The Illustrated
BIBLE

eagle

Published by Eagle Publishing Ltd,
6 Kestrel House, Mill Street, Trowbridge,
Wiltshire BA14 8BE.

British Library Cataloguing in Publication Data.
A catalogue record for this book is available from the British Library.

The Illustrated Bible was designed,
edited and produced by
McRae Books
info@mcraebooks.com
Publishers: Anne McRae, Marco Nardi

General Editor: John Griswood, in cooperation with following
Consultants: Simon Goulden, Agency for Jewish Education
Dr. Stephen Motyer, London Bible College
Reverend Dom Jerome Hodkinson
Text: Neil and Ting Morris
Main illustrations: Francesca d'Ottavi
Documentary illustrations: Paola Ravaglia, Studio Stalio
(Alessandro Cantucci, Fabiano Fabbrucci, Andrea Morandi,
Ivan Stalio), Lorenzo Cecchi, Leonardo Meschini, Franco Autuori,
Gian Paolo Faleschini
Art Director: Marco Nardi
Layout and picture research: Laura Ottina
Cutouts: Filippo Delle Monache
Colour separations: Litocolor, Florence and Fotolito Toscana, Florence

ISBN No. 086347 587 6

Printed by STIGE, Italy

Table of Contents

THE NEW TESTAMENT

7

INTRODUCTION

Illuminated Bible
Until the invention of printing, every book had to be copied and illustrated by hand. In the Middle Ages, Christian monks produced beautifully decorated copies of sacred texts. These books were works of art that took many months to produce, and were bound in precious covers like the one above.

The Bible is not really a single book but a library for it contains a collection of books – the *Book of Genesis*, the *Book of Kings*, the *Book of Psalms* and so on. The word Bible comes from Greek and Latin words which mean 'books'. These books were written over a long period dating from about 1450 BC. Most of the authors of these books are unknown. The earliest authors wrote down the traditions of the Jewish people that had previously been handed down through the generations by word of mouth.

The Christian Bible is divided in two parts – the *Old Testament* and the *New Testament* ('testament' is a word that means agreement). The Old Testament, which was written mainly in Hebrew (and is often referred to as the Hebrew Bible) is sacred to both Christians and Jews. In the Christian Bible the books of the Old Testament are grouped in four sections which are different from the Jewish Hebrew Bible where the books are grouped in three main sections.

THE OLD TESTAMENT IN CHRISTIAN BIBLES
The Pentateuch (Torah)

The first five books in both the Jewish and Christian Bible are called the *Pentateuch* (the Greek for five books) or '*Torah*', a word meaning 'law' or 'teaching' in Hebrew. The *Torah* is particularly important to Jews, who believe the books to have been revealed by God to Moses on Mount Sinai.

Genesis tells the story of the Creation, of Abraham and his son Isaac, the conflict between the brothers Jacob and Esau and the story of Joseph.

Exodus records how Moses leads the people of Israel out of Egypt and how God establishes a covenant with his people at Sinai.

Leviticus 'the priestly book' contains laws and commandments and deals with rituals, feasts and fasts.

Numbers is an account of events during the Israelites' journey through the desert to the borders of the Promised Land.

Deuteronomy continues the story of the Israelites up to the death of Moses. It also contains more laws or instructions.

The Historical Books

These books tell the story of the people of Israel from the entry into the Promised Land to the return from exile in Babylon.

Joshua, Judges, Ruth 1 & 2, Samuel 1 & 2, Kings 1 & 2, Chronicles, Ezra, Nehemiah, Esther

Wisdom Literature

The Wisdom books are very varied. *Psalms* is concerned with how to praise God. The *Song of Songs* asks questions about the meaning of human love. *Job* examines life's inequalities and sufferings.

Job, Psalms, Proverbs, Ecclesiastes, Song of Songs

Printed Bible
The first printed book, a Latin Bible, was produced by the German craftsman Johannes Gutenberg in 1455.

The Prophets

Isaiah, Jeremiah, Lamentations, Ezekiel, Daniel, Hosea, Joel, Amos, Obadiah, Jonah, Micah, Nahum, Habakkuk, Zephaniah, Haggai, Zechariah, Malachi

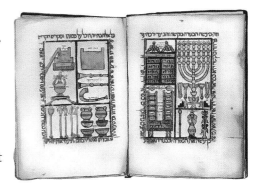

THE JEWISH BIBLE

After *Deuteronomy* in the *Torah*, the second main division of the Jewish Bible begins. It is called the *Prophets*. It shows major differences in the classification and order of the books.

Former Prophets

Joshua, Judges 1 & 2, Samuel 1 & 2, Kings

Latter Prophets

Isaiah, Jeremiah, Ezekiel, Hosea, Joel, Amos, Obadiah, Jonah, Micah, Nahum, Habakkuk, Zephaniah, Haggai, Zechariah, Malachi

The Writings

Psalms, Proverbs, Job, Song of Songs, Ruth, Lamentations, Ecclesiastes, Esther, Daniel, Ezra, Nehemiah 1 & 2, Chronicles

Jewish Bible
This illuminated Hebrew Bible is called the Perpignan Bible after the area in southern France where it was produced in the 13th century.

There are small differences between the Catholic and Protestant Bible. The so-called *Deutero-Canonical Books* which include *Tobit*, *Judith* and the *Maccabees* are not generally accepted by Protestants or are published separately as *The Apocrypha*.

THE NEW TESTAMENT

The 27 books of the New Testament were written in Greek and form the spiritual foundation of Christianity (both Old and New Testaments are also sacred to Muslims). The first four books – the *Gospels* (a Saxon word meaning 'good news') – were written by Matthew, Mark, Luke and John and describe the birth, life, miracles, teachings, death and resurrection of Jesus. Christians believe that Jesus, as the son of God, was the Messiah or Christ promised by the prophets who brings forgiveness of all sin (salvation) and the promise of the kingdom of God. This was the new covenant or testament between God and his people.

The *Acts of the Apostles* (almost certainly written by Luke) tell of the growth of the Christian church and of the journeys of Paul.

The 21 *Epistles* are letters from Christian leaders (mostly Paul) to keep in touch with Christians living all around the Mediterranean.

The *Book of Revelation* (probably written by the apostle John) is a collection of visions and prophecies written to encourage believers to hold on to their faith even under persecution.

The Gospels
This mosaic shows the four Gospels in a cupboard. The Gospels' narration mainly focuses on the last three years of Jesus's life. They were probably written about 50 years after his death.

THE OLD TESTAMENT

God Creates the World

At the very beginning of time God created the world. Everything was dark and empty at first, so God said, "Let there be light." Then God made a time of light and a time of darkness. He called the light "day" and the darkness "night". This was the first day of creation.

On the second day, God separated the waters of the earth from the sky above. On the third, He pulled the waters of the earth apart, to make dry land between the oceans. Then God commanded the land to produce trees and plants that could make their own fruit and seeds. God looked at what He had created, and saw that it was good.

On the fourth day, God created the sun to shine down on earth. He also made the moon and the stars, to glow and twinkle during the night from the dark heavens above the earth. These would serve as signs to mark the days, years and changing seasons.

Next God made creatures to fill the oceans and the sky above the earth. He made all kinds of sea creatures, from the tiniest fish to the mightiest whale. He gave birds wings,

so that they could fly in the sky above the oceans and the dry land. Then, on the sixth day, He made animals that could live and move about on the land. The forests and plains came to life with all kinds of creatures. God made them all so that they could bear their own young and increase in number to fill the earth.

On the seventh day, God rested from his work. He looked at everything that He had created in the heavens and on the earth, and He saw that it was good.

GOD MAKES PEOPLE

God shapes Eve from Adam's rib

The story of the creation of humanity stresses the unity of male and female and their mutual need. God creates the woman to be the suitable partner for man and to rule with him over the garden of Eden.

for him." He caused Adam to fall into a deep sleep, and while he was asleep, God took out one of his ribs. From the rib God created a woman, and we call her Eve.

God blessed Adam and Eve and said to them, "Have children so that human beings may increase in number and look after the earth and every creature that lives on it. I have made plants and fruit to feed you and all the other creatures on earth."

When God had finished making the earth and the heavens, He said, "Now I will make human beings. They will be in charge of the fish of the sea, the birds of the air, and all the animals that live on land."

First God formed a man from the dust of the ground. He breathed the breath of life into the man so that he became a living being, and we call this first man Adam. God took Adam and placed him in a beautiful garden. Then God said, "It is not good for the man to be alone. I will make a companion

AND THE LORD GOD FORMED MAN OF THE DUST OF THE GROUND, AND BREATHED INTO HIS NOSTRILS THE BREATH OF LIFE; AND MAN BECAME A LIVING SOUL.

(Genesis 2.7)

In the Garden of Eden

The beautiful place where God had placed Adam and Eve was called the Garden of Eden. It was full of wonderful trees, and they had fruit that was good to eat. A river flowed through the garden and watered it. In the middle of the garden were two special trees, called the tree of life and the tree of knowledge of good and evil. God said to Adam and Eve, "You may eat as much fruit as you like from all the trees in the garden except one. That is the tree of knowledge of good and evil. If you eat fruit from that tree, you will die."

Then God brought all the animals and birds to Adam, so that he could give them names. One by one Adam named all the animals that God had made. Adam and Eve, the first man and the first woman, were happy in the Garden of Eden.

Adam gives animals their names
This story, while explaining how animals got their names, implies that man has control over them. This same concept was already expressed in another passage of the story of creation where God grants humanity dominion over all the living creatures of the earth.

15

THE FIRST SIN

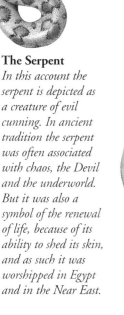

The Serpent
In this account the serpent is depicted as a creature of evil cunning. In ancient tradition the serpent was often associated with chaos, the Devil and the underworld. But it was also a symbol of the renewal of life, because of its ability to shed its skin, and as such it was worshipped in Egypt and in the Near East.

T he snake was the most cunning of all the animals in the Garden of Eden. It slithered up to Eve and said, "Did God really say you must not eat fruit from any of the trees?"

"No," Eve replied. "God said we could eat fruit from all the trees except one. If we eat fruit from that one tree in the middle of the garden, we will die."

"That's not true," the snake hissed. "But God knows that when you eat that tree's fruit you will understand good and evil and be as wise as he is."

The snake's cunning words made Eve look more closely at the fruit of the special tree. It certainly looked very good to eat, and Eve couldn't help thinking how wonderful it would be to be wise. Without further thought she picked a fruit from the tree and bit into it.

Then Eve gave some of the fruit to Adam, and he ate it, too. At once their eyes were opened, but not in the way the snake had promised. Instead, they both suddenly felt ashamed that they were naked, and they hurried off to find some fig leaves with which to cover themselves.

The Fall of Mankind
This story points out that alone of all animals, humans reason and choose what they do. Choosing wrongly separates humans from God. Adam and Eve's disobedience is also known as the Fall of Mankind. This medieval Christian mosaic shows Adam and Eve with the snake in the Garden of Eden.

GOD'S JUDGEMENT

As the day grew cooler, God went walking in the Garden of Eden. Adam and Eve felt so ashamed of themselves that they hid from him among the trees. "Where are you, Adam?" God called.

Adam and Eve came out of their hiding place. "I heard you in the garden," Adam said, "and I was afraid because I was naked, so I hid."

"Who told you to be afraid?" God asked. "Have you eaten fruit from the tree that I ordered you not to touch?"

"It wasn't my fault," said Adam. "The woman you put here with me gave me some fruit, and I ate it."

"What have you done?" God asked Eve.

"It wasn't my fault," Eve replied. "The snake tricked me into eating it."

God then explained the consequences of what Adam and Eve had done. He told Eve that it would be more painful for her to bear children. And he told Adam that thorns and thistles would grow among his crops, so that his daily work would be long and hard. And one day, he and Eve would die. "You came from dust, and one day you will return to dust," God said.

Then God made clothes of skin for Adam and Eve and sent them out of the Garden of Eden. He placed angels at one end of the Garden and a flaming sword to guard the way to the tree of life.

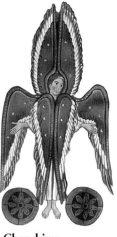

Cherubims
To guard the Garden of Eden, God put Cherubims, heavenly creatures usually represented with four or six wings covered with eyes.

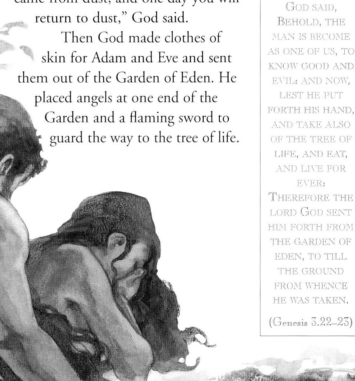

AND THE LORD GOD SAID, BEHOLD, THE MAN IS BECOME AS ONE OF US, TO KNOW GOOD AND EVIL: AND NOW, LEST HE PUT FORTH HIS HAND, AND TAKE ALSO OF THE TREE OF LIFE, AND EAT, AND LIVE FOR EVER: THEREFORE THE LORD GOD SENT HIM FORTH FROM THE GARDEN OF EDEN, TO TILL THE GROUND FROM WHENCE HE WAS TAKEN.

(Genesis 3.22–23)

CAIN AND ABEL

After Adam and Eve had been sent out of the Garden of Eden, Eve gave birth to two sons. The older boy, whose name was Cain, grew up to be a farmer who raised crops. His brother, Abel, became a shepherd.

Animal offerings
The ancient populations of the Middle East frequently offered sacrifices of animals and crops to their gods. Above, a bull is taken to be sacrificed in Mesopotamia, about 1700 BC.

One day, the two young men decided to make special offerings to God. Cain offered some crops from his harvest, and Abel made a present of a new-born lamb from his flock. God could see into their hearts. He looked favourably on Abel and accepted his offering, but he did not look favourably on Cain's offering because he knew that he was a proud and jealous man.

Cain was very upset and angry, but God said to him, "Why are you angry? If you do what is right, you will be accepted. Remember that evil is always there, trying to overpower you. You must fight against it and win the battle." But as God was speaking to him, all Cain could think of was how jealous he was of his brother.

Then Cain asked Abel to come for a walk in the fields. While they were there, Cain suddenly struck his brother over the head with a rock and killed him. As Cain walked back to his fields, God asked him, "Where is your brother?"

AND THE LORD SAID UNTO CAIN, WHERE IS ABEL THY BROTHER? AND HE SAID, I KNOW NOT: AM I MY BROTHER'S KEEPER? AND HE SAID, WHAT HAST THOU DONE? THE VOICE OF THY BROTHER'S BLOOD CRIETH UNTO ME FROM THE GROUND.

(Genesis 4.9–10)

How should I know?" Cain replied in an offhand way. "Am I supposed to watch out for him all the time?"

But God knew what Cain had done. "Your brother's blood cries out to me from the soil where it was spilt," he said. "Now whenever you till the soil, it will no longer give you crops. You are cursed and must spend the rest of your life as a homeless wanderer."

The punishment is more than I can bear," Cain cried. "Whoever finds out what I have done will kill me." But God told Cain that he would protect him and that anyone who killed him would suffer vengeance seven times over. Then he put a mark on Cain so that no one who found him would kill him.

So Cain left his home and went to live in a region to the east of Eden, called the Land of Nod.

Shepherds and farmers
One of the themes of this story is the tension between the different ancient ways of life of shepherds and farmers. Cain, originally a farmer, becomes a nomadic shepherd after murdering his brother, and is traditionally considered to be the ancestor of the Kenites, a nomadic people who lived close to the Israelites.

19

THE FIRST MURDER

☞ This story shows the consequences of Cain's act of violence: he is banished by God and becomes a homeless wanderer. It is the first in a series of narrations which illustrate humanity's increasing tendency to sin after expulsion from Eden. In all of these stories God's severe judgment is in the end mitigated by his mercy.

NOAH'S ARK

As the number of people increased on earth, so did their wickedness. God saw that the world had become so full of sin and violence that there was nothing for him to do but wash it clean and start all over again.

God knew one man who was true to him and entirely innocent of the sins of the world. The man's name was Noah and God told him what he was going to do. "People have filled the world with wickedness," God said, "and I am going to put an end to all of them. I am going to bring floodwaters that will destroy all life on earth. You must make an ark of cypress wood, covered and sealed inside and out with pitch."

God told Noah exactly how the ark, or boat, must be built. It was to be very big – about 140 metres long – with lower, middle and upper decks, a door at the side and a roof on top. This

20

was far bigger than the room needed for Noah and his wife, as well as his three sons and their wives. Then God explained why. "As well as your family," he told Noah, "you are to bring into the ark two of every kind of animal and bird that you can find on earth, one male and one female of each kind. You must also store food for your family and the animals, so that you can all stay alive and survive the flood."

Noah started to build the ark at once, and he followed God's instructions to the letter. This must have amused all those who saw Noah and his sons at work. Imagine building a huge boat on dry land, far away from the nearest sea!

When the ark was finished, God said to Noah, "Now collect all the animals and birds and take them into the ark two by two. Seven days from now it will start to rain, and when it does, it will rain non-stop for forty days. The flood will wipe the face of the earth clean."

Noah did exactly as God commanded him.

THE GREAT FLOOD

Just as God had commanded, Noah filled his ark with pairs of all the different kinds of animals and birds that lived on earth. Each pair was made up of a male and a female, so that they could produce young in years to come and fill the earth again. Noah and his three sons also collected all the food that would be needed by them and the animals. Seven days later, the ark was full.

On that very day, just as God had said, the heavens opened and rain fell – on Noah's land, on the roof of the ark and all over the world. The heavy rainfall never stopped and it soon caused the oceans to rise and floods started covering the land. The floodwaters rose slowly as the rain kept falling. One day the floods reached the land where Noah had built his ark, though people had laughed at him for building a boat so far from the sea. Soon the ark was gently lifted up and floated on the water. Noah and his family were glad that he had built the huge boat so well and sealed it with pitch. The torrential rain and floods pounded against the ark, but the boat was strong enough to stay afloat.

It rained and rained for forty days, just as God had said. The floodwaters kept on rising, until at last they even covered the highest mountain tops on earth. All that could be seen from the ark was water. Apart from those on board, all the people and animals on earth had disappeared beneath the waves of the flood.

But God had not forgotten Noah, and at last the rain stopped falling, as He had promised. The floodwaters were so deep that for a long time things continued to look exactly the same outside the ark – just a huge ocean everywhere. The waters were slowly going down, however, and after several months the ark at last again touched land. It came to rest on the mountains of Ararat.

Noah waited for a few more weeks, hoping that the waters would continue to go down. Then he sent

out a raven, to see if there was land for it to settle on. But the raven just flew around without sighting any land. So Noah sent out a dove, but it too came flying back to the ark without finding anywhere to land. Noah decided to wait for another week, and then he sent the dove out again. This time it came back with an olive leaf in its beak and Noah knew that the floodwaters had indeed gone down. He waited patiently for another week, before sending the dove out for a third time. This time it did not return, and Noah knew

that they could leave the ark.

Noah and his family let all the animals out of the ark. They could see that there was dry land all around, so Noah at once built an altar and offered thanks to God for saving them. Then God blessed Noah and his family, and said to them, "Never again will floods destroy all life on earth. As a sign of this promise to you, I have made a rainbow in the sky. Whenever you look up and see a rainbow, remember the promise that I have made."

AND THE FLOOD WAS FORTY DAYS UPON THE EARTH; AND THE WATERS INCREASED, AND BARE UP THE ARK, AND IT WAS LIFT UP ABOVE THE EARTH. AND THE WATERS PREVAILED, AND WERE INCREASED GREATLY ON THE EARTH; AND THE ARK WENT UPON THE FACE OF THE WATERS.

(Genesis 7.17–18)

THE TOWER OF BABEL

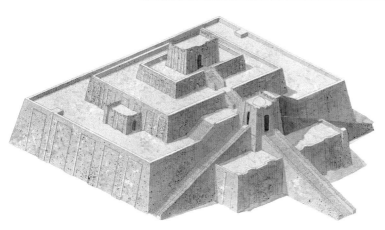

The ziggurat
The Tower of Babel was probably based on the great ziggurat of Babylon, built in the 6th century BCE by King Nebuchadnezzar. Ziggurats were massive temple-towers built of mudbricks. They were constructed as a series of platforms crowned by a small temple accessible only to kings and priests and to which the gods were thought to descend.

24

After the terrible flood, Noah planted vines and began farming the land again. His sons Shem, Ham and Japheth and their wives had many children, and Noah's grandchildren eventually had many children, too. Their families gradually spread to different parts of the world, just as God had intended when he first spoke to Noah. But still all the people in the world spoke the same language.

One group of wandering people settled down on the plains of a region called Babylonia. They wanted to make a name for themselves and decided to build a city, with a tower tall enough to reach right up to the sky. "The great tower will make us famous," they said, "and we can enjoy life here instead of wandering all over the world."

They started work at once by making bricks from mud and baking them hard in the heat of the sun. They used these mudbricks instead of stone, fixing them together with tar as they built the walls of their tall tower. They worked quickly and well and their tower made rapid progress.

But God looked at the city and the tower that the Babylonians were building and was not happy. He saw that once again people were pleasing themselves and becoming too full of pride and self-importance. Soon they would be as bad as those who lived on earth before the flood. God decided to upset their plans by giving them different languages, so that they could not understand each other so easily.

Once they did not all speak the same language, the people could no longer plan and work together. They stopped building the city and its tall tower, which we call the Tower of Babel. People went on wandering to other regions, taking their different languages and spreading them around the world.

AND THEY SAID, GO TO, LET US BUILD US A CITY AND A TOWER, WHOSE TOP MAY REACH UNTO HEAVEN; AND LET US MAKE US A NAME, LEST WE BE SCATTERED ABROAD UPON THE FACE OF THE WHOLE EARTH.

(Genesis 11.4)

The confusion of languages
God punishes people because they want to build the tower out of presumption, to reach heaven and challenge his authority. This story refers to the beginnings of urban life and it gives an explanation to the existence of different languages and nations. Above, the Tower of Babel *as painted by Pieter Bruegel in 1563.*

25

GOD CALLS ABRAM

"People of God"
The story of the Hebrew people begins with Abraham (above).

Ur
Ur was perhaps the greatest city in Mesopotamia and possibly in the world when Abram was living there. Among the many beautiful objects found in the royal tombs was the Standard of Ur, dated from about 2500 BCE. Decorated with lapis lazuli and shell mosaics, it shows the king's activities in times of peace and war. Below, a detail of the Standard of Ur.

Many of the descendants of Noah's son Shem lived on a fertile plain near the River Euphrates. A man named Abram lived there, in a city called Ur. One day God spoke to Abram. "You must leave your father's house, your city and your people," God said, "and travel to a land that I will show you. I will make your name great and bless you, and then you will be a blessing to people everywhere."

So Abram left Ur, together with his father Terah, his wife Sarai and his nephew Lot. They took with them servants, sheep and cattle, and travelled north along the course of the Euphrates. At night they rested in tents, and finally they arrived at the city of Haran, where they stayed until Abram's old father died. Then they continued on their journey.

From Haran, Abram and his family headed west, towards the land of Canaan, always guided by God. At a place called Bethel, God appeared to Abram and said, "I will give this land to your children and all their descendants." Abram thanked God by building an altar to him there.

Abram went on travelling through Canaan, looking for water and the best grassland for his herds. But then famine struck the land, and so he went south to Egypt. In Egypt, he pretended that his beautiful wife Sarai was in fact his sister, because he feared that otherwise the Egyptians would kill him because of her beauty.

26

When the pharaoh of Egypt discovered that Abram had deceived him about Sarai, he ordered him to leave the country.

By now both Abram and Lot had large flocks of sheep and herds of cattle and it was difficult to find enough grazing land and water for them. When quarrels broke out between their herdsmen, Abram said to Lot, "Families should not quarrel like this. There is a whole land for us and others to share. Choose which way you want to go, and I will go the other way."

Lot decided to travel south towards the valley of the River Jordan. He chose to settle near the city of Sodom. When he had gone, God said to Abram, "Look around you in every direction. All the land that you see belongs to you and your descendants for ever."

As agreed, Abram went in the opposite direction from Lot. He headed north and settled in the area around Hebron, where he built another altar to praise the Lord.

28

Abram's journeys

From Ur, Abram and his family moved first up the Euphrates valley to Haran, situated on the trade routes in the north. Then, in response to God's command, they moved south to Canaan, an area already inhabited by various tribes known as Canaanites. During a time of famine, Abram journeyed to Egypt, following the trade route from Syria. He finally settled in the area around Hebron, while Lot settled in the region of Sodom.

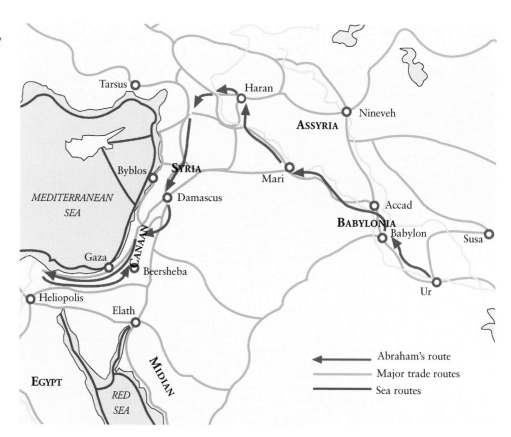

Abram and Hagar

AND THE ANGEL OF THE LORD SAID UNTO HER, BEHOLD, THOU ART WITH CHILD, AND SHALT BEAR A SON, AND SHALT CALL HIS NAME ISHMAEL; BECAUSE THE LORD HATH HEARD THY AFFLICTION.

(Genesis 16.11)

Sarai, Abram's wife, had an Egyptian servant girl named Hagar. One day Sarai said to Abram, "God has not blessed me with children, but if you had a child with my servant, we could bring it up as our own."

Abram agreed with his wife's plan and slept with Hagar. The servant girl soon found that she was expecting a baby and she was happy about this. But Hagar began to look down on her mistress and treated her with less than her usual respect. Before long this was too much for Sarai. "This is all your fault," she complained to Abram. "I gave my servant to you, and now she despises me."

"She's your servant," Abram replied. "Do whatever you think best."

Sarai treated Hagar so badly that it was not long before the girl ran away. She wandered around the barren desert, and when at last she rested by a spring God spoke to her. "Where are you going?" he asked.

"I'm running away from my mistress," Hagar replied sadly.

"Go back to her and serve her again," God said gently. "I have heard of your misery, and I will look after you so that you will have many more children. You will soon have a baby son and you must call him Ishmael."

God's words comforted Hagar and she returned at once to Sarai and Abram. "I have now seen the One who sees me," she said happily to herself. Soon she gave birth to a son and Abram gave him the name Ishmael.

Ishmael and the Arabs
In Genesis 17, God promises that Hagar's son Ishmael "will be the father of twelve rulers and I will make him into a great nation". Ishmael holds an important role in Muslim tradition. It is told that he and Abram built the Ka'bah, Islam's holiest shrine, at Mecca in Arabia. Above, tile depicting the Ka'bah.

THE THREE STRANGERS

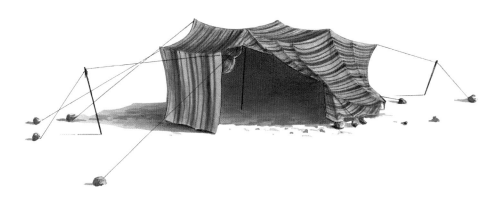

Abram's camp

Abram and his family probably lived in a portable tent similar to modern Bedouin ones (right). If the family became larger, the tent could be extended, or divided into separate rooms by hanging curtains.

AND THE LORD SAID UNTO ABRAHAM, WHEREFORE DID SARAH LAUGH, SAYING, SHALL I OF A SURETY BEAR A CHILD, WHICH AM OLD? IS ANY THING TOO HARD FOR THE LORD? AT THE TIME APPOINTED I WILL RETURN UNTO THEE, ACCORDING TO THE TIME OF LIFE, AND SARAH SHALL HAVE A SON.

(Genesis 18.13–14)

When war broke out around the city of Sodom, Abram's nephew Lot was taken prisoner. Abram soon heard of this and took a band of trained men to set his nephew free. At the same time he helped some of the chiefs of the region, but he refused to accept a reward from them because he did not want anyone to be able to say that they had made him rich.

Then God said to Abram, "I will give you a very great reward." There was only one thing which Abram and his wife wanted and did not have – a child of their own. But Sarai was too old to have children. "When I die," Abram said sadly, "one of my servants will inherit all I have."

When God heard Abram's words, he led him outside his tent and said, "Look up at all the stars in the night sky — there are too many to count. That is how many descendants you will have. From now on your name will be Abraham, meaning "father of many". And the mother of many will be your wife, who from now on is named Sarah. I give the whole land of Canaan to you and your descendants, and I will be their God. That is my promise to you. As a

FATHERS OF THE PEOPLE

☞ The origins of the people of Israel are traced back to Abram and his descendants, Isaac, Jacob and Joseph. These men were the Patriarchs, which means male leaders, or fathers, of a family. Abram's great trust in God began when he left the city of Ur for Canaan. Because of this trust, God made a special agreement, or covenant, with Abram and his descendants, that they would be his people and he would be their God.

sign of our agreement, you must make sure that every male among your people is circumcised."

A few days later, while Abraham was sitting at the entrance to his tent during the heat of midday, three strangers approached. Abraham jumped up and invited them to rest and refresh themselves under the shade of a tree. Then he rushed off to have a suitable meal prepared for his guests.

Abraham stood near the strangers while they ate. "Where is your wife Sarah?" one of them asked.

"In our tent," said Abraham.

"I will return at the same time next year," the man said, "and your wife will have a son."

Sarah could hear what was being said from inside the tent and she laughed gently to herself. How could she possibly have a son by this time next year, when she was far too old?

"Why did Sarah laugh?" the man asked Abraham. "Is anything too hard for the Lord? I will do as I promised and Sarah will have a son."

Abraham realised that the stranger spoke with the voice of God. The three men got up to go and Abraham walked with them to see them on their way.

The three angels
The three divine messengers who visited Abraham have often been depicted in Orthodox Christian art. The Russian icon above was painted by Andrey Rublev (1370–1430).

31

AT LOT'S HOUSE

AND THE LORD SAID, BECAUSE THE CRY
OF SODOM AND GOMORRAH IS GREAT, AND
BECAUSE THEIR SIN IS VERY GRIEVOUS;
I WILL GO DOWN NOW, AND SEE WHETHER
THEY HAVE DONE ALTOGETHER
ACCORDING TO THE CRY OF IT, WHICH IS
COME UNTO ME; AND IF NOT, I WILL KNOW.

(Genesis 18.20–21)

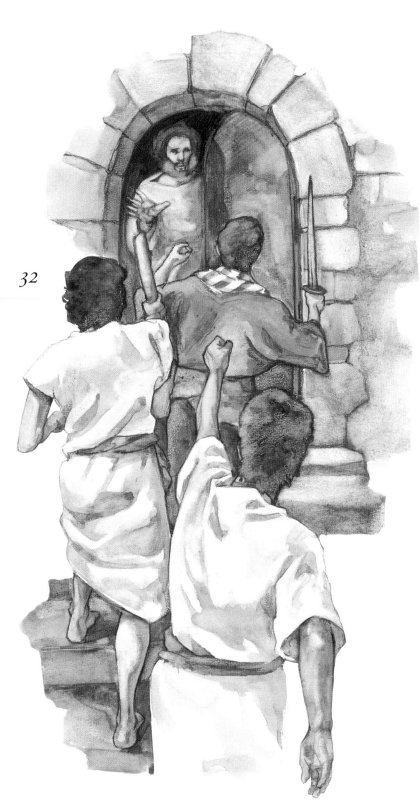

The cities of Sodom and Gomorrah were so full of sin that God decided it would be best to destroy the cities completely. God told Abraham about this and Abraham at once thought of his nephew Lot, who lived in Sodom. Abraham asked God to spare the cities if there were even ten good people living there and God agreed to do so.

That evening two angels arrived at the gates of Sodom to see if there were any good people at all living there. Lot was sitting at the entrance to the city and he greeted the strangers and invited them to take refreshment and spend the night in his house.

Later, while the visitors were eating their meal, men from all over Sodom came and surrounded Lot's house. They shouted at Lot to send out his visitors, whom they wanted to ill-treat. Lot opened his door to plead with the men of Sodom, but they did not listen. "Get out of the way," they yelled, "or we'll treat you even worse than them!"

The two visiting angels pulled Lot back into his house and bolted the door shut. Then they struck blind the large crowd of men gathered shouting outside the house, so that they could no longer find the door.

THE PILLAR OF SALT

T he visiting angels told Lot that they had been sent by God to destroy the city and that he and his wife and two daughters must leave immediately.

When he heard this, Lot rushed to warn the two young men who were going to marry his daughters. "You must get out of this place at once," he yelled. "God is going to destroy the whole city!" But the young men just laughed: they thought that Lot was joking.

As dawn approached, the two angels urged Lot and his family to hurry. When Lot hesitated, they grabbed him, his wife and two daughters by the hand and led them out of the city. As soon as they were outside the gates of Sodom, one of the angels said, "Now run for your lives! Go up into the hills or you will be swept away. Don't stop once and don't look back!"

Lot was not sure he could make it to the hills and he begged to be allowed to go to the nearby town of Zoar. They granted his request, but told him to get there as quickly as possible.

By the time Lot and his daughters reached Zoar, the sun had risen. Then fire and burning stone rained down on Sodom and Gomorrah, and the whole of the surrounding countryside. But Lot's wife had stopped running. She couldn't resist looking back just once at Sodom, the city which had been her home. The moment she did so, she turned into a pillar of salt.

Isaac and Ishmael

> And Abraham rose up early in the morning, and took bread, and a bottle of water, and gave it unto Hagar, putting it on her shoulder, and the child, and sent her away; and she departed, and wandered in the wilderness of Beersheba.
>
> (Genesis 21.14)

Drinking water

It was very important to carry water when travelling, because it was not always easy to find water sources in the semi-desert. The "bottle" of water that Abraham gave to Hagar was probably a goatskin (above).

34

God kept his promise to Abraham and Sarah and in due course Sarah gave birth to a baby boy. Abraham named his son Isaac, which means "he laughs", because his wife had laughed when she heard that she was to have a son.

When the baby was eight days old, Abraham circumcised him, as God had ordered. Sarah was very happy. "God has brought me joy and laughter," she said, "and everyone who hears about my baby will laugh with me. Who would have thought that I would nurse a child at my age?"

One day, when Isaac was still a boy, Sarah saw Hagar's son making fun of him. She was furious. "Get rid of that slave woman and her son," she told Abraham. "He will never share in Isaac's inheritance."

Abraham was upset at this, because Ishmael was also his son. But God said to him, "Do as Sarah says. I will look after Ishmael."

Early next morning Abraham took some food and a goatskin ("bottle") of water to Hagar and wished her and Ishmael farewell. The servant girl and her son wandered off through the desert of Beersheba.

When they had eaten the food and drunk all the water, Hagar knew that they could not survive for long in the hot, barren desert. She laid Ishmael down in the shade of a

Circumcision

From the time of Abraham, Jewish boys have been circumcised (circumcision is a small operation involving the removal of the foreskin). This is a sign in the Jewish faith that they are one of the people who have a special relationship with God. Right: ritual instruments used for circumcision.

bush and sat down a little way off, for she did not want to hear the boy crying or to see her own son die. Then she herself began to sob.

But God had heard Ishmael crying and he said to Hagar, "Don't be afraid. Go to your son and take him by the hand, for I will look after him and make his children into a great family."

Then God led Hagar to a well of pure water. Hagar filled her goatskin with water and put it to her son's lips. God had saved Ishmael and he continued to watch over him as he grew up into a young man.

ABRAHAM IS PUT TO THE TEST

The ram in the thicket
This statue of a male goat with its horns and forelegs caught in a tree was discovered in the royal tombs of Ur. It is a reminder of the story of Abraham being told at the last minute to sacrifice a ram, instead of his son Isaac, to God. Abraham finds the ram caught in a nearby bush.

One day God told Abraham to take his son Isaac to the land of Moriah. "There you will sacrifice your beloved son on a hill that I will show you," God said.

Abraham loved his son very much, but he did as God commanded. The very next morning he got up early and saddled his donkey. Then he woke Isaac and told him that they were going on a journey. Abraham also took two of his servants with him. Before they left, they collected a bundle of firewood, which they loaded onto the donkey. Only Abraham knew what this was for — to make a fire for the sacrifice of his son.

They travelled for three days, until at last they reached the land of Moriah. In the distance Abraham could see a hill and knew that this was where he had to take his son. He told the servants to wait for them. "Stay here with the donkey," Abraham said. "The boy and I are going to worship on the hill."

Abraham told Isaac to carry the bundle of firewood up the hill, while he took a brazier of fire and his knife. "Father?" Isaac said as they walked. "We have got the wood and the fire, but where is the lamb for the offering we are going to make?"

"God will provide the lamb for the offering, my son," Abraham said in as firm a voice as he could

manage. Father and son carried on up the hill. Abraham told Isaac to help him gather stones to build an altar. They put the firewood on top and everything was ready for the sacrifice. Then Abraham swiftly bound his son's hands and feet and lifted him gently on to the altar.

Abraham took his knife and raised it high, ready to make his greatest sacrifice. But just at that moment, he heard a voice. "Abraham! Abraham!" an angel of the Lord called out. "Do not lay a hand on the boy. There is no need to harm him, for now God knows that you will always obey him. You have shown that you are even prepared to sacrifice your own son to him."

Abraham lowered his knife, untied his son and took him down from the altar. Then he looked up and saw a ram caught by its horns in a nearby bush. Abraham quickly killed the ram with his knife and lifted it on to the altar in place of his son. He lit the fire and sacrificed the ram to God. Then the angel spoke again. "For offering your own son God will bless you and all your descendants. And through them all nations on earth will be blessed."

Abraham and Isaac went back to the servants to begin the long, happy journey home. They knew that God did not want people to make any more human sacrifices.

AND THEY CAME TO
THE PLACE WHICH
GOD HAD TOLD HIM
OF; AND ABRAHAM
BUILT AN ALTAR
THERE, AND LAID
THE WOOD IN
ORDER, AND BOUND
ISAAC HIS SON, AND
LAID HIM ON THE
ALTAR UPON THE
WOOD.
(GENESIS 22.9)

A Wife for Isaac

> AND THE
> SERVANT RAN TO
> MEET HER, AND
> SAID, LET ME, I
> PRAY THEE,
> DRINK A LITTLE
> WATER OF THY
> PITCHER.
> AND SHE SAID,
> DRINK, MY
> LORD: AND SHE
> HASTED, AND
> LET DOWN HER
> PITCHER UPON
> HER HAND, AND
> GAVE HIM
> DRINK.
>
> (Genesis 24,
> 17–18)

By the time Isaac grew up, his father Abraham was an old man. When Isaac's mother Sarah died, Abraham was very sad. But he never forgot that God had blessed him and promised that his descendants would become a great nation. This made him think about a wife for Isaac, so one day he called for his chief servant. "It is time that my son Isaac had a wife," Abraham said. "But I do not want him to marry one of the daughters of the Canaanites, among whom we live. So I want you to travel to Mesopotamia, the land I originally came from. There you must find a wife for Isaac from among my own people. Promise me faithfully that you will do this."

"But what if the chosen woman does not want to make the long journey back to Canaan with me?" the servant asked. "What shall I do then? Should I take your son to meet her there?"

"No," Abraham replied firmly. "God led me away from Mesopotamia and when he brought me to this land, he promised that he would give it to my children and their descendants. I know that he will help you find the right wife for my son.

If the chosen woman is unwilling to travel back with you, then you are free from your promise." So Abraham's servant set out on the long journey to the land of Mesopotamia, taking with him ten camels and valuable gifts from his master.

When at last they reached the far-off land, they stopped at a well outside the town of Nahor. It was evening, which the servant knew was the time when the young women of the town came out to collect water. So the servant knelt down and prayed to God. "Please, Lord," he said, "let me meet the woman that you have chosen as a wife for your servant Isaac. I will ask a young woman for a drink, and if she also offers water to my camels, I will know this is a sign that she is the chosen one."

Before the servant had even finished his prayer, a young woman came to the well to fetch water. The servant rushed over, just as the young woman raised her jar full of water. "Please give me a little water to drink," the servant said.

"Drink, my lord," the young woman replied politely. "And I see that your camels need water, too." When the woman had filled a water trough for the animals, the servant was delighted and asked her who she was.

"My name is Rebekah," the young woman said. "I am the daughter of Bethuel and granddaughter of Nahor." This only confirmed to the servant that his prayer had been answered, for Nahor was the name of his master's brother.

He at once took out a gold ring and beautiful bracelets, which he gave to Rebekah. Then he asked if there was room for him to stay at her father's house. "We have room for you and plenty of straw and fodder for your camels," Rebekah replied. She ran off to tell her family what had happened.

By the time Abraham's servant arrived at Rebekah's house, her father and brother were waiting to greet him. They offered him food, but he said, "Before I eat, I must tell you why I have come." And so they sat down and listened to his story. He told them who he was and why his master Abraham had sent him on this special journey. Then he told them how he had prayed at the well and met Rebekah. After listening very carefully to everything the servant said, Rebekah's family all agreed that it was God's will that she should marry Isaac.

Abraham's servant gave gifts of fine clothes and jewels to Rebekah and her mother, before at last settling down to eat and drink. Next morning, the servant got up early and prepared at once to return to the land of Canaan, intending to take Rebekah with him. But Rebekah's mother and brother asked if they could have time to prepare for her departure. "Please do not make me wait," the servant said. "Since God has granted success to my journey, I would like to carry out my master's wish at once."

"Let my sister decide," Rebekah's brother said. He asked her, "Do you want to go with this man?"

Golden jewellery
Craftworkers in Canaan were highly skilled in making gold and silver bracelets, necklaces and pendants like the ones above. Golden anklets and jewelled rings for noses, ears and fingers were also worn by Canaanite women.

39

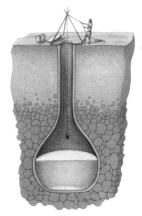

Water supply
People depended mainly on springs, rainwater and wells for drinking, household use and farming. Rainwater was stored in deep underground cisterns with narrow necks (above), which prevented the water from drying up or becoming polluted. Few houses had their own well or cistern, so women fetched water every day from the local spring or well, where everyone met to gossip and chat.

Camels
Their speed, strength and ability to survive without water for long periods made camels invaluable for desert travelling. Above, an Israelite with a heavily laden camel, from an Assyrian relief, about 700 BCE.

40

Rebekah did not hesitate. "I will go," she replied.

Abraham's servant prepared his camels, while Rebekah said goodbye to her family. She knew that she was about to go on a long journey to a strange land, to marry a man she had never even met.

When at last the travellers drew near to Isaac's house, Rebekah saw a man from a long way off. It was Isaac, who was out walking in the fields. He looked up at the same time and saw the line of camels approaching. As he came toward them, Rebekah asked Abraham's servant, "Who is that man coming to meet us?"

"That is my master's son, Isaac," the servant replied, as Rebekah modestly lifted a veil to cover her face.

Isaac loved Rebekah as soon as he met her, and they were both very happy that she was to become his wife.

JACOB AND ESAU

For a long time after they were married, Rebekah and Isaac had no children. Isaac prayed to God to let his wife become pregnant, and soon Rebekah was expecting not just one baby, but twins. God told Rebekah that the two children would themselves be the founding fathers of different peoples and that the younger child would be stronger than the older one.

The first twin to be born was named Esau. The second twin was born holding on to his brother's heel, and they named him Jacob. As the two boys grew up, their parents saw that they were very different characters. Esau loved the outdoors, and he soon became a skillful hunter. This made him his father's favourite, because Isaac loved eating the meat of wild animals. Jacob, on the other hand, was much happier staying at home, and was his mother's favourite.

One day, when Jacob was cooking some lentil soup, his brother came rushing in from the fields. Esau was very hungry and said to Jacob: "Quick, give me some of that soup, I'm starving!"

Jacob saw an opportunity to get something out of his brother, so he replied: "I'll give you some soup if you'll agree to give me your rights as the first-born son."

"Well, I'm dying of hunger," Esau replied, "so I might as well." Before handing over the soup, Jacob made Esau promise to give up his birthright to him. Esau promised, and Jacob gave him a bowl of steaming soup and some bread. Esau ate it quickly and then got up and left. He didn't give another thought to the birthright he had just promised away.

Some years later, when Isaac was old and blind, he called for Esau, his first-born son. Isaac knew that he did not have long to live and he wanted to give Esau his blessing. "My son," he said, "Take your bow and arrows and hunt some deer, so that you can make me some of the stew that I like to eat. Then I will give you my blessing."

41

> AND THE LORD SAID UNTO HER, TWO NATIONS ARE IN THY WOMB, AND TWO MANNER OF PEOPLE SHALL BE SEPARATED FROM THY BOWELS; AND THE ONE PEOPLE SHALL BE STRONGER THAN THE OTHER PEOPLE; AND THE ELDER SHALL SERVE THE YOUNGER.
>
> (Genesis 25.23)

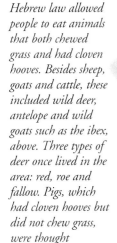

Rebekah overheard her husband's words, and when Esau had gone hunting, she rushed to Jacob. She told her favourite son what Isaac had said. "Listen carefully and do exactly as I say," Rebekah went on. "Go and get me two of our best young goats, so that I can make some stew for your father just the way he likes it. Then you can take it to him and get his blessing before he dies."

But Jacob was worried. "What if my father touches me?" he asked. "Esau is much hairier than me, and if my father realises that I am trying to trick him, he may curse me instead of blessing me."

Rebekah had a plan for this,

Wild animals
Hebrew law allowed people to eat animals that both chewed grass and had cloven hooves. Besides sheep, goats and cattle, these included wild deer, antelope and wild goats such as the ibex, above. Three types of deer once lived in the area: red, roe and fallow. Pigs, which had cloven hooves but did not chew grass, were thought "unclean" and their meat was forbidden.

too. She gave Jacob some of Esau's clothes to wear, and wrapped a hairy goatskin around his smooth arms and neck. Then she made a tasty stew from the goats' meat and gave a bowl to Jacob to take to his father.

"Who is it?" Isaac asked as Jacob approached him.

"It's Esau, your first-born son," Jacob replied.

Isaac could smell the tasty stew, but he thought the voice sounded like Jacob's. "How did you hunt the deer so quickly?" he asked. "The Lord God gave me success," said Jacob. "Come closer, my son," said Isaac. When he touched Jacob's hairy arms, Isaac was convinced that it was Esau. He blessed his son as the head of the whole family.

Just after Jacob had left his father, Esau came in from hunting and made a stew from the deer he had caught. Then he took a bowl of it to Isaac.

"Who is it?" Isaac asked.

"It's your first-born son, Esau," came the reply.

When Isaac heard Esau's voice, he was horrified. "Who was it who came earlier?" he wailed. "And who have I just blessed?"

Both Isaac and Esau knew very well who it must have been. "This is the second time that Jacob has deceived me," Esau cried. "First he took my birthright and now he has taken my blessing."

As he left his father, Esau was so furious that he vowed to kill his brother. When Rebekah heard of this, she went straight to Jacob and told him that he must leave at once. She said that he should go to the city of Haran and stay with his uncle, Laban. Then she told Isaac that she thought Jacob should go back to Mesopotamia, where she had come from and find a wife for himself. Isaac agreed and so Jacob left his home and set out on a long journey.

43

The Edomites
Believed to be the descendants of Esau, the Edomites settled in the land of Edom — dry, mountainous country south of the Dead Sea. They were enemies of the Hebrews, who conquered them many times and thought of them as "enemies of God". Above, a horned head of an Edomite goddess.

JACOB'S DREAM

Sacred stone pillars
In the time of the patriarchs, it was a religious custom to carve stone pillars, which people visited when they wanted to worship their gods. The one above is from a Canaanite temple dedicated to the Moon god. Such pillars were forbidden in Hebrew law.

Jacob left his own home and set out for his mother's home town of Haran, a journey that would take many days. When it started to get dark at the end of the first day, Jacob stopped to rest for the night. He found a flat stone to use as a pillow and lay down to sleep. He was so tired that he fell asleep at once.

During the night, Jacob had a dream. In it he saw a long staircase that stretched all the way from earth to heaven. Angels were going up and down the staircase and at the very top was God, who spoke to Jacob. "I am the God of your grandfather Abraham and your father Isaac," he said. "I will give you and your children the land on which you are lying. Your descendants will spread out from this land all over the earth and I will bless all the people of the world through you and your children. I will be with you and take care of you wherever you go."

When Jacob woke up, he thought: "God must be in this wondrous place, even though I was not aware of it when I stopped here. This must be the house of God and the gate of heaven."

Early next morning, as soon as it was light, Jacob took the stone that he had used to rest his head and set it up as a pillar. He poured oil on top of the stone and named the place Bethel, which means "house of God".

Then Jacob made a solemn vow. "If God will take care of me on this journey and bring me safely home again, then he will be my Lord for ever." Having made his vow, Jacob left the stone pillar and continued on his journey to Haran.

Jacob's dream
Jacob's vision was a very important story. It shows that God can still make promises to someone who does not always obey him. He tells him, "I will not leave you until I have done all that I have promised you." Right: Jacob's dream, from a medieval manuscript.

AND JACOB WENT OUT FROM BEERSHEBA,
AND WENT TOWARDS HARAN.
AND HE LIGHTED UPON A CERTAIN PLACE,
AND TARRIED THERE ALL NIGHT, BECAUSE
THE SUN WAS SET; AND HE TOOK OF THE
STONES OF THAT PLACE, AND PUT THEM
FOR HIS PILLOWS, AND LAY DOWN IN THAT
PLACE TO SLEEP.
AND HE DREAMED, AND BEHOLD A
STAIRCASE SET UP ON THE EARTH, AND THE
TOP OF IT REACHED TO HEAVEN: AND
BEHOLD THE ANGELS OF GOD ASCENDING
AND DESCENDING ON IT.

(Genesis 28.10–12)

Jacob Meets Rachel

And it came to pass, when Jacob saw Rachel the daughter of Laban his mother's brother, and the sheep of Laban his mother's brother, that Jacob went near, and rolled the stone from the well's mouth, and watered the flock of Laban his mother's brother. And Jacob kissed Rachel, and lifted up his voice, and wept.

(Genesis 29.10–11)

46

Jacob continued on his way to the city of Haran. Just outside the walls of the city he came to a field, where he saw a small group of shepherds looking after their flocks of sheep. There was a well in the field, which was covered by a large, flat rock. At the end of each day, when the sheep were thirsty, they would all gather around the well. Then the shepherds would push the stone away from the mouth of the well, draw water, and let their sheep drink.

Jacob asked the shepherds where they were from. He was pleased when they replied that they lived in Haran. "Then you must know my uncle Laban?" Jacob asked.

"Yes, we know him," one of the shepherds replied.

"Are he and his family well?" Jacob asked.

"No, it's too early," said another of the shepherds. "We only move the rock aside and give the sheep water when they have all gathered at the well."

By this time Rachel had arrived with her sheep. Jacob stepped forward, pushed the stone away from the well and drew water for the sheep. Rachel was grateful for his help. Then Jacob told her with a smile that he was the son of Rebekah, her father's sister.

Rachel was delighted to meet her cousin and Jacob embraced her. Then she ran off to tell her father the good news. As soon as Laban heard about Jacob, he rushed out of the city to meet him. There was soon another joyful meeting, and Laban told Jacob that he must come and stay at his house in Haran.

There Laban introduced Jacob to his other daughter, whose name was Leah. She was older than Rachel, but not nearly as beautiful. Jacob was pleased to meet her, but he only had eyes for her younger sister. He was happy to be able to stay at their father's house, and he soon made himself useful by helping to look after the flocks of sheep.

"Yes, they are well," answered the shepherd. "In fact, Laban's daughter Rachel is just coming this way across the field with some of her father's sheep."

Jacob looked round and saw a beautiful young woman leading sheep towards the well. "The sun is still high in the sky," Jacob said to the shepherds, "but isn't it time to give your sheep water?"

Sheep and goats
A family's wealth was often measured by the number of animals it kept. Sheep and goats provided valuable milk, meat, wool and leather and goatskins were made into bottles for storing water, wine or milk. Herds of sheep and goats were allowed to graze freely together, watched over by shepherds, who guarded them from thieves and wild animals. Both sheep and goats were used in religious sacrifices. This stone bowl (below), made about 3000 BCE, is decorated with longhorn sheep.

47

Jacob Works Long and Hard

Jacob was very happy at the house of his uncle, Laban. When he had been staying there for a month, his uncle took him to one side. "Just because you are my nephew, it doesn't mean that you should work for me for nothing," he said. "Tell me what I can pay you."

Jacob was in love with Laban's younger daughter Rachel, so he knew immediately what to ask for. "I'll be very happy to work for you for seven years without any pay," Jacob said, "if you will then let me marry your daughter Rachel."

Jacob was overjoyed when Laban agreed to his suggestion. His love for Rachel was so strong that time passed quickly as he worked for his uncle. Seven long years seemed little more than a few short weeks to him, though he never forgot their agreement for a single hour.

When the seven years had passed, Jacob went to Laban and reminded him of his promise. Laban stuck to their agreement and made arrangements at once for a great wedding feast. He invited all the people of the neighbourhood to celebrate the marriage of Jacob and Rachel. After the feast, however, when Laban was supposed to take the bride to her husband, he took his older daughter, Leah, instead. Since it was already dark, he knew that Jacob would not realise that his bride was Leah rather than Rachel.

Laban's plan worked, but when dawn broke the next day, Jacob saw at once that he had spent the night with the wrong sister. He ran to his uncle to complain. "Why have you done this to me?" Jacob cried. "I have served you for seven years, and all you can do is cheat me."

"It is not our custom for a younger daughter to get married before an older one," Laban explained calmly. "But if you will celebrate your marriage to Leah for a week, then you can marry her younger sister as well — in return for another seven years' work, of course."

At that time it was not unusual for a man to have several wives and Jacob was still as keen as ever to marry Rachel. So he agreed to another seven years' work. A week later, when the celebrations of his marriage to Leah were over, Rachel became Jacob's second bride.

Jacob was happy to go on working for his uncle now that Rachel was also his wife, for he loved her dearly. Leah was sad that her husband had so little love for her, but she was pleased when she became pregnant before her younger sister. She soon gave birth to a baby boy and she named him Reuben, which means "See, a son". When she had given birth to three more sons before Rachel had even become pregnant, Leah said: "God has listened to my prayers. He has given me children because he knows that my husband does not love me."

Rachel was very jealous of her sister and she was desperate to have a child. "Give me a baby or I'll die!" she screamed at Jacob. But this just made her husband angry. "Do you think I am God?" he asked. "He has kept you from having children, not me."

As the years passed, Jacob took the sisters' maidservants as his third and fourth wives. They too gave birth to sons, and Rachel could only watch and weep as the other women brought up Jacob's children. Then God remembered Rachel and took pity on her. Before long she too gave birth to a son, and she named him Joseph.

The bride
On her wedding day, the bride wore a veil and her own special wedding clothes. She also wore jewels, some of which were gifts from her husband-to-be. She may have looked similar to this modern Berber girl (above), who is dressed for marriage.

49

The wedding feast
In Bible times, people married young, as they do in many places today. Weddings were arranged by the parents, often to someone within the same family. The groom's family had to pay a "bride-price" to the girl's father. Sometimes, as in Jacob's story, it was paid with work. In return, the bride's family gave a "dowry", a present to the groom's family, which might be land, property or servants. When the new home was ready, the wedding took place. A banquet was held (left), accompanied by music and dancing.

JACOB AND ESAU BECOME FRIENDS AGAIN

Household gods
God's people often deserted him to worship the "false gods" of their neighbours. Above, this small statue of Astarte, a Canaanite goddess, might have been like one of the household idols that Rachel stole from Laban. Perhaps she hoped that it would bring prosperity to her new family, or would grant her and Jacob many children.

One night God appeared to Jacob in a dream and told him to go home to Canaan. Next morning, while Laban was out in the fields, Jacob told his wives and children to get ready for the journey. Rachel quickly took her father's treasured household gods and, without telling Jacob, put them with her belongings.

The whole family set off without telling Laban. As soon as he found out that they had gone, he hurried after them. Eventually he caught up with Jacob and his family, who were resting in their tents. Laban was very angry. "Why did you carry off my daughters and grandchildren?" he asked his nephew. "You didn't even let me say goodbye, and to make things worse, you stole my gods."

"I was afraid you would stop your daughters from coming with me," Jacob replied. "But I did not take your gods, and if you find them here, whoever took them will die."

So Laban searched Jacob's tent, but found nothing. Next he searched Leah's tent, and finally he went to Rachel. His younger daughter had hidden the gods inside her camel's saddle, and she was sitting on it in her tent. Laban quickly looked through the tent, but found nothing. Jacob was quick to point out to his uncle that he had been mistaken, and Laban accepted this. The two men agreed that they had both been wrong

JACOB BECOMES ISRAEL

☞ The change of Jacob's name means that the old cheating Jacob is no more. The wrestling may have happened inside himself rather than with a real person. Jacob's name now becomes that of the nation Israel, and his twelve sons become the ancestors of the Twelve Tribes of Israel.

— Jacob for leaving without warning, and Laban for accusing him of stealing. They promised never to behave badly to each other again.

Next morning, Laban returned home, and Jacob and his family continued on their journey. Jacob sent messengers to his brother Esau to tell him that he was coming home. He also sent presents of sheep, cattle and goats. That night he sent the others on ahead so that he could be alone to think. When it was dark, a man appeared from nowhere and took hold of Jacob. The two men wrestled with each other for hours, but neither would give in. Finally the stranger touched Jacob on the hip and put it out of joint. He asked Jacob's name, and then he said: "You will no longer be called Jacob. From now on your name will be Israel, because you have succeeded in your struggles with God and your fellow human beings."

With that, the stranger disappeared. Israel means "he struggles with God" — and Jacob knew then who the stranger he had wrestled with must be.

Jacob was very nervous about seeing his brother again, and was even more worried when he heard that Esau was coming to meet him with four hundred men. Thinking they might be attacked, Jacob moved Rachel and Joseph to the back of the party, where he thought they would be safe. Then he went on ahead to face his brother. Esau ran up to him, threw his arms around him and wept tears of joy.

"Why did you send me those presents?" Esau asked.

"To win back your friendship," Jacob replied.

"I have more than enough," said Esau. "Keep what you have, brother." But to please Jacob, he accepted the presents and the brothers became friends again.

AND ESAU RAN TO MEET HIM, AND EMBRACED HIM, AND FELL ON HIS NECK, AND KISSED HIM: AND THEY WEPT. AND HE LIFTED UP HIS EYES, AND SAW THE WOMEN AND THE CHILDREN; AND SAID, WHO ARE THOSE WITH THEE? AND HE SAID, THE CHILDREN WHICH GOD HATH GRACIOUSLY GIVEN THY SERVANT.

(Genesis 33.4–5)

JOSEPH AND HIS BROTHERS

J acob and his favourite wife, Rachel, were delighted when she gave birth to her first child, who was named Joseph.

Sadly, Rachel died a few years later giving birth to her second son, whose name was Benjamin. Jacob also had many children by his other wives — he had twelve sons altogether. This meant that young Joseph grew up in a large family, surrounded by his half-brothers.

Jacob's undying love for Rachel meant that Joseph was his favourite son. This did not escape the notice of Joseph's half-brothers, who were angry that their father loved Joseph more than any of them. They hated Joseph even more when his father gave him a special present — a beautiful, multi-coloured robe.

Joseph was a dreamer, and this annoyed his brothers, too. He insisted on telling them about his dreams, in which he always seemed to be superior. One day Joseph said to his brothers: "I had an amazing dream last night. Just listen to this! We were all together out in the fields, tying up sheaves of corn. Suddenly the sheaf I was tying stood up straight, all on its own. Then your sheaves all made a circle around mine and bowed down to it."

The dream annoyed the brothers. "Do you expect us to bow down to you?" one of them asked Joseph. "What do you want — to rule over us?" another snarled as he wandered off.

A few days later Joseph had another strange dream, and once again he described it to the others. "Listen to this," he said. "I dreamed that the sun, the moon and eleven stars in the sky were bowing down to me." This time the brothers said nothing, but they all noticed that Joseph said he dreamed of eleven stars — then Joseph went to tell his father about the latest dream, Jacob noticed what the brothers had noticed. To Joseph's surprise, Jacob told him off. "What is this dream supposed to mean?" the old man asked. "Is it that you expect your parents and all your brothers to bow down to you?" The strange dream made Jacob think: perhaps his favourite son had been chosen to play

Migrations
In Joseph's time, there was a constant flow of people moving from Canaan to Egypt in search of work and food. Some, like Joseph, were sold into slavery. The Egyptian fresco below shows a group of Hebrew wanderers — perhaps on their way to trade or possibly to settle. Joseph's "coat of many colours" may have been like the brightly patterned clothes worn by the men, centre right.

a special role in the family?

Some weeks later, Jacob called for Joseph to send him on an errand. "Your brothers are out in the fields near Shechem, grazing the sheep," Jacob said. "Go and see if everything is all right with them and the flocks. Hurry there, then come back and let me know."

"Very well, father," Joseph replied, setting off at once. But when he reached Shechem, there was no sign of his brothers or the sheep. A man told him that they had moved on toward Dothan, so Joseph hurried on to look for them there.

Near Dothan, one of the brothers spotted Joseph from a long way off. "Here comes that dreamer in his colourful robe!" he said. "This is our chance. Let's kill him and throw his body into a pit. We can say that a wild animal must have killed him. Then we'll see what comes of his fancy dreams."

When Leah's son Reuben heard this, he tried to dissuade the others. "Let's not shed any blood," he said. "We could just throw him into a pit to teach him a lesson." As Reuben was the oldest, the other brothers listened to him. When Joseph arrived, they grabbed him, stripped him of his multicolored robe and threw him into a deep pit. Reuben went off to tend the sheep and the other brothers sat down to eat their midday meal. As they ate, the brothers saw a group

54

Slavery
In the time of Joseph, buying slaves was an accepted, though not a usual, way of obtaining servants or labourers. Prisoners of war were made slaves of the nation that captured them. In ancient Egypt, slaves were generally treated well. Above, statue of an Egyptian slave.

of merchants approaching. Their camels were loaded with spices, which they were taking to Egypt. One of the brothers, whose name was Judah, had an idea. "Why don't we sell Joseph to those merchants?" he said. "That way we'll earn something from him."

The other brothers thought this was an excellent idea and stood up to greet the merchants. A price was soon agreed and Joseph was sold as a slave for twenty pieces of silver. The merchants and their camels slowly went on their way.

When Reuben came back from tending the sheep, he looked into the pit and saw that it was empty and was very upset — he had intended to save Joseph later and take him back home. "Where can he be?"

he asked his brothers. Then they told him about the merchants. As they did so, they realised that they would have to make up a story for their father.

One of the brothers killed a goat and dipped Joseph's robe in its blood. Then they went home and showed the blood-stained robe to Jacob. "Is this Joseph's robe?" they asked innocently.

Jacob recognised the multi-coloured robe at once. "This is my own dear son's robe," he cried. "He must have been killed by a wild animal and torn to pieces." All Jacob's sons and daughters came to comfort him, but he would not be consoled. He could only weep and say: "I will go to my own grave mourning the death of my dear son Joseph."

THE TWELVE TRIBES OF ISRAEL

☞ The families of Jacob's twelve sons grew to become the twelve tribes of Israel. This family tree shows Abraham's descendants and the names of Jacob's twelve sons, corresponding to the names of the tribes that later made up the nation of Israel.

56

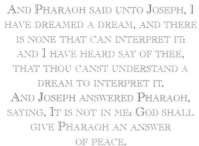

**Mistress of
the house**
*Wealthy Egyptian
women lived in a
separate area of the
house from their
husbands. They had
many servants who
took care of the
housework and also
helped them with
their make-up and
clothes. Above, two
Egyptian ladies with
flowers at a banquet.*

THE PHARAOH'S DREAMS

When the merchants who had bought Joseph from his brothers reached Egypt, they sold him to the captain of the pharaoh's guard. Joseph lived in the house of his new Egyptian master, whose name was Potiphar, and before long became his personal attendant. Joseph was such a good worker that he was soon put in charge of the entire household.

Joseph was a handsome man, and Potiphar's wife took a great liking to him, but Joseph's behaviour made it clear that he was not prepared to deceive his master. Then one day he was left alone with the mistress of the house, and she took the opportunity to try and persuade him to make love to her. Joseph was horrified. "My master has put his whole house in my care," he said to Potiphar's wife. "He has made me the most important person in the house, apart from you. How could I ever let him down?"

But the mistress, who was not to be put off, took hold of Joseph's cloak. As Joseph quickly made a move to leave, Potiphar's wife tore the cloak from him. She was furious and screamed and called for her servants. When the servants came running in, she said that Joseph had tried to force himself upon her. When Potiphar came home, she repeated her story and showed him the cloak. "That Hebrew slave of yours forced his way into my room," she cried. "When I screamed for help, he ran away so fast that he left his cloak."

Potiphar had Joseph thrown straight into prison. There, Joseph again proved himself very useful. He helped the jailers and was put in charge of looking after other prisoners. When the pharaoh's chief butler and baker were sent to prison for displeasing their master, they were put into Joseph's care.

One night the two new prisoners both had strange dreams and next morning they told them to Joseph. The butler had dreamed of a grapevine with three branches, from which he took ripened grapes and squeezed wine into the pharaoh's cup. He wanted to know what the dream meant. "The three branches are three days," Joseph explained. "In three days the pharaoh will give you your old position back, and you will put wine in his cup, just as you used to. When this happens, please remember me and mention me to the pharaoh, so that I can get out of prison, too."

Next, the baker told Joseph his dream. "I had three baskets on my head," he said. "There were loaves of bread for the pharaoh in the top basket and birds flew down and pecked at them. What can it mean?"

"The three baskets are three days," Joseph said. "In three days the pharaoh will have you hanged and birds will peck at you." And what Joseph forecast came true. Three days later the pharaoh celebrated his birthday with a feast, for which he called the butler back into his service. But he had the baker hanged.

Unfortunately for Joseph, the butler forgot to mention his name to the pharaoh. Then, two years later, the pharaoh had strange dreams and asked who could interpret them for him. He sent for all the wise men of Egypt, but no one could make any sense of them. Only then did the butler remember Joseph. He told his master how the young Hebrew had explained his dream correctly. So the pharaoh sent for Joseph and told him two of his own strange dreams.

In the first dream, the pharaoh had seen seven fat cows come out of the River Nile. They were followed by seven thin cows, which ate up the fat ones, but themselves remained thin. In the second dream, the pharaoh had seen seven ripe ears of wheat growing on a single stalk. Then seven scrawny ears swallowed up the ripe wheat. What could the dreams mean?

"Both dreams mean the same thing," Joseph explained. "The fat cows and ripe ears of wheat are seven

Wine
Grapes grow well in Israel and the northern Delta region of Egypt. Besides being eaten fresh, grapes were dried to eat as raisins or fermented to make wine. Below, a wall-painting of Egyptians harvesting grapes.

years of plenty, and the thin cows and scrawny ears of wheat are seven years of famine. Egypt will soon have seven years of good harvests, followed by seven years of famine. You must put one of your men in charge of all food supplies, so that extra grain is stored for use in poor years."

"Your plan is a good one," the pharaoh told Joseph and he made him his chief minister, in charge of all the food in Egypt. Before long, Joseph was travelling up and down the River Nile, building storehouses in the cities and organizing the collection of grain.

Cereal crops
Barley and wheat were widely grown in ancient Egypt. Both were ground to make flour for baking. Barley was also used to brew beer. After being harvested, the grain was winnowed (above) to separate it from the chaff. The grain was stored in granaries, or barns.

58

CHIEF MINISTER OF EGYPT

As chief minister to the pharaoh, Joseph was an important man. He dressed in robes made of the finest linen and, with the pharaoh's agreement, married the daughter of an Egyptian priest. In due course, his wife gave birth to two sons. Joseph — as the pharaoh expected — was a good chief minister, organizing the country well. Every Egyptian city began storing grain, harvested from the fields alongside the River Nile.

At first the harvests were good. Just as Joseph had predicted, there was a seven-year period of plenty in Egypt. Huge quantities of grain were stored in the cities. Before long, the storehouses were so full that Joseph lost count of just how much grain they held. But, just as Joseph had said, when the seven years of plenty came to an end, they were followed by seven years when the crops failed to grow.

The harvests were so poor that severe famine struck the whole of Egypt, as well as neighbouring lands. The Egyptians turned to their ruler, the pharaoh, for help. He told them to go to Joseph, who began opening the storehouses and selling grain to the Egyptians. There was so much stored grain that Joseph also sold quantities of it to people from other starving countries.

Famine had struck the land of Canaan, too, and Joseph's father, Jacob — who thought that his favourite son had been killed by a wild animal — decided to send his sons to buy grain in Egypt. Jacob sent all his sons but one: he was afraid that harm might come to his youngest son, Benjamin, so he kept him at home.

When ten of Jacob's sons reached Egypt, they went to see the famous chief minister who governed the sale of grain. As they approached him, the brothers all bowed down — not realizing that this was their own brother. Joseph recognised them at once, but pretended not to. He was thinking of the dreams he had had all

The Nile
Life in Egypt depended on the yearly flood of the great River Nile. Each year the water would overflow its channels, depositing rich soil on the surrounding land. This yearly flood allowed farming, hunting and fishing to flourish. If the flood failed, there was no water for the crops and no food to eat.

59

Chief minister
The chief minister, the highest of a group of officials who administered the kingdom of Egypt, was second only to the pharaoh. Above, a bronze statue of a chief minister.

AND JOSEPH SAW HIS BRETHREN, AND HE KNEW THEM, BUT MADE HIMSELF STRANGE UNTO THEM, AND SPAKE ROUGHLY UNTO THEM; AND HE SAID UNTO THEM, WHENCE COME YE? AND THEY SAID, FROM THE LAND OF CANAAN TO BUY FOOD. AND JOSEPH KNEW HIS BRETHREN, BUT THEY KNEW NOT HIM.

(Genesis 42.7–8)

those years ago. "Where are you from?" he asked the brothers.

"From Canaan, my lord," one of the brothers replied. "We have come to buy grain."

"I don't believe you!" Joseph cried. "You are spies, come to find out what's going on in Egypt."

The brothers protested their innocence. "We are honest men, all

brothers," said one. "There were twelve of us, but our father would not let our youngest brother come with us, and another brother is dead."

"I will give you a chance to prove your honesty," Joseph said. "You can take grain back to your starving land, but then you must bring your youngest brother to me. Then I will know that you are telling the truth. In the meantime, one of you must stay here as my prisoner."

The brothers knew that they had little choice but to agree. "I told you not to harm our brother Joseph," Reuben said to the others. "But you wouldn't listen, and now we are being punished for it." The brothers did not realise that the chief minister could understand what they were saying, because he had spoken to them through an interpreter. Joseph turned away as he felt tears spring to his eyes, but he quickly recovered himself, and his brothers were too frightened and worried to notice his strange behaviour.

When the brothers had paid in silver, Joseph had their sacks filled with grain. Then he secretly told his men to slip the pouches of silver into the grain sacks. Simeon, the second son of Leah, agreed to stay as a hostage, and Joseph ordered him to be bound and imprisoned, while the others set off on their donkeys.

When they reached home, the brothers told Jacob of all that had happened to them in Egypt. Then, as they emptied their sacks, they each found their own pouch of silver as well as the grain. This worried Jacob, because it didn't make sense. "My son Joseph is dead, my son Simeon is in prison and now you want to take my youngest son Benjamin away from me," he cried. "But if any harm were to come to him, it would surely kill me. No, you cannot take Benjamin to this chief minister in Egypt."

Canaanite visitors
This Egyptian wall-painting from the 14th century BCE shows Canaanites offering gifts to the pharaoh. The sort of pots they are carrying were used to hold expensive oils, spices or fine wine.

Grain storage
This wall painting, made about 1400 BCE, shows servants measuring and recording a harvest of grain. Most people's taxes were paid in grain, which was sent to state-owned granaries under the authority of officials such as Joseph.

Benjamin and the Silver Cup

Israel in Egypt

☞ The story of Joseph is important because it explains how the children of Israel came to be in Egypt, which remained their homeland for the next 300 years. The book of Genesis ends with Joseph's last words to his brothers: "I die: and God will surely visit you, and bring you out of this land unto the land which he sware to Abraham, to Isaac and to Jacob."

62

When his family had eaten all the grain that had been brought from Egypt, Jacob told his sons to go back and buy more. They reminded him that the Egyptian chief minister had said they could only return if they brought their youngest brother Benjamin with them, but Jacob would not agree to this. Then Judah, the brother who had suggested selling Joseph to the merchants on their way to Egypt, spoke up. "You can hold me personally responsible for the safety of my youngest brother," he told Jacob. "If I do not bring him back to you, I will bear the blame all my life."

Jacob reluctantly agreed, telling his sons to take twice as much silver as last time, as well as gifts of nuts and spices for the chief minister of Egypt. The brothers set off at once. When they arrived in Egypt, Joseph was overjoyed to see his youngest brother with them, for Benjamin was his full brother (unlike the others, who were his half-brothers). Joseph told his men to take the brothers to his house and to release Simeon so he could join them.

When Joseph came home, the brothers all bowed to him before presenting their gifts. Joseph was so moved to see Benjamin again that he found it hard to hold back his tears. After the

brothers had been served a lavish meal, Joseph told his men to fill their sacks with grain. Then he told his steward to slip the pouches of silver into the grain sacks and put a special silver cup in Benjamin's sack.

Next day, the eleven brothers set off for home. They had not gone far when an Egyptian horseman caught up with them. It was the minister's steward, who accused them of stealing his master's silver cup. The brothers agreed to open their sacks and, when Benjamin opened his, there — to their horror — was the cup. They were arrested and taken back to the chief minister's house.

When Joseph heard the steward's report, he said: "The one who was found with the cup must stay as my servant. The rest of you can go back to your father." Joseph's plan for keeping Benjamin with him in Egypt appeared to have worked, until Judah stepped forward and said that they could never return without Benjamin, for it would break their father's heart. This was too much for Joseph, who sent his servants away and spoke to the brothers for the first time in their own language. At last it was time to tell them the truth. "I am Joseph, your long-lost brother," he said gently.

Joseph's brothers couldn't believe their ears. They looked very frightened. "Don't blame yourselves for selling me here," Joseph told them. "God sent me ahead of you to save lives. Now hurry back to our father and tell him what has happened. Ask him to come here with the whole family, children and grandchildren, as well as all his flocks and herds. We have had only two years of famine and there are another five to come." Then Joseph hugged them all, beginning with his younger brother Benjamin.

The brothers returned happily to Canaan. With the Pharaoh's agreement, Joseph sent carts, donkeys and bread as presents for his father, and these convinced Jacob that his sons' amazing story must be true. The whole family packed up their belongings and travelled with their animals to Egypt. There they settled in the region of Goshen, and Joseph looked after them and gave them food during the long years of famine.

When Jacob died some years later, his sons took his body back to Canaan to be buried, as he had wished. The Pharaoh sent some of his officials to see them safely on their way and ordered the Egyptian people to mourn Jacob for a period of seventy days. After burying his father in Canaan, Joseph returned to Egypt with his brothers, where they lived happily.

Mourning
When a person died, there was a public demonstration of grief by family and friends. They would weep, wail, tear their clothes, throw ashes over their heads and beat their breasts. Usually the period of mourning lasted seven days, but it was longer for someone as important as Joseph. Above, Egyptian women mourners.

63

AND JOSEPH SAID UNTO HIS BRETHREN, COME NEAR TO ME, I PRAY YOU. AND THEY CAME NEAR. AND HE SAID, I AM JOSEPH YOUR BROTHER, WHOM YE SOLD INTO EGYPT. NOW THEREFORE BE NOT GRIEVED, NOR ANGRY WITH YOURSELVES, THAT YE SOLD ME HITHER: FOR GOD DID SEND ME BEFORE YOU TO PRESERVE LIFE.

(Genesis 45.4–5)

In the Land of Egypt

The pharaoh
The king of Egypt, also called the pharaoh, had absolute power: he was the earthly ruler, military leader and chief priest of his people. In this sculpture, above, Pharaoh Menkaure, builder of the third pyramid at Giza, stands between two Egyptian goddesses.

All but three per cent of Egypt is desert. In biblical times, the prosperity of the whole country depended on the annual mid-summer flooding of the River Nile, which left a deposit of rich, fertile soil across the valley floor. Without this, crops could not grow and people starved. Nomadic herdsmen and their families from the Arabian deserts were allowed to settle in a valley in the eastern delta. This valley was known then as the "Land of Goshen". Among these wanderers were the Israelites, who must have been amazed and awed by Egypt's splendid temples, palaces and pyramids. In time, many of the Israelites who settled in Egypt themselves became rich and held important positions.

The pharaoh was looked upon as a living god. While he was alive, he was the god Horus, and after his death he was worshipped as the god Osiris. The official religion included 2,000 gods and goddesses. At their head were Amun and the sun god Ra. In the Egyptians' religion, death and the afterlife were of great importance. The bodies of important people were preserved (mummified) and placed in tombs deep inside the pyramids, together with things it was believed they would need in the afterlife. All these preparations for death helped the Egyptians to develop medical knowledge, as well as skills in maths, writing and building.

The pharaoh was the head of government, society and religion, but most of his duties were performed by city-governors, who were themselves helped by other officials.

Sometime during the New Kingdom (1570–1075 BCE) — perhaps when Egyptian power and

Ramses II
Ramses II in his war chariot. He lived from 1279 to 1213 BCE. A famous military leader, he led his armies successfully against the Hittites, a warlike people living in what is now Greece and Turkey.

Mummification
The Egyptians developed a method of preventing dead bodies from decaying. It was called mummification. This picture shows a mummy being prepared by a priest, who wears a mask of the jackal-headed god of the dead, Anubis.

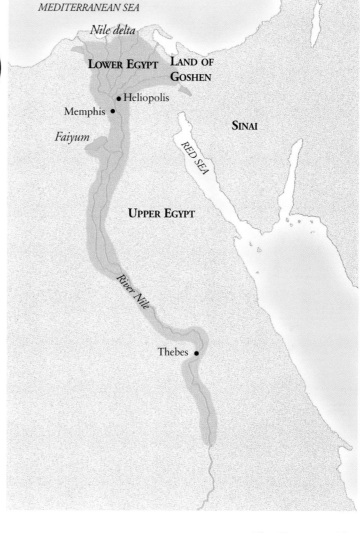

influence was declining — a new pharaoh (probably Ramses II) turned against settlers such as the Israelites who had come to Egypt from other countries. He pressed them into slavery and put them to work on building sites, where they provided valuable labour.

It was the departure, or Exodus, of the Israelites from Egypt, led by Moses, that marked the birth of Israel as a nation.

The Giza pyramids
More than 80 royal pyramids were built in Egypt. They were amazing feats of engineering and construction, built using huge stone blocks that fitted precisely together. The great age of pyramid building reached its peak with the three giant pyramids, left, at Giza, north of Memphis.

BABY MOSES

The people of Egypt thought that there were too many Israelites in their land. So the Pharaoh ordered that every baby boy born to the people of Israel must be thrown into the River Nile to drown.

Shortly after this command had been given, an Israelite woman gave birth to a beautiful baby boy. The mother could not bear to lose her baby, so she hid him for three months. But as the baby grew bigger and his cries got louder, she knew that she could not go on hiding him.

The woman took a basket made of reeds and coated it with pitch to make it waterproof. Then she put her baby in the basket and carried it to the river. She placed the basket in the water, among the tall bulrushes that grew near the bank.

The woman's young daughter, Miriam, had gone with her mother, and waited on the bank to see

what would happen to her baby brother.

Soon the Pharaoh's daughter came to the river to bathe. She saw the basket in the bulrushes, and told one of her servants to bring it to her.

When the princess looked into the basket, the baby woke up and started to cry. "This is one of the Israelite babies," the princess said, feeling sorry for the child.

Just then, Miriam came out of her hiding place. "Shall I fetch one of the Hebrew women to nurse the baby?" she asked. The princess said yes, and the little girl rushed off home to call her mother.

Having no idea who she was, the Pharaoh's daughter said, "Take this baby, nurse him for me, and I will pay you." The mother carried her baby home, rejoicing that her clever plan had saved his life.

When the child was older, his mother took him to the Pharaoh's daughter. The princess named him Moses, and brought him up as her son.

Women in Egypt

Egyptian girls did not go to school, but stayed at home and learned from their mothers how to cook and weave. Most girls married young and devoted themselves to their families, but a few other occupations were available to them. They could work as servants, dancers, musicians, midwives, cloth-makers or professional mourners.

AND WHEN SHE COULD NO LONGER HIDE HIM, SHE
TOOK FOR HIM AN ARK OF BULRUSHES, AND DAUBED IT
WITH SLIME AND WITH PITCH, AND PUT THE CHILD
THEREIN; AND SHE LAID IT IN THE FLAGS BY THE
RIVER'S BRINK. AND HIS SISTER STOOD AFAR OFF, TO
WIT WHAT WOULD BE DONE TO HIM. AND THE
DAUGHTER OF PHARAOH CAME DOWN TO WASH
HERSELF AT THE RIVER; ... WHEN SHE SAW THE ARK
AMONG THE FLAGS, SHE SENT HER MAID TO FETCH IT.

(Exodus 2, 3–5)

Moses and the Burning Bush

Moses had been born and brought up in Egypt, but he never forgot that he was an Israelite. One day he saw an Egyptian savagely hitting a Hebrew slave as he was trying to make mudbricks. This made Moses very angry and, seeing no one else around, he rushed over, killed the Egyptian and hid the body.

Next day, Moses saw two Israelites fighting each other and rushed over to separate them. "Why are you hitting a fellow Israelite?" he asked one of the men. "What is it to you?" the man replied. "Are you thinking of killing me like you did that Egyptian?"

Now that his secret was out, Moses knew it would not be long before the Pharaoh heard of it. He fled at once to the barren land of Midian. There he met the seven daughters of a priest named Jethro, and helped them water their flocks. They invited him to their house, and some months later Moses married one of the daughters, Zipporah.

Moses became a shepherd. One day, when he was looking after Jethro's flocks, he saw a bush burning on the side of a hill. As he came closer, Moses saw that although the

AND MOSES SAID UNTO THE LORD,
O MY LORD, I AM NOT ELOQUENT,
NEITHER HERETOFORE, NOR SINCE
THOU HAST SPOKEN UNTO THY
SERVANT: BUT I AM SLOW OF SPEECH,
AND OF A SLOW TONGUE.
AND THE LORD SAID UNTO HIM,
WHO HATH MADE MAN'S MOUTH? OR
WHO MAKETH THE DUMB, OR DEAF,
OR THE SEEING, OR THE BLIND?
HAVE NOT I, THE LORD?
NOW THEREFORE GO, AND I WILL BE
WITH THY MOUTH, AND TEACH THEE
WHAT THOU SHALT SAY.

(Exodus 4,10–12)

bush was on fire, it was not being destroyed – it just kept burning. Then he heard the voice of God coming from the bush. "Moses, do not come any closer," the voice said. "Take off your sandals, for you are standing on holy ground."

God said that he had heard the cries of the Israelites who were suffering as slaves in Egypt, and that Moses must go back there to rescue them. "I am sending you to the Pharaoh to bring my people, the Israelites, out of Egypt," God said, as the bush went on burning. "You will bring them to a land that I promised to give to Abraham's descendants."

Moses was very worried by this task, and asked God to send someone else to do it. But God said he would be with Moses and that his brother Aaron would also help him convince the Egyptians to let the Israelites leave. Finally, God told Moses to keep his shepherd's stick with him, because he would be able to perform miracles with it. Moses knew that he must obey God.

Mount Horeb or Mount Sinai?
The location of Mount Horeb, or Mount Sinai — the place where God first revealed himself to Moses in the burning bush (left), and where Moses received God's laws — has never been identified.

LET MY PEOPLE GO

Moses put his wife and two sons on a donkey and set off for Egypt, which he knew was now ruled by a new Pharaoh. He was still not sure that he would be able to convince the new ruler to let the Israelites go, but he was pleased when he met Aaron on the way. Moses told his brother everything that God had said, including the miracles that he promised he would be able to perform.

When they arrived in Egypt, the two brothers called the Israelite elders together. Aaron told them everything that God had said to Moses, and the elders rejoiced that God had seen their people's misery. Then Moses and Aaron went to see the Pharaoh. Aaron told him that his Lord, the God of Israel, had commanded him to come and tell the Egyptian ruler: "Let my people go."

This only made the Pharaoh angry. "Who is this God and why should I obey him?" he asked. "I will not let the Israelites go. Instead, I will make them work harder!" The Pharaoh immediately issued orders to his slave-drivers that they were to stop supplying the Hebrew workers with straw for making mudbricks. The slaves would have to find their own straw wherever they could, but they still had to make the same number of bricks each day as they had done before. The Egyptians needed many bricks for their new city buildings.

The Israelites did all they could to find scraps of straw, but this held them up in their work and they made fewer bricks each day. "They are just being lazy!" said the Pharaoh, and he ordered his slave-drivers to beat the workers and their Israelite overseers. Before long the overseers went to Moses and Aaron, complaining that they had upset the Egyptians and made the situation much worse.

Moses was in despair. This task was just as difficult as he had thought when he first heard the voice in the burning bush. He asked God for help. "Why should the Pharaoh listen to me when I cannot even persuade my own people?" Moses asked.

"Your brother Aaron is to tell the Pharaoh once again to let my people go," God told Moses. "The Pharaoh will not listen, but I will perform mighty acts and the Egyptians will know that I am the Lord when I take my people out of their land. You and Aaron must go and see the Pharaoh again, and Aaron must throw down his stick in front of him."

Moses and Aaron did as God had commanded. When the Pharaoh again refused even to think about letting his Israelite slaves go, Aaron threw his stick down on the ground before him. At once the stick turned into a snake. Instead of being amazed, however, the Pharaoh called his

Brickmaking
Egyptians used sun-dried mudbricks in all their buildings, except the most important ones, which were made of stone. The mud was mixed with sand and straw to make it more workable and prevent it from cracking. Then it was put into moulds and baked in the sun. Below, slaves at work making mudbricks, from a wall painting at Thebes.

magicians and told them to throw down their sticks, just as Aaron had done. When the magicians obeyed, all their sticks turned into snakes. But before they could congratulate themselves, Aaron's snake gobbled up all the others.

Surely the Pharaoh will change his mind now, Moses thought. But he was wrong. The Egyptian ruler still refused to listen to them or to the command of God.

> AND AFTERWARD MOSES AND AARON WENT IN, AND TOLD PHARAOH, THUS SAITH THE LORD GOD OF ISRAEL, LET MY PEOPLE GO, THAT THEY MAY HOLD A FEAST UNTO ME IN THE WILDERNESS.
>
> (Exodus 5.1)

THE PLAGUES OF EGYPT

The plagues
Many scholars think that there may be natural explanations for the plagues sent by God to Egypt. Crops were often destroyed by migrating locusts, for example, and swarms of frogs appeared every year at the end of the Nile flood. This illustration, right, from a 14th century Hebrew manuscript from Spain, depicts the plague of frogs, gnats, flies and the death of livestock.

72

God had told Moses that he would perform mighty acts so that the Egyptians, who believed in many other gods and goddesses, would know that he was the true Lord. Now he told Moses and his brother Aaron to go down to the banks of the River Nile early in the morning, when the Pharaoh was there. "Touch the river with your stick," God said, "and its water will turn into blood." Moses and Aaron did as God commanded, telling the Pharaoh what they were going to do because he would not set their people free. But the Pharaoh took no notice.

Moses reached out and touched the river with his stick. At once the water turned into thick red blood. The Pharaoh's attendants were horrified, as it meant the Egyptians would have no water to drink. Soon all the fish of the Nile died and the river stank. But the Pharaoh said nothing. He simply went back to his palace as if nothing had happened.

Seven days later, God told Moses what to do next. Once again Moses went to see the Pharaoh. "God says that you must let his people go," Moses said. "Otherwise, there will be a plague of frogs throughout your land." When the Pharaoh refused, Aaron stretched his hand over the River Nile and thousands of frogs came jumping out. They hopped out of every pond, stream and canal and got into all the people's houses, including the royal palace. They also covered the farmers' fields. At last it seemed as if the Pharaoh was prepared to change his mind. He agreed to let the Israelites go if their God would take all the frogs away – and the very next day every single frog died. But when the Pharaoh saw this, he changed his mind and went back on his promise.

Then God told Aaron to touch the ground with his stick, and all the dust that lay there turned into gnats. Before long all the people and animals in Egypt were being tormented and bitten by millions of whining gnats. By now the Pharaoh's magicians were convinced that the plagues were being caused by the Israelite God, but their ruler would not listen to them.

God next sent swarms of flies and the buzzing insects got everywhere. Even the royal palace was full of them. But God made sure that there was not a single fly in the region of Goshen, where the Israelites lived. This was an extra sign of his power and it seemed to have an effect on the Pharaoh. Once again, he agreed to let the Israelites go if the plague of flies was lifted from the land. But once again he went back on his promise when God relieved his land of the plague.

Then God caused a deadly disease to strike the Egyptians' animals. All their horses, donkeys and camels were struck down, as well as their sheep and goats. But he left the Israelites' animals untouched. When the Egyptian ruler ignored this plague, God told Moses and Aaron to find handfuls of soot and throw them into the air. The soot covered everything with a fine dust, and soon all the Egyptian people were covered in painful, septic boils. Even the royal magicians fell ill, but it still did not persuade their ruler to agree to Moses' request.

God said to Moses: "Tell the Pharaoh that I could easily have wiped him and his people off the face of the earth, but I have spared them so that everyone can see my power. If the Pharaoh still will not let my people go, I will send the worst hailstorm ever to strike Egypt."

Moses did as he was commanded, but the Pharaoh still refused to listen. Then Moses stretched up his hand toward the sky, causing thunder to boom and lightning to flash across the land. Soon huge hailstones beat down everywhere, except on the region of Goshen. The hail struck down people and animals, stripped trees of their branches and leaves, and flattened crops.

At last, the Pharaoh called for Moses and said he would agree to let the Israelites go. "This time I realise that I am in the wrong," the Egyptian ruler said. "Your Lord is right, and I will let your people go, if only he will stop the hail and thunder." Moses stretched up his hand toward God in heaven and the storm

THUS SAITH THE LORD, IN THIS THOU SHALT KNOW THAT I AM THE LORD: BEHOLD, I WILL SMITE WITH THE ROD THAT IS IN MINE HAND UPON THE WATERS WHICH ARE IN THE RIVER, AND THEY SHALL BE TURNED TO BLOOD.
AND THE FISH THAT ARE IN THE RIVER SHALL DIE, AND THE RIVER SHALL STINK; AND THE EGYPTIANS SHALL LOATHE TO DRINK OF THE WATER OF THE RIVER.

(Exodus 7.17–18)

73

stopped as quickly as it had started. Moses felt sure that this time the Pharaoh would keep his word, but once the problem had gone away, he changed his mind yet again: the Israelites must stay in Egypt.

This time, God said he would send a plague of locusts to eat everything that was left in Egypt. When Moses told the Pharaoh this, his officials begged him to do something. So the Pharaoh told Moses that he would let the Israelite men go, but their women and children must stay in Egypt. When God heard this, he said to Moses, "Stretch out your hand over Egypt, and locusts will swarm over the land." Moses obeyed and a plague of locusts was blown in on the wind. There were millions of them and soon there was nothing green left in

the whole of Egypt – the locusts ate every single leaf.

When the Pharaoh agreed to let the Israelites go, God changed the direction of the wind and the locusts were blown away. But as soon as every locust had gone, the Pharaoh again changed his mind. So God told Moses to stretch up his hand to the sky and bring darkness over the land. Moses did as God said, and the whole of Egypt went dark – except in the region where the Israelites lived. It stayed dark for three whole days.

Finally the Pharaoh said: "If your God will stop these plagues, I will let your men, women and children go. But you must leave behind your animals." When Moses said this was impossible, the Pharaoh flew into a rage. "Get out of my sight!" he cried. "I will never let your people go!"

PASSOVER

God told Moses that the Pharaoh would refuse once again to let the Israelites leave Egypt, even when he was threatened with the final, worst plague of all. But this plague was going to be so terrible that the Egyptian ruler would be forced to change his mind at last and let God's people go. Moses went once more to the Pharaoh and told him what God had said. "At midnight the Lord God will visit Egypt," said Moses. "Then every first-born son will die, and this will include every Egyptian family, from the royal family of the Pharaoh to the poorest prisoner's family. Even the first-born of all your cattle will

die. A terrible cry will be heard throughout the land, but among the Israelites not a single child will be harmed. This is what God has told me. And after this, you and your officials will beg me and my people to leave Egypt." The Pharaoh still refused to listen, as Moses knew he would. Then Moses and his brother Aaron went to tell their fellow Israelites what God had told them to do to avoid the terrible disaster that awaited the Egyptians. God had said: "The father of every family must take a healthy young lamb or kid and slaughter it at twilight. Then they must take some of the animal's blood and daub it on

Lamb sacrifice
Moses told his people to sacrifice a lamb and to mark their doors with its blood, so that death would "pass over" their houses. Jewish families still celebrate the Passover today. They eat a special meal and retell the story of that last night in the land of Egypt.

75

Pesach

During the festival of Pesach (Passover), Jews celebrate the escape from Egypt by holding a special meal called Seder, at which the story of the Exodus is read. Below, a Seder plate, with sections for the different symbolic foods. These include roast lamb, unleavened bread (called matzoh), bitter herbs (a reminder of the slaves' tears) and haroseth, a mixture of honey, apples and nuts – symbolic of the mortar that the Israelites used when they worked as brick-makers in Egypt.

76

the door frame of their house. This will be a sign to me that the house is to be left alone when the Lord God comes to kill the first-born of Egypt. When I see the blood, I will pass over you and you will be safe."

Moses told the Israelites that there was more for them to do. The mother of each family was to roast the meat of the animal over a fire. Then the family were all to eat the roast meat, along with bitter herbs and bread made without yeast. They were to stay indoors during this special meal, but must keep on their outdoor cloaks and sandals, so that they could leave in a hurry. It was important that

all the Israelites should obey these instructions given by God. God had told Moses that future generations of Israelites would remember this day and celebrate it with a special meal. And when their children asked, "What does this ceremony mean?" they would reply, "It is the Passover feast, in memory of the night when God passed over our homes when he struck down the Egyptians." God said that during the festival of Passover, the Israelites were to have no yeast in their houses and to eat only bread made without yeast. They were to do no work during Passover, except for preparing food. The Israelites listened carefully to what Moses told them, and did as God commanded. At midnight the Lord God struck down all the first-born sons in Egypt, from the highest and richest in the land to the lowest and poorest. Every single Egyptian house was affected and the Pharaoh and all his officials got up during the night when they heard a terrible wailing throughout the land. Then the Pharaoh found that his own first-born son was dead. Once again he knew that God had done exactly as he had said he would do. This was the tenth plague that the Egyptians had suffered and it was the most

terrible of all, especially for their ruler, the Pharaoh. The Pharaoh called Moses and Aaron to his palace, and said: "You can go, you and all the Israelites! Every man, woman and child must go, along with all your animals."
The Pharaoh's people were overjoyed that he had at last given way, and the Egyptians even gave their former slaves gold and silver to take with them. They were prepared to do anything, just so long as the Israelites left their land as quickly as possible.

"Otherwise, we will all die!" one of the Egyptians cried. All the Israelites gathered together to leave Egypt at once. They picked up their bread dough just as it was, without yeast, wrapped it up and carried it on their shoulders. There were about six hundred thousand Israelites, not counting the women and children. They had lived in Egypt for more than two hundred years and now, at last, they were free to leave. Moses took Joseph's bones with him, as his ancestor had asked his people to do when they at last left Egypt.

CROSSING THE RED SEA

God had told Moses that he would lead his people out of Egypt to the Promised Land. But he did not take them by the shortest, most direct route, since he did not want them to have to do battle with unfriendly peoples on the way. If they were faced with war, the Israelites might change their minds and go back to Egypt. So God took them along the desert road that led to the Red Sea, guiding them from the front with a column of cloud by day and a pillar of fire by night. Then God told Moses, who was leading the Israelites on their journey, to make camp near the Red Sea.

The Egyptian Pharaoh, who had so wanted the Israelites to leave his country after their God had plagued it with disasters, now began to have second thoughts. "What have we done?" one of the Pharaoh's officials said. "Now that the Israelites have gone, we have lost our supply of slaves." This was too much for the Pharaoh, who had already forgotten about all the terrible things that had happened to him. He issued orders that his powerful army – including six hundred chariots and his best horsemen – was to rush after the Israelites, capture them and bring them back by force.

It did not take long for the Egyptian army to catch up with the Israelites. At their camp near the Red Sea, some of Moses' people saw a dust cloud approaching a long way off. They were terrified when they realised that this was an army of Egyptians charging across the desert towards them. The news spread quickly through the camp and panic broke out. Many of the people blamed Moses. "Why did you make us leave our homes in Egypt?" one of them cried. "We said we would rather serve the Egyptians. Anything would have been better than dying out here in the desert."

79

The Egyptian army
Egypt had a highly trained army of charioteers and foot-soldiers. The commander-in-chief was usually one of the Pharaoh's sons. This model of an infantry company, from about 2000 BCE, was placed in a tomb to protect the dead person in the next life.

of the Red Sea. When Moses did so, a great wind blew up and the waters parted in front of him. Between two great walls of water ran a pathway over the seabed, wide enough for the Israelites to cross on foot.

Before Moses and his people had all reached the far side of the sea, the Egyptian army started out along the pathway that God had created. But their wheels got stuck in the mud and the Egyptian chariots were soon crashing into each other. Some of the chariots tried to turn around, but this only made things worse.

When the last of the Israelites were safely on the far shore, God again told Moses to stretch out his hand over the Red Sea. Moses did as God commanded and the waters closed together, covering the seabed and drowning the entire Egyptian army. Seeing this, the Israelites knew that they could always put their trust in God and in Moses, his servant.

While the Israelites rested on the far shore of the Red Sea, Moses sang a song of praise to God. His sister Miriam picked up a tambourine and sang, too. Then the other women followed her example, and soon the Israelite camp was full of music and dancing. The words of Miriam's song rang in their ears. "Sing to the Lord, for he has had a glorious triumph," she sang. "He has thrown the horse and his rider into the sea." The Israelites had been saved. Now they were ready to continue their long journey to the Promised Land.

Moses remained calm at the approach of the Egyptian army. "Don't be afraid," he said. "God will look after us and save us from the Egyptians." While the Israelites all looked back to see how fast the Egyptians were approaching, God told Moses to raise his stick and stretch out his hand over the waters

TRAVELS IN THE DESERT

After they had crossed the Red Sea, the Israelites continued on their journey to Canaan. Once again they did not take the shortest route. Moses led them south into the land of Sinai, to avoid the trade routes used by the Egyptians.

Sinai was a hot, dry desert region, where travellers could go for days without finding water. The Israelites began to slow down and complain to Moses, but he told them to be patient, as he was leading them to a small oasis. When they got there, however, they found that the water was foul and tasted bitter. After going without water for so long, the people were very disappointed. They were desperately thirsty, but where would they ever find anything good to drink? Then God told Moses to pick up a small piece of wood that was lying beside the pool of foul water and throw it in. When Moses did so, the water became sweet and fit to drink. This gave people the strength to carry on and before long they came to a bigger oasis, named Elim.

There were palm trees and springs at this settlement, and the Israelites made camp near the water. Next time they moved on, however, they walked for many days without coming to another oasis. By now almost all of the people were complaining. "We had as much food and drink as we wanted in Egypt," one of them told Moses. "It would have been better if God had killed us there, rather than you leading us out into the desert to die." When God heard this, he told Moses that he would feed the people, but that they must do as he told them.

Oases
Oases are areas of fresh water in the middle of a desert. Some are just tiny springs surrounded by a few palm trees. Others are so big that they can be used to irrigate land and supply water for towns. Offering water and shade, oases are important stopover points in the desert for people and animals. The water at an oasis comes from underground sources that build up above layers of solid rock. The water seeps up through cracks or faults in the rock.

Worship in the desert
This clay dish shows Moses preaching to a crowd of Israelites. It was found in the Sinai desert.

82

Possible routes of the Exodus
This map shows four possible routes the Israelites might have taken on their way to the Promised Land. Nobody can be certain which way they went. They may have travelled south, close to the Red Sea (more correctly named the Sea of Reeds) and then inland. Exactly where Mount Sinai was located is uncertain.

MEDITERRANEAN SEA
Gaza
Qantir
Avaris
Succoth
Pithom
Northern route
EGYPT
Kadesh Barnea?
Mt Sinai (?)
Mt Sinai (?)
Central route (1)
Central route (2)
Mt Sinai (?)
GULF OF SUEZ
Southern route
Eilat
GULF OF EILAT
Mt Sinai (?)
Mt Sinai (?)
Mt Sinai (?)
RED SEA

"Tell the people that by evening they will eat meat," God said, "and that in the morning there will be more food for them to eat. They may gather as much food as they need for six days, but on the seventh day they must rest."

That evening flocks of quail flew over the camp and the people caught the birds and roasted them. And next morning, when they left their tents, they found that there was a layer of dew all around the camp. When the dew had been burned off by the sun, they saw that thin white flakes had been left on the ground. "What is it?" they asked Moses. "It is the food that God promised he would provide for you to eat," Moses replied. So the people gathered the flakes and when they ate them, found that they tasted like honey. They were delighted and named the food manna, which means "what-is-it?" Every morning the people gathered as much manna as they needed for that day. On the sixth morning, Moses reminded them that the next day was the Sabbath, or day of rest, and they found that there was twice as much manna as usual for them to gather. They baked some of the food, boiled some of it and saved the rest for the next day, when they were not supposed to work. Some people did not save any of the manna, however, and went out on the seventh day to gather some. That morning there was not a single flake to be found and God was angry that they had disobeyed him.

The Israelites continued on their long journey through the desert. At last they came to a settlement named Rephidim, but there was no water there for them to drink. Once again they complained to Moses. "Why do you always complain to me?" he asked. "When you moan at me, you are really complaining about God, who brought us out of Egypt and who always looks after us." But some of the people went on blaming Moses for all their troubles and he was worried that they were about to attack him. Moses turned to God and asked what he should do. As always, God answered him and promised that he would help him. Moses gathered

AND IT CAME TO PASS, THAT AT
EVEN THE QUAILS CAME UP, AND
COVERED THE CAMP: AND IN THE
MORNING THE DEW LAY ROUND
ABOUT THE HOST.
AND WHEN THE DEW THAT LAY
WAS GONE UP, BEHOLD, UPON
THE FACE OF THE WILDERNESS
THERE LAY A SMALL ROUND
THING, AS SMALL AS THE HOAR
FROST ON THE GROUND.
AND WHEN THE CHILDREN OF
ISRAEL SAW IT, THEY SAID ONE
TO ANOTHER, IT IS MANNA: FOR
THEY WIST NOT WHAT IT WAS.
AND MOSES SAID UNTO THEM,
THIS IS THE BREAD WHICH THE
LORD HATH GIVEN YOU TO EAT.

(Exodus 16.13–15)

together some of the leaders of the people and asked them to follow him out of the camp. They walked in the desert until they came to a small, rocky hill, which Moses knew would be there. While the others watched, Moses hit one of the rocks with his stick. To their astonishment, water came gushing out of the rock. When the leaders tasted it, they found that it was clean and fresh. The Israelites knew that once again God had looked after them and that they could trust him always to keep his promises.

Battle with the Amalekites

Now that they had water, the Israelites were happy to stay at the oasis of Rephidim to rest, before the next stage of their journey. Moses reminded his people that God would always watch over and protect them, but that they must trust him and obey his commands.

The Israelites were not alone in the desert. Apart from the constant threat from wild animals, there were other people in the land of Sinai. The Amalekites were a wandering tribe who did not like having to share their oases with newcomers. When they saw that Rephidim was occupied, they crept up to the Israelite camp to see how well-defended it was, and then attacked.

Moses picked out a brave young man named Joshua, and told him to choose the strongest men to fight against the Amalekites. Next morning, Moses climbed a nearby hill with his brother Aaron and another man named Hur. Moses held up the stick that God had told him always to have with him. Seeing this gave the Israelites courage to fight harder. Later, when Moses grew tired and lowered his arms, the Amalekites surged forward. But when he raised his arms again, the Israelites attacked the enemy with great force and drove them back.

When they saw what was happening, Aaron and Hur sat Moses down on a rock and stood to either side of him, each holding up one of his arms. This meant that Moses could keep his arms raised, although by now he was exhausted. By evening the Israelites had managed to fight off the Amalekite army. Moses thanked God by building an altar on the hill overlooking Rephidim.

> BUT MOSES' HANDS WERE HEAVY; AND THEY TOOK A STONE, AND PUT IT UNDER HIM, AND HE SAT THEREON; AND AARON AND HUR STAYED UP HIS HANDS, THE ONE ON THE ONE SIDE, AND THE OTHER ON THE OTHER SIDE; AND HIS HANDS WERE STEADY UNTIL THE GOING DOWN OF THE SUN.
>
> (Exodus 17.12)

85

GOD GIVES HIS LAWS TO MOSES

The Ten Commandments

In these ten laws, God gives the Israelites rules to live by and shows them how to behave towards him and towards each other. They are the heart of the covenant that God made with his people at this time. Right, an illustration from a Spanish Bible of 1422, showing Moses holding up the two tablets with the Ten Commandments written on them.

When the Israelites arrived at the foot of God's holy mountain, Mount Sinai, they set up camp. Moses left them and climbed the mountain so that he could be close to God.

God spoke to Moses. "Tell the Israelites that they must obey my commands and keep to my agreement with them," God said. "Then your people will be a treasured, holy nation. In three days' time I will come down to Mount Sinai to speak with you further. I will come as a thick cloud, and after the people hear me talking to you, they will always put their trust in you. Prepare the people to hear my words, but until that time make sure that no one climbs the mountain or even goes near its lower slopes."

Moses hurried back down to the camp and told his people what God had said. He asked them to wash their clothes very carefully, in preparation for the important day when God was going to speak to them. He also warned them that anyone who tried to climb the mountain would be killed.

On the morning of the third day there was a tremendous thunderstorm. Mount Sinai was covered in cloud and lightning flashed all around. Suddenly there was a loud trumpet blast, which

Moses knew was the sign that the people could at last approach the mountain. He led them out of the camp – most were shaking with fear at the terrible storm. The Israelites stood at the foot of the mountain and saw that it was belching fire. The ground shook. The sound of the trumpet grew louder and louder and Moses knew that God was calling him to the top of the mountain.

When God spoke to Moses at the top of Mount Sinai, he gave him ten sacred commands to take back down to his people. They later came to be known as the Ten Commandments. God said:

"I am the Lord, your God, who brought you out of slavery in Egypt, and you must not worship any other god.
You must not make or worship any images or idols.
You must not misuse my name.
Remember the Sabbath and keep it holy by not working on that day.
Honour your father and your mother.
You must not commit murder.
You must not commit adultery.
You must not steal.

AND MOUNT SINAI WAS ALTOGETHER ON A SMOKE, BECAUSE THE LORD DESCENDED UPON IT IN FIRE: AND THE SMOKE THEREOF ASCENDED AS THE SMOKE OF A FURNACE, AND THE WHOLE MOUNT QUAKED GREATLY.

(Exodus 19.18)

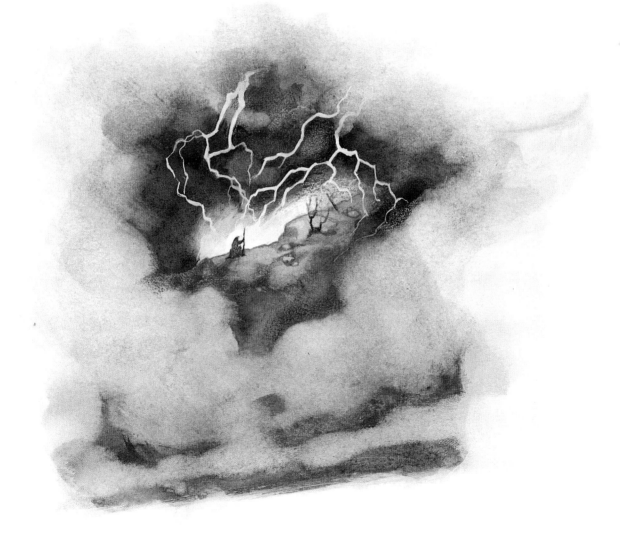

The laws of Hammurabi
This stone pillar (stela) from 1700 BCE is inscribed with the law code devised by the Babylonian king, Hammurabi. The scene at the top shows the god Shamash presenting Hammurabi with the laws, many of which are very similar to those of the Israelites.

The tablets of the law
In Jewish synagogues, the tablets containing the Ten Commandments are kept at the top of a cupboard called the Ark. This is surmounted by a crown. Usually only the first phrase of each Commandment is written out.

You must not give false testimony against your neighbour.
You must not jealously desire your neighbour's house, or your neighbour's wife, or anything else that belongs to your neighbour."

God said that Aaron and seventy of the leading Israelites could come up the mountain to pray. All the others were to stay at the foot of the mountain. Only Moses was allowed to go to the very top and be close to God. God told Moses of many other laws that the Israelites were to obey. There were rules about how to treat their servants, how to settle quarrels and deal with disagreements and how to look after poor people, widows and orphaned children. All the rules were about events in the everyday lives of ordinary people.

Then Moses went down and built an altar at the foot of the mountain. It was made of twelve large stones, which represented the twelve tribes of Israel. He made burnt offerings and animal sacrifices to God on the altar. Moses told the people what God had said and they agreed to live by the laws that their Lord had given them.

Moses knew that God had much more to tell him, so he went back up the mountain. He stayed on Mount Sinai for a total of forty days and forty nights. When God had finished speaking to him, he gave Moses two stone tablets. These were inscribed with God's laws. Moses got ready to carry the tablets down the mountain to the camp.

THE GOLDEN CALF

While Moses was on Mount Sinai listening to the words of God, the Israelites grew bored and restless in their camp. They said to Aaron, "We don't know what has become of that fellow Moses who led us out of Egypt. Make us a god to lead us farther."

Aaron asked them to bring him their earrings and any other jewellery made of gold. He melted the jewellery down over a fire and molded the metal into the shape of a calf. The people were delighted. "This is our god," they shouted when they saw the golden calf. "And tomorrow we will hold a festival," said Aaron.

Next day the people got up early and made offerings to the golden calf. Some danced around the idol, while others sat down to eat and drink the day away.

God was angry and sad when he saw what was happening. He told Moses to go back to his people at once. "They have broken my law already," God said. Moses did his best to offer excuses for the Israelites' behaviour, and then hurried down the mountain, carrying the two stone tablets engraved with God's laws.

On the way he met Joshua, who was puzzled by the noise as they approached the camp. "It sounds as if there's a battle going on," he said. But Moses knew that it was the noise of drunken singing and dancing. "That is not the sound of victory or defeat," he said sadly.

When Moses finally reached the camp and saw people dancing around the golden calf, he was overcome by anger. He threw the stone tablets to the ground, smashing them to pieces. Then he grabbed the calf idol and hurled it into the fire. "Why did you let them do this?" he shouted at Aaron.

"Don't be angry with me," Aaron begged. "These wicked people wanted me to make them a god. They brought me their earrings, and when I threw them into the fire, out came this calf!" Moses took the idol from the fire and ground it to dust. Then he mixed the gold dust with water and made all the Israelites drink it.

"You have committed a great sin," Moses told the people. "Now all I can do is go up to God and beg him to forgive you." So Moses once again climbed Mount Sinai and asked God's forgiveness for the people's wickedness. God said, "I will blot the sinners out of my book, and when the time comes, I will punish them. Now go and lead the people on to the land I promised Abraham and his descendants, and my angel will go ahead of you."

89

Bull worship
Aaron may have made a golden calf because he knew of Apis, the Egyptian bull god, or the Canaanite god, Baal. This bronze bull, below, was found at Samaria.

AND IT CAME TO PASS, AS SOON AS HE
CAME NIGH UNTO THE CAMP, THAT HE
SAW THE CALF, AND THE DANCING; AND
MOSES' ANGER WAXED HOT, AND HE
CAST THE TABLES OUT OF HIS HANDS,
AND BRAKE THEM BENEATH THE MOUNT.

(Exodus 32.19)

THE TENT OF THE LORD

Before Moses returned to his people from the top of Mount Sinai, God told him that he wanted him to build a special tent – a tabernacle, or Tent of Meeting – as a dwelling place for God in the Israelite camp. The rest of the camp was made up of ordinary tents, used by the people travelling from Egypt to the Promised Land. Like the other tents, the tabernacle could be taken down and carried when the Israelites moved on from one oasis to the next. This meant that they would always have a place where they could worship God and pray to him. God gave Moses detailed instructions about the exact way in which he was to make the tabernacle. It was to be made of ten curtains of the same size, made of fine white linen, sewn with blue, purple and scarlet yarn, and decorated with beautiful figures of cherubim. The curtains were to be fastened together with gold clasps to make a tent shape, over a framework made of acacia wood overlaid with fine gold. The whole structure was to be covered with a curtain of goat's hair and a layer of sheepskins, fastened together

with bronze clasps. Moses knew that he was going to need expert craftsmen and the very best materials, including gold and silver, to make the tabernacle. God told him that the Israelites would provide him with everything he needed, and when Moses went back to his people, they gladly gave him all the precious materials. The gold and silver came from the gifts that the Egyptians had presented to the Israelites when they left Egypt, because they were so glad to see them go. The people gave Moses their brooches, rings and ornaments. Then Moses chose a master-craftsman named Bezaleel to build the tabernacle. He was helped by all those men and women in the camp who were skilled at carpentry, metalwork and embroidery. They set to work at once, making the tabernacle and the many other items that God had given detailed instructions about. Inside,

The priesthood
Each time the Israelites set up camp, the priests put up the tabernacle. The High Priest wore a tunic with a breastplate decorated with twelve jewels, representing the twelve tribes of Israel.

The tabernacle
In the courtyard was the tent sanctuary, divided into two rooms. The first room, the holy place, held a menorah, an incense altar, and a table onto which twelve loaves were placed each week, one for each of the twelve tribes of Israel. The Holy of Holies contained the Ark, which stood for the presence of God. Its curtains were always kept closed — the Most Holy Place was too holy to be seen.

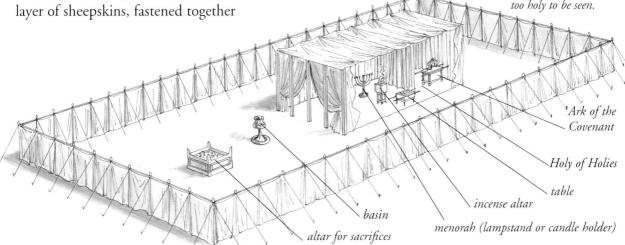

Ark of the Covenant

Holy of Holies

table

incense altar

menorah (lampstand or candle holder)

basin

altar for sacrifices

The menorah
The menorah, a seven-branched candlestick, was the tabernacle's only source of light. It has become a symbol of Judaism and is part of the emblem of the state of Israel.

92

The Ark of the Covenant
The ark contained the stone tablets inscribed by God with the Ten Commandments. It was the most sacred object in Jewish history, a reminder of God's covenant that he would always be with his people. The Ark was stolen by the Babylonians when they captured Jerusalem in 587 BCE.

the tabernacle was divided into two rooms by some fine white curtains. The outer room was called "the holy place", and for it the craft-workers made three special items: a table made of acacia wood with gold mouldings, on which they placed an offering of bread made without yeast; an altar made of acacia wood overlaid with bronze, where fragrant incense could be burned; and a decorated, seven-branched candlestick or lampstand made of pure gold, where lamps of olive oil could be kept burning. The inner room, called the "most holy place" or the "holy of holies", contained the most important item of all: a chest made of acacia wood, overlaid with pure gold inside and out, and decorated with two gold cherubim on its lid. This sacred chest was called the "Ark

of the Covenant" and was specially made to hold the two stone tablets on which God had written the laws that he gave to the Israelites. Of course, God knew that Moses had broken the original tablets when he saw his people worshipping the golden calf, so he told him to make new ones. "Chisel out two stone tablets just like the first ones," God told Moses, "and come to me at the mountaintop." Moses did as God commanded and God wrote the words of the Ten Commandments and laws on the new tablets. The tabernacle and all its holy contents had special carrying rods, so that it could be picked up and carried as the Israelites continued on their journey. God told Moses to have sacred garments made for his brother Aaron, who was to serve as High Priest, with his four sons. After certain animal sacrifices had been made, the priests were ordained and the tabernacle was consecrated. The tabernacle stood within a court, which was enclosed by curtains. It opened towards the east and faced the altar where the people could bring their sacrifices. The court also contained a bronze basin, where Moses and the priests could wash their hands and feet before entering the tabernacle. The tabernacle was set up – with the tablets of the laws inside the Ark of the Covenant – on the first day of the second year after the Israelites left Egypt. A column of cloud covered the tabernacle, which meant that the glory of God filled this special tent. Moses and the Israelites had completed their task and were ready to move on towards the Promised Land.

IN SIGHT OF THE PROMISED LAND

When the Israelites continued their journey from Mount Sinai, men from Levi's tribe carried the tabernacle with them. They headed north across the deserts of Sinai and eventually reached a hilly region and a settlement named Kadesh. There they made camp, knowing that they were now within reach of Canaan.

Moses chose twelve men, one from each of the tribes of Israel, to go ahead and explore the land. "See what this place is like," Moses told them. "Is the soil fertile, what sort of people live there, and are their towns fortified?" The twelve chosen men set out to answer these questions and were gone for forty days.

When they returned, the twelve spies were carrying luscious fruits – grapes, pomegranates and figs – to show that the land was indeed fertile. They reported that it was a wonderful place, but that the powerful people who lived there had built large cities that were well defended. "The people there are so big and strong," said one of the spies, "that we felt like tiny grasshoppers

Poisonous snakes
Some snakes are well adapted to living in dry, sandy desert conditions. Most of them are harmless, but some have the power to kill. This model snake, above, from the 14th century BCE, was found at the copper mines of Timna, near the Gulf of Aqaba.

The land of milk and honey
Right: honeybees are shown returning to their hives in this illumination. The Promised Land was described as flowing with milk and honey — a way of saying that it had good grass for cattle and plentiful flowers for honeybees.

beside them. We cannot possibly hope to take land from those giants." Only Caleb, who had represented the tribe of Judah on the spying trip, and Joshua, from the tribe of Ephraim, disagreed. "Of course we can take possession of the land," said Caleb. "Don't be afraid. God is with us, and he will look after us in the land flowing with milk and honey." But the others had forgotten what God had promised them and could not be won over by Caleb.

God was angry that the people did not trust him and he called Moses to the tabernacle. "Those of your people who disobeyed and distrusted me will never see the Promised Land," God said. "Their children will live to enjoy the land that they have rejected, and so too will Caleb and Joshua, who showed their trust in me. The rest of you will wander the desert for forty years — one year for each of the days that your spies explored the land — and

you will die there." When Moses told the people what God had said, they changed their minds and wanted to enter the land of Canaan at once. Moses warned them that this was useless, since God would not be with them, but some went ahead anyway. It did not take long for the Canaanites and Amalekites who lived there to drive the Israelites away. They realised then that they must indeed wander for forty years in the desert, as God had said. Before long, many of the people began complaining to Moses of their hardship, and especially the lack of water. "Why did you bring us to this terrible place?" they cried. Moses went to the tabernacle and asked God what he should do. "Take your stick," God said, "and lead the people to a rock that I will show you. When you speak to the rock in front of the people, it will gush with water." Moses did as God told him, but he was so angry with the rebellious people that when he got to the right place, he raised his stick and struck the rock twice. Water came gushing out, but God was displeased with Moses for losing his temper, disobeying his instructions and doing things his own way. "Since you did not trust me," God told Moses, "you will not lead your people into the land I have promised them."

This was a very difficult time for Moses. His sister Miriam had died at Kadesh and his brother Aaron died when the Israelites set out into the

AND ALL THE CHILDREN OF ISRAEL
MURMURED AGAINST MOSES AND AGAINST
AARON: AND THE WHOLE CONGREGATION
SAID UNTO THEM, WOULD GOD THAT WE HAD
DIED IN THE LAND OF EGYPT! OR WOULD
GOD WE HAD DIED IN THIS WILDERNESS!
AND WHEREFORE HATH THE LORD BROUGHT
US UNTO THIS LAND, TO FALL BY THE SWORD,
THAT OUR WIVES AND OUR CHILDREN SHOULD
BE A PREY? WERE IT NOT BETTER FOR US TO
RETURN INTO EGYPT?

(Numbers 14.2–3)

desert once more. The people soon grew impatient again and continued to complain about God and Moses. When God saw this, he sent poisonous snakes slithering into the Israelites' camp. Many people were bitten by the snakes and some died. Others came to Moses and begged him to ask God to take away this new punishment.

When Moses prayed, God told him what to do. "Make a model snake and put it on a pole," God said. "Anyone who is bitten only has to look at the snake to be saved." So Moses made a snake out of bronze and put it up on a wooden pole. Just as God had said, when victims trusted his promise and looked at the bronze snake, they got better at once.

BALAAM AND HIS DONKEY

As the Israelites approached Canaan after their many years in the desert, they had to fight with those who already lived in the region. They defeated Sihon, king of the Amorites, who lived to the east of the Dead Sea, and then Og, the king of Bashan, near the Sea of Galilee. These victories alarmed the Moabites, who lived near the River Jordan. Their king, Balak, was worried for his people when he heard that the Israelites had set up camp across the river from Jericho. The Moabites convinced their neighbours from Midian that they must join forces to fight the huge number of Israelites. Then Balak sent messengers and gold to a wise man named Balaam, asking him to come and curse the Israelites so that they could be defeated and driven away. Balaam agreed to consider the request, but that night God visited him in a dream. "You must not put a curse on my people," God told Balaam, "because they are blessed." The Moabites were disappointed when Balaam refused to help them, and their king sent his princes with the promise of a very handsome reward if Balaam would change his mind. Once again Balaam prayed to God, and this time he was told that he could go to Moab, but that he must follow exactly all of God's commands. Next morning Balaam set off for Moab on his donkey. He had not gone far when the faithful donkey suddenly shied away and turned off the path into a field. Balaam beat her with his stick, and they moved on. But they had not gone much farther when the donkey again took fright. This time they were on a narrow path between two walls, and when the terrified donkey pressed up against one of them, it crushed Balaam's foot. Once again he beat the donkey and forced her to carry on. Balaam did not see what was frightening his donkey: it was God's angel, standing in front of them barring the way. When the donkey saw the angel a third time, she simply lay down and refused to budge, despite the beating. Then, to Balaam's astonishment, the donkey spoke to him. "Why are you beating me?" the donkey asked. "Do I usually refuse to go where you tell me?" "No," Balaam replied truthfully, and

96

Beasts of burden
In the Bible lands, donkeys were both ridden and used to carry or pull heavy loads. Kings usually rode on donkeys in Old Testament times. Horses were mainly used in battle.

then God opened his eyes and he too saw the angel ahead of them. "Why did you beat your donkey?" said the angel. "I came here to bar your way, and your donkey has saved your life by stopping three times. Now you may carry on, but you may only say what I tell you." King Balak was delighted when he saw Balaam approaching. Together they made ready to put a curse on the Israelites by sacrificing animals on seven altars. But when Balaam

was ready to deliver his curse, he could only utter the words that God told him to say. "How can I curse people who are not cursed by God?" Balaam said. The Moabite king was furious, and insisted that Balaam try again. "God has blessed these people, and I cannot change it," said Balaam. Instead of cursing the Israelites, he could only bless them — however much gold he was offered by the angry king.

THE DEATH OF MOSES

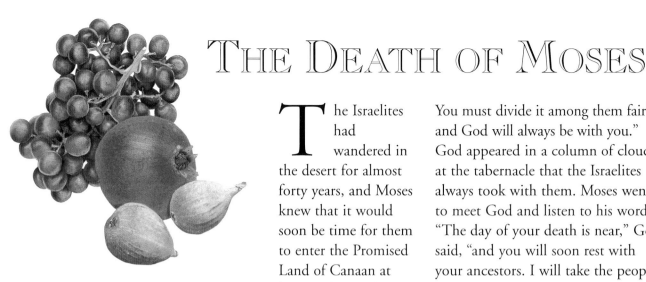

Canaan's fruits

The Promised Land was rich in fruit. Grapes were eaten fresh, dried as raisins or made into wine. Figs were also eaten fresh and dried and pressed into fig cakes. Pomegranates had juicy flesh that quenched thirst and the rind was made into a medicine and also a red dye.

98

The Israelites had wandered in the desert for almost forty years, and Moses knew that it would soon be time for them to enter the Promised Land of Canaan at last. He had willingly helped his people through all their troubles, but God had told him many years before that he would not reach the Promised Land himself, and he knew that nothing could change this. As they drew close to the River Jordan — the border of Canaan — God decided that it was time to pass on the leadership of his people to someone else. Moses first went out and spoke to the Israelites. "I am one hundred and twenty years old," Moses announced, "and I am no longer able to lead you. I will not myself cross the River Jordan, but God will go on ahead of you. You need not be afraid of anyone, for God will never abandon you." Then Moses went to see Joshua, who had been acting for many years as his second-in-command, and said to him: "Be brave and strong, for you must lead your people into the land that God promised their ancestors.

You must divide it among them fairly, and God will always be with you." God appeared in a column of cloud at the tabernacle that the Israelites always took with them. Moses went to meet God and listen to his words. "The day of your death is near," God said, "and you will soon rest with your ancestors. I will take the people into the land flowing with milk and honey, as I promised their ancestors. But then they will turn to other gods and break our agreement. I know this even before I take them into the land I promised them. Now write down all that I have told you." Moses wrote everything that God had told him in a book, and when he had finished, he went to the Levites, who carried the Ark of the Covenant. He told them to take his book and place it in the tabernacle, beside the sacred chest. Then he called the people together and made a farewell speech, in which he praised God and told the people that they must always obey him. "Our God is great," Moses said. "He is the rock. Everything he does is perfect. He is true, just, and right."

That very day God called Moses and told him to climb Mount Nebo, which lay across the River Jordan from Jericho. From there he

HAPPY ART THOU, O ISRAEL: WHO IS LIKE UNTO THEE, O PEOPLE SAVED BY THE LORD, THE SHIELD OF THY HELP, AND WHO IS THE SWORD OF THY EXCELLENCY! AND THINE ENEMIES SHALL BE FOUND LIARS UNTO THEE; AND THOU SHALT TREAD UPON THEIR HIGH PLACES.

(Deuteronomy 33.29)

would be able to see the fertile land of Canaan, which God was giving to his fellow Israelites. "You will die on the mountain and be gathered to your people," God told Moses. Before leaving the Israelite camp, Moses blessed each of the twelve tribes of Israel in turn. He had special words for the descendants of Joseph, the favourite son of Jacob, who had originally taken his people to Egypt. "May God bless his land with the best gifts of the earth, for he was a prince among brothers."

Then Moses left his people and climbed to the top of Mount Nebo. From there he had a wonderful view of Canaan, with its fertile valleys, rivers, lakes and cities. "This is the land I promised to the descendants of Abraham, Isaac and Jacob," God said to Moses. "I have let you see it with your own eyes." Moses died on the mountain overlooking Canaan. He had performed mighty deeds on behalf of his people and brought them to the very border of their Promised Land. He was buried in a nearby valley, though to this day it is not known exactly where his grave is.

THE HISTORICAL BOOKS

Jericho
One of Canaan's largest fortified cities was Jericho, located next to a water spring in the arid lands north of the Dead Sea. Its history goes back to the Middle Stone Age, between 10,000 and 7500 BCE, when agriculture began. Above, a pottery vase from Jericho, shaped like a head, about 15th century BCE.

100

The twelve historical books in the Old Testament in Christian Bibles tell the history of the Israelites from their entry into the Promised Land to their return from Exile in Babylon. (In Hebrew Bibles, six of these books are collected with the prophets.)

Joshua relates how, in fulfilment of God's promise to Abraham, the Israelites conquer Canaan, the Promised Land.

Judges contains dramatic stories of how, in times of crisis, God chose brave leaders — judges — who rallied the people and brought them back to God when they were losing faith or falling into idolatry. Such people include Deborah, Gideon and Samson.

Ruth is a short book, the story of a widow's love, her loyalty to her mother-in-law and her faith in God.

1 & 2 Samuel narrate the history of the last of Israel's judges, Samuel (not a warrior-hero like previous judges, but a judge in the

modern sense) and the establishment of the monarchy under King Saul, followed by King David.

1 & 2 Kings describe the reign of King Solomon and how, after his death, his kingdom is divided into Israel (the northern kingdom) and Judah. Israel is conquered by the Assyrians; Judah falls to the Babylonians.

1 & 2 Chronicles, written later than *Kings*, describe many of the same events, concentrating on Judah and its kings.

Ezra tells of Ezra's leadership after the return to Jerusalem from exile and the rebuilding of the Temple.

Nehemiah describes Nehemiah's role in rebuilding the walls of Jerusalem.

Esther is the story of a Jewish woman who became queen of Persia and saved her people from a plot.

Roman Catholic and Orthodox Bibles often include books that do not appear in Jewish Bibles, and which Protestants place in a separate volume known as the *Apocrypha*. These include: *Tobit*, *Judith* and *1 & 2 Maccabees*.

Judith
The beautiful Jewish widow, Judith, is the heroine of the Book of Judith. According to the Bible, when Nebuchadnezzar, king of Assyria, sent his general Holofernes to attack her city in Judah, Judith cut off his head and saved the city. Left, detail of a painting of Judith by Sandro Botticelli (1444–1510).

RAHAB AND THE SPIES

After Moses' death, God told Joshua to lead his people into the Promised Land. "Be brave and strong," God said, "and obey my laws. Then you will be successful, and I will be with you wherever you go."

Joshua told the Israelites that they would soon cross the River Jordan. But first he chose two men to go ahead and explore the land. They secretly made their way to the city of Jericho, and there met a woman named Rahab, whose house was built into the high, thick wall that surrounded the city.

Rahab took the men in and, knowing that the king of Jericho was on the lookout for spies, led them up to the roof, where she hid them under stalks of flax that had been laid out to dry. Sure enough, the Israelites had been seen entering the city. The king's men rushed to Rahab's house to look for the spies.

Rahab said that the two unknown men who had been in her house had left before the city gates were closed for the night. The soldiers rushed off to try and find them. Then she went to the Israelites and said, "Just as I have shown kindness to you, be kind to me and spare my family when you conquer this land."

The men agreed. "Say nothing about our visit and bring your family to this house," they said. "Tie a red cord in your window so that our soldiers will know not to harm you or your family." Rahab then gave the two men a long rope so that they could let themselves down from her window and escape into the night.

THE FALL OF JERICHO

The shofar
The ram's horn trumpet called a "shofar" was used in war to give signals and sound alarms. It was also blown during celebrations, including the king's coronation. The shofar can still be heard in synagogues on the New Year festival and on other holy days.

Joshua's spies reported that the people of Jericho were fearful of an invasion. The Israelites were sure that God would give the land to them, but they did not know how they would all be able to cross the River Jordan.

God told Joshua what to do. Following God's instruction, Joshua sent the priests who carried the Ark of the Covenant on ahead of everyone else. As soon as the priests' feet touched the waters of the River Jordan, the river stopped flowing and dry ground appeared before them. They carried the golden chest to the middle of the dry riverbed and all the people walked to the other side.

Joshua told one man from each of the twelve tribes to pick up a stone from the middle of the riverbed. Then the priests carried the Ark into Canaan, and the waters of the River Jordan started to flow again. That night, when they made camp near the city of Jericho, Joshua piled up the twelve stones into a heap to remind everyone in years to come how God brought his people into the Promised Land. "This will be a reminder to the people of Israel for ever," Joshua said.

A man armed with a sword appeared to Joshua and told him what he and his people were to do for the next seven days. Joshua made sure that the instructions were carried out exactly according to God's wishes. For the next six days, the Israelites marched once around the city, carrying the Ark behind seven priests blowing ram's-horn trumpets. On the seventh day, they all marched around Jericho seven times. Then, as Joshua had been told by God's messenger, the priests sounded a long, loud blast on their trumpets. At the same time the Israelites shouted at the tops of their voices, and suddenly the walls of the city came crashing to the ground.

Israelite soldiers charged into the city at once and captured it. The men who had visited Rahab went straight to her house and rescued her and her family, as they had promised. Then the soldiers set fire to the city.

AND IT SHALL COME TO PASS, THAT WHEN THEY MAKE A LONG BLAST WITH THE RAM'S HORN, AND WHEN YE HEAR THE SOUND OF THE TRUMPET, ALL THE PEOPLE SHALL SHOUT WITH A GREAT SHOUT; AND THE WALL OF THE CITY SHALL FALL DOWN FLAT, AND THE PEOPLE SHALL ASCEND UP EVERY MAN STRAIGHT BEFORE HIM.

(Joshua 6.5)

People of Canaan
The Canaanites were a mixture of different peoples living in the area that roughly corresponds to modern Syria, Israel and Lebanon. Above, an Egyptian glazed brick shows a Canaanite noble from the time when the Israelites had settled in the land of Canaan.

The Promised Land
The settlement of Israel dates to about 1200–1000 BCE. The Promised Land was already inhabited by various tribes: Canaanites, Amorites, Edomites, Amalekites, Moabites, Ammonites, Midianites. The land was divided into small city-kingdoms, which were often at war with each other.

104

After conquering Jericho, the Israelites went on to fight many more battles against the Canaanites. Their next conquest was the powerful city of Ai. When the people of Gibeon heard about this, they decided to trick the Israelites into making a peace agreement with them. Their city was not far off, to the west of the Israelite camp at Gilgal, but the Gibeonites pretended to come from a distant land. They sent a group of men to Joshua, making sure that they wore tattered clothes and old, patched sandals. In their packs they carried moldy old bread.

"Who are you and where do you come from?" Joshua asked.

"We come from far away," one of the Gibeonites replied. "We heard reports of you and your God, and set out to make peace with you. We brought fresh food with us, but we have travelled for so many days that our bread has gone stale. The long journey has even worn out our clothes." Joshua believed what he heard and saw, and agreed not to fight the Gibeonites and to help them if they needed it.

Just days later, the Israelites learned that they had been tricked, but they kept their promise. When the five kings of the Amorites heard of this, they were worried that they too might be conquered, so they joined forces to attack the city of Gibeon. At this the Gibeonites sent word to Joshua's camp and appealed for the help that he had promised to give. Joshua honoured his agreement, and the Israelite army marched all through the night from Gilgal to Gibeon. Their arrival took the Amorite kings by surprise, and they soon saw that they could not hold the city. The Amorite soldiers turned and fled down the hills from the city. As the Israelites chased after them, God sent a violent storm and huge hailstones rained down on the Amorites, making it impossible for them to escape. Then the sun stood still over the region, so that darkness did not fall until the battle was over and the Israelites were victorious.

Joshua's army went on to win many more battles and conquer Canaan. The Israelites defeated thirty-one kings altogether, starting with the king of Jericho and ending with the king of Tirzah. At last they could think about peace, as they settled down in their Promised Land.

Map:
MEDITERRANEAN SEA
Sidon
Damascus
Tyre
PHOENICIA
ARAM
Galilee
Megiddo
CANAAN
AMMON
River Jordan
AMOR
Gezer
Gaza
PHILISTIA
Dead Sea
MOAB
Negev Desert
AMALEK
EDOM

AND THE MEN OF
GIBEON SENT UNTO
JOSHUA TO THE CAMP TO
GILGAL, SAYING, SLACK
NOT THY HAND FROM
THY SERVANTS; COME UP
TO US QUICKLY, AND SAVE
US, AND HELP US: FOR
ALL THE KINGS OF THE
AMORITES THAT DWELL
IN THE MOUNTAINS ARE
GATHERED TOGETHER
AGAINST US.

(Joshua 10.6)

105

It was now time for Joshua to divide the land so that each of the tribes of Israel had its own territory. He was helped in this task by the High Priest Eleazar, who was Aaron's son, and by the heads of the twelve tribes. Land to the east of the River Jordan was shared by the tribes of Gad, Reuben, and half the people of Manasseh. To the west of the river, the land was divided among the tribes of Asher, Benjamin, Dan, Ephraim, Issachar, Judah, Naphtali, Simeon, Zebulon and the other half of Manasseh. The Levites did not receive their own region, since they had been chosen to serve God as priests, but they were given towns and pasturelands throughout the others' territories.

Joshua reminded the Israelites that God had kept all his promises to them. He had looked after them on their long travels and brought them all safely to their new home. They must continue to serve God faithfully and must always do whatever he asked of them.

New Leaders in Times of Trouble

The Iron Age
The period from 1200 BCE to the destruction of the First Temple in 586 BCE is called the Iron Age. During this time, while the Israelites were settling in Canaan, some peoples learned how to use iron to make weapons and tools. They kept this skill secret from the Israelites, who had to buy iron weapons from them. Above, an elaborate Canaanite stand from the 10th century BCE.

Canaanite kings
Right: This ivory plaque from the fortress town of Megiddo, about 13th century BCE, shows a Canaanite court scene. The ruler is sitting on a throne in front of his wife, while a musician plays the harp and people bring offerings. A war chariot and a foot soldier are leading two bound prisoners.

After Joshua died, some of the Israelites forgot their promises and stopped obeying God's commands. Groups of Canaanites and other peoples still lived among them, and before long young Israelites were marrying the sons and daughters of these peoples. Some even began to worship their neighbours' gods, including their main god, Baal. This gave the Canaanites power and made it easier for outsiders to attack the people of Israel. But whenever the Israelites turned back to God, he sent them a new leader, or judge, to save them from their troubles.

One of the judges, Ehud, lived at a time when Israel had been conquered by the Moabites. Ehud was forced to go to the palace of Eglon, to pay taxes to the king of Moab. Before leaving home he hid a special double-edged dagger under his robe. As Ehud was left-handed, he hid the dagger on his left side, knowing that any Moabite searching for weapons would look only on the right side. When Ehud arrived at the palace, he told King Eglon that he had a secret message for him, so that they would be left alone. Then he quickly drew his dagger and, before the king could even cry out, plunged the weapon into his body and killed him. Ehud quickly left, locking the door so that the king's servants would not find the body until Ehud had got away. Then he gathered an army together and drove out the leaderless Moabites.

After Ehud's death, the Israelites came under the rule of a Canaanite king named Jabin. Israel's new leader was a woman named Deborah, a prophet who settled her people's disputes from a special place beneath a palm tree. When people told her of King Jabin's great cruelty, Deborah sent for a soldier named Barak and told him that he was ordered by God to fight the Canaanites. Barak knew that Jabin's commander, Sisera, had a vast army that included 900 iron chariots, but Deborah persuaded him to obey God's command. So Barak took an army of 10,000 men up into the hills. Sisera's chariots were massed in a narrow valley below, but when they tried to attack the Israelites, they got stuck in the river running through the valley. The charioteers were all killed, but Sisera got away. When he came to a

camp of the Kenites, he thought that he was safe. Jael, the wife of Heber the Kenite, invited him into her tent and gave him milk to drink and a blanket to cover himself. As soon as Sisera fell asleep in the tent, Jael picked up a tent peg and hammered it into his head, killing him instantly.

When the Israelites next turned away from God and worshipped others, their lands were invaded by Midianites. One day a young man of the Manasseh tribe, named Gideon, was visited by an angel while he was harvesting wheat that he had hidden from the invaders. The angel told Gideon that he had been chosen to lead Israel to freedom. The young man did not think of himself as a leader, and asked for a sign that this truly was God's command. He set out meat and bread as offerings to God, and the angel made fire flare out of solid rock to burn Gideon's offerings.

God told Gideon that he must first destroy his people's altar to Baal. Gideon was afraid of what the townspeople would think if he did this, so he waited until nightfall. Then he smashed the altar with a great rock, cut down Baal's sacred trees and

AND THE ANGEL OF THE LORD APPEARED UNTO HIM, AND SAID UNTO HIM, THE LORD IS WITH THEE, THOU MIGHTY MAN OF VALOUR. AND GIDEON SAID UNTO HIM, OH MY LORD, IF THE LORD BE WITH US, WHY THEN IS ALL THIS BEFALLEN US? AND WHERE BE ALL HIS MIRACLES, WHICH OUR FATHERS TOLD US OF, SAYING, DID NOT THE LORD BRING US UP FROM EGYPT? BUT NOW THE LORD HATH FORSAKEN US, AND DELIVERED US INTO THE HANDS OF THE MIDIANITES.

(Judges 6.12–13)

built an altar to God. Next morning the people of the town were horrified and demanded that whoever was responsible should be punished. But Gideon's father replied, "If Baal really is a god, surely he can look after himself?"

Before he started fighting the Midianites, Gideon asked for another sign that God really had chosen him to be his people's leader. He put a woolen fleece on the ground and said to God, "If the fleece is wet with dew but the ground is dry, I will know that you have called me to save Israel." Next morning Gideon saw that the fleece was indeed soaked with dew, while the ground around it was bone dry. But he still asked for one final sign – and next morning the fleece was dry while the ground was wet. At last Gideon was convinced that he really had been chosen by God, and he called the men of Israel to form his army.

Many thousands of men answered the call, but God told Gideon that he did not need such a large army. Those who were afraid were told that they were free to leave, while the rest were taken to a spring

to drink. Gideon watched as the men quenched their thirst. Most ran to kneel or lie down by the water, lapping it up like thirsty dogs, but a few cupped their hands and drank quickly, still watching out for any danger. God said that those few would be enough to rescue Israel, though there were only three hundred of them.

Gideon gave each of his men an earthenware jar, a flaming torch and a trumpet. That night they crept close to the Midianite camp, hiding the light of their torches inside their jars. At a signal from Gideon, the Israelites suddenly gave a huge blast on their trumpets, startling the sleeping Midianites. Then the Israelites cried aloud, "The sword of the Lord and of Gideon!" as they took out their torches and smashed the jars on the ground. When the Midianites heard the terrible crashing noise and saw the blaze of torchlight, they grabbed their swords and started hitting out in every direction. In their panic, they wounded and killed many of their own soldiers, while some simply turned and ran off into the darkness. Gideon's small army had beaten the Midianites without striking a single blow.

Jephthah's Promise

Israelite society
At the time they settled in Canaan, the Israelites lived in large family groups called clans, which included husband and wife (or wives) with their unmarried daughters and their sons and families. The clans were grouped into tribes. Decisions were made by general assemblies of men or by elders, who acted as leaders. Above, ivory carving of a well-born Canaanite girl, from Megiddo.

It was not long before the Israelites forgot their promise to God and again turned to worship other gods. As on the previous occasion, they were invaded by their neighbours. This time the Ammonites were the conquerors. After some years the people of Israel realized that once again they had done wrong. So they turned again to God and looked for a leader who could free them from the rule of the Ammonites. The elders from Gilead thought that a local man named Jephthah might be able to lead them in their struggle. He was known by everyone to be a powerful warrior.

Jephthah was the son of a man named Gilead and a woman who was not his father's wife. This had led to him falling out with the rest of his family. When they grew up, the sons of Gilead and his wife – Jephthah's half-brothers – had turned against him. "You will never inherit anything from this family," they told Jephthah, "because you are the son of an unmarried woman and an outsider." Unwelcome in his own family, the unhappy Jephthah left home and went to live in a neighbouring region. There he was the leader of a group of fighting men.

When the invading Ammonites camped in the region of Gilead, the elders sent for Jephthah and asked him to be their commander. He had never expected to be invited back or welcomed, by his half-brothers or anyone else. "None of you cared when I was thrown out of my father's house," Jephthah told the elders, "so why should I help you now?"

The Gileadites had no answer except to say that if Jephthah helped them now, they would make him leader of the whole of Gilead. This was enough to persuade Jephthah, and he prayed to God for help in the battle to come. "If you give me victory over the Ammonites, Lord," he foolishly promised, "I will sacrifice to you the first living thing I see when I return home in triumph." Then Jephthah gathered together a powerful army of Israelites and led his men against the Ammonites. The Israelites destroyed many of their enemy's settlements and won a great victory. Because of Jephthah, the land of Israel was free once more.

Jephthah went back home in triumph. As he approached his house, his daughter came out to greet him, singing and dancing

> AND JEPHTHAH CAME TO MIZPEH UNTO HIS HOUSE, AND, BEHOLD, HIS DAUGHTER CAME OUT TO MEET HIM WITH TIMBRELS AND WITH DANCES: AND SHE WAS HIS ONLY CHILD; BESIDE HER HE HAD NEITHER SON NOR DAUGHTER.
>
> (Judges 11.34)

happily with a group of her friends. Jephthah's happiness turned to horror as he watched his only child. He could hardly bear to tell her of the promise he had made to God. But when he managed to speak to her at last, his daughter replied: "You have given your word to the Lord, father. Now that he has granted you victory, you must keep your promise. I ask just one thing – that you allow me a little time to weep in sorrow with my friends."

Jephthah granted his daughter's request, and then kept his promise to God and sacrificed his only child. Of course, he should not have done this, for God had clearly shown Abraham long ago that he did not want humans to be sacrificed to him. He asked only for the love and obedience of his people.

The Ammonites
The Ammonites were said to descend from Lot. At first they did not fight with the Israelites, but later the two peoples often struggled for control of the land. Above, a sculpture of a king or god from Ammon.

SAMSON AND THE LION

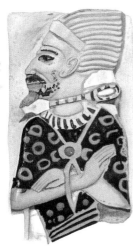

The Philistines
The Philistines were one of the "Sea Peoples" (possibly from Crete), who invaded the Middle East at the end of the 13th century BCE. They settled on the coast of Canaan about the same time as the Israelites, and set up five city-states. They were a constant threat to Israel, as both peoples wanted to control the same territory. Above, an Egyptian portrait of a Philistine prisoner.

When the Israelites again forgot God, they were attacked by Philistines from the Mediterranean coast. The invaders ruled Israel for forty years, while the Israelites waited for a leader strong enough to fight them off.

One day God sent an angel to an Israelite couple, Manoah and his wife, who had no children. For many years they had longed to have a baby. The angel told Manoah's wife that she would soon give birth to a son. He said that the boy was to be a Nazirite – which was someone dedicated to the service of God. "To show this, you must never cut his hair," the angel told them, "and when he grows up, he will free Israel from the Philistines."

When the baby boy was born, his parents named him Samson. At last they were a family. As the boy grew tall and strong, they let his hair grow long, just as the angel had commanded. One day, when Samson was a young man, he noticed a pretty Philistine girl in the town of Timnah. When he got home, he told his parents that he wanted to marry the girl. They were unhappy at this, because they wanted him to marry a girl from their own people. But Samson had made up his mind.

The next time Samson went to Timnah, an amazing thing happened. As he was walking through a vineyard, a lion suddenly sprang out at him. Anyone else would have been terrified, but Samson was so strong that he fought the lion and strangled the ferocious beast with his bare hands. Then he carried on to Timnah, telling no one what had happened. To his great joy, the Philistine girl agreed to marry him.

On his return to Timnah for the wedding feast, Samson saw that the lion's carcass was still lying in the vineyard. As he passed, he heard a swarm of bees inside the carcass. Putting his hand carefully into the hole, he scooped out some honey, which he ate as he walked on to Timnah. When he arrived, he set the young Philistine men a riddle. He said that if they could answer it within seven days of the wedding celebrations, he would give them all rich presents. But if they could not, they must give the same to him. The riddle he told them went like this: "Out of the eater came something to eat, out of the strong came something sweet."

The young men spent several days trying to solve the puzzle, but it was beyond them. Then they went to Samson's new wife and threatened her.

AND THE SPIRIT OF THE
LORD CAME MIGHTILY UPON
HIM, AND HE RENT HIM AS HE
WOULD HAVE RENT A KID,
AND HE HAD NOTHING IN HIS
HAND: BUT HE TOLD NOT HIS
FATHER OR HIS MOTHER
WHAT HE HAD DONE.

(Judges 14.6)

"If you don't get the answer for us," they said, "we'll burn your father's house down." So Samson's wife begged him for the answer, and when he refused to tell her, she burst into tears and said he didn't love her. This went on for a few days, until at last Samson tired of his wife's tears and told her the answer. She rushed off at once to tell the Philistine men.

Before sunset on that same, last day of the feast, the young men came to Samson and said proudly: "What is sweeter than honey, and what is stronger than a lion?" Samson was furious, because he knew that his wife had given away the answer. Determined to get revenge on the Philistines, Samson left his wife and stormed off to his father's house.

SAMSON AND DELILAH

Samson did not have an Israelite army, but his enormous strength meant that he could fight the Philistines single-handed. In one battle he killed a thousand men by striking them down with the jawbone of a dead donkey. On another occasion, he was trapped inside the Philistine city of Gaza, but he managed to escape by tearing the city gates and gateposts right out of the ground with his bare hands. The Philistines knew that he was simply too strong for them.

When Samson fell in love with a young Philistine woman named Delilah, his enemies realized that they might be able to bribe her

AND THE LORDS OF THE PHILISTINES CAME UP UNTO HER, AND SAID UNTO HER, ENTICE HIM, AND SEE WHEREIN HIS GREAT STRENGTH LIETH, AND BY WHAT MEANS WE MAY PREVAIL AGAINST HIM, THAT WE MAY BIND HIM TO AFFLICT HIM: AND WE WILL GIVE THEE EVERY ONE OF US ELEVEN HUNDRED PIECES OF SILVER.

(Judges 16.5)

Samson the hero
Samson's tragic story is one of the most popular stories in the Old Testament, and has inspired dramas, painting, operas and movies. Left, Samson and Delilah, from a 13th century French manuscript. In the left-hand picture Delilah is cutting off Samson's hair — the secret of his great strength; on the right, he is being tied up and blinded by the Philistines.

115

and use her against him. Philistine leaders visited Delilah and offered her a thousand pieces of silver if she could find out the secret of Samson's great strength and tell them how he could be overpowered. When she asked Samson why it was that he could never be captured, he said, "If you tied me up with seven new bowstrings, I would be as weak as everyone else."

Next time Samson went to see Delilah, she brought out seven new bowstrings and playfully started to tie him up, just to test his strength. Samson did not know that Philistine soldiers were waiting outside, but it wouldn't have made any difference to him. When Delilah cried "Samson, the Philistines are coming!"he simply burst out of the bowstrings as if they weren't there. The next time Delilah asked about his strength, Samson claimed that new ropes that had never been used would be too much for him. But when she tied him up and warned that the Philistines were coming, he simply snapped the ropes as if they

were thin threads. "It's unfair to treat me like a fool," Delilah said. "How can you say you love me when you keep secrets from me?" Samson tried to put her off, but when she kept on at him day after day about his strength, he finally gave in. "No razor has ever been used on my head," he told her. "This is to show that my life is dedicated to God. But if someone were to cut off my hair, my strength would be gone and I would be as weak as any other man."

Delilah told the Philistine leaders that at last she knew the secret of Samson's strength. When Samson next came to see her, soldiers were ready in hiding. First she lulled him to sleep, and then she quickly cut off all his hair. When she had finished, she cried out: "Wake up, Samson, the Philistines are coming!" Samson leapt up at once, thinking he could take on any number of soldiers. But instead, he found that all his strength had gone and he had no power to resist. The Philistines seized Samson, blinded him, bound him in heavy chains and dragged him away.

SAMSON IN THE PHILISTINES' TEMPLE

Philistine religion
The chief god of the warlike Philistines was Dagon, according to the Bible. They also worshipped the goddess Astarte and a god named Baalzebub. Above, a Philistine coffin from the 12th century BCE.

> AND SAMSON CALLED UNTO THE LORD, AND SAID, O LORD GOD, REMEMBER ME, I PRAY THEE, AND STRENGTHEN ME, I PRAY THEE, ONLY THIS ONCE, O GOD, THAT I MAY BE AT ONCE AVENGED OF THE PHILISTINES FOR MY TWO EYES.
>
> (Judges 16.28)

Once they had captured and blinded Samson, the Philistines dragged him off to a prison in the city of Gaza. The Israelite leader had once broken out of this city by lifting its gates with his bare hands, but now he was weak and powerless. The Philistines set him to work grinding grain in their prison.

All the Philistines, from the leaders to the ordinary people, were delighted to have overpowered their great enemy at last. The leaders decided to celebrate by holding a huge feast and making special offerings to their chief god, Dagon. The people believed that it was Dagon who had handed Samson over to them, and they were only too ready to praise their god. They all made their way to the temple in the city that was dedicated to Dagon. Outside the building, some began to shout to their leaders, "Let us see this great Samson! Bring the Israelite out so that he can entertain us!"

The Philistines believed that Samson was no longer a threat to them. Not one of them noticed that in prison, his hair had grown again. A guard was sent to fetch Samson from prison. As he was led through the streets, the people jeered at him and mocked him

for being blind and weak. Inside and out, the temple of Dagon was crowded with men and women of the city. The Philistine leaders were all there. People even stood on the rooftops to watch the fun. They were sure that Samson would put on a great performance, whether he wanted to or not.

As he was being led into the temple, Samson asked the guard to put him in the middle of the building so that he could lean against the central pillars. Then he asked for his hands to be guided to the pillars. The guard did this, thinking that Samson would otherwise fall over in his weakness. Once he felt the two great pillars with his hands, Samson prayed silently to God: "Please, Lord," he prayed, "give me strength just one more time, so that I can take revenge on those who blinded me."

Then Samson pressed his hands against the two pillars, gathered his returning strength and pushed with all his might. As the pillars started to move, Samson cried, "Let me die with the Philistines!" With that the mighty pillars swayed and fell, bringing the whole temple crashing down on all those crowded inside.

Samson had led the Israelites for twenty years: now he died with his Philistine enemies. His proud but sorrowful family collected Samson's body and took him back to be buried in the same tomb as his father.

Ruth and Naomi

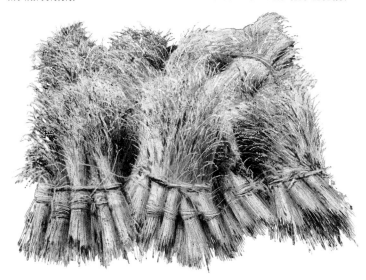

Women's work
Israelite women's daily domestic tasks included fetching water, caring for children and animals, cooking, grinding flour and baking bread (above, pottery figurine of a woman kneading dough). Women also carded and spun wool, wove cloth and sometimes worked in the fields and tended flocks.

Harvest time
The harvest season lasted about seven weeks, from spring to early summer. Barley and wheat were cut with sickles. After the crops were gathered in, poor people were allowed by law to go gleaning — they could collect any stalks left behind by the harversters.

During the time that Israel was ruled by judges, a man named Elimelech lived in Bethlehem with his wife Naomi and their two sons. One year the harvest was so poor that the family went to live in neighbouring Moab. When Elimelech died there, his wife Naomi was left to bring up her two sons. In time, both sons married Moabite women. About ten years later, both sons also died, and Naomi decided to return to her homeland.

Naomi's two daughters-in-law, Ruth and Orpah, went with her. But on the way Naomi tried to persuade them to go back to their own country, where they might find new husbands. Orpah tearfully agreed and turned back, but Ruth was determined to stay with her mother-in-law. "Wherever you go, I will go," Ruth said lovingly to Naomi. "Your people will be my people, and your God will be my God."

It was harvest time when the two women arrived in Bethlehem, and Ruth went to work in the fields.

She spent all day gleaning after the harvesters, picking up any barley stalks that they had left behind. Ruth worked hard without a rest and was soon noticed by Boaz, the man who owned the land. Boaz spoke kindly to Ruth, telling her to stay with his workers until they had finished in his fields. He showed her where there was water to drink and bread to eat, and even helped her in her work by quietly telling his harvesters to leave some barley stalks for her as they reaped. Ruth asked Boaz why he was being so good to her. "I have heard of your kindness to your mother-in-law and how you left your own people," Boaz replied. "May the Lord repay you for what you have done."

Naomi was delighted when Ruth told her what had happened. "Boaz is a relative of my late husband," Naomi said. "He will look after you." One evening, after Boaz and his men had been celebrating a harvest party, Ruth went to the threshing ground and found Boaz asleep. She quietly lay down nearby. When Boaz woke next morning, he was glad to see that Ruth felt so safe with him, and he decided to try and help her further.

Boaz knew that Naomi had inherited a small plot of land from her husband. He also knew a man who was a close relative of Naomi and he said to this man, "Naomi is going to sell her husband's land. The law says you have first claim on it – but if you buy it, the law says that you must also marry Ruth, to give

THEN SAID BOAZ UNTO HIS
SERVANT THAT WAS SET
OVER THE REAPERS, WHOSE
DAMSEL IS THIS?
AND THE SERVANT THAT
WAS SET OVER THE REAPERS
ANSWERED AND SAID, IT IS
THE MOABITISH DAMSEL
THAT CAME BACK WITH
NAOMI OUT OF THE
COUNTRY OF MOAB:
AND SHE SAID, I PRAY YOU,
LET ME GLEAN AND
GATHER AFTER THE
REAPERS AMONG THE
SHEAVES: SO SHE CAME, AND
HATH CONTINUED EVEN
FROM THE MORNING UNTIL
NOW, THAT SHE TARRIED A
LITTLE IN THE HOUSE.

(Ruth 2.5–7)

119

her a home." "I don't want to marry
her," said the man. "You can buy the
land. I give up my claim." So Boaz
bought the land and married Ruth,
and he made sure that after his death,
all the land would go to her children.
Naomi was delighted that Ruth's
kindness had been so richly rewarded.

Naomi was just as pleased as
the new parents when Ruth gave
birth to a baby boy. It was almost as
if she had a new son herself. The
baby was named Obed, and in years
to come he became the father of
Jesse, who in turn was the father of
David, the future king of Israel.

SAMUEL

☞ The two books of Samuel tell the story of how Israel developed from a group of tribes at the time of the Judges to become a united nation under King Saul and King David.

SAMUEL IS CALLED

Each year the people of Israel visited the tabernacle in Shiloh, where the Ark of the Covenant was kept. One visitor was Hannah, the wife of Elkanah. She was sad because she had no children. At the doorway of the tabernacle she prayed to God, promising that if only she had a son, he would be the Lord's servant for his whole life. A priest named Eli saw how distressed Hannah was. "Go in peace," Eli said as she left, "and may God answer your prayer."

In the course of time Hannah did indeed give birth to a baby boy. She was overjoyed and named him Samuel, meaning "asked of God". Remembering her promise, she waited until Samuel was old enough to feed himself and then took the little boy to Shiloh. There she gave her son to Eli, so that he could help the priest and be God's servant. Eli already had two sons, but they were greedy young men who broke many of God's laws, so he was pleased when he discovered what a pleasant, useful boy Samuel was. Hannah missed her son, and every year she brought him a new robe when she visited the tabernacle.

One night Samuel was woken by a voice calling his name and he ran to Eli. But the priest had not called him. After this happened three times, Eli realised that God was calling Samuel. He told the boy to reply, "Speak, Lord, your servant hears you." Samuel obeyed, and God told him that Eli's wicked sons were going to die. From that day young Samuel was a prophet of the Lord, and the people of Israel listened to him.

AND SHE VOWED A VOW, AND SAID, O LORD OF HOSTS, IF THOU WILT INDEED LOOK ON THE AFFLICTION OF THINE HANDMAID, AND REMEMBER ME, AND NOT FORGET THINE HANDMAID, BUT WILT GIVE UNTO THINE HANDMAID A MAN CHILD, THEN I WILL GIVE HIM UNTO THE LORD ALL THE DAYS OF HIS LIFE, AND THERE SHALL NO RAZOR COME UPON HIS HEAD.

(I Samuel 1.11)

THE CAPTURE OF THE ARK

The Israelites were often at war with the Philistines. After suffering heavy defeats, the Israelites took the Ark of the Covenant from the tabernacle at Shiloh and carried it into battle. Though the Ark gave them confidence, the Israelites lost again. The two men carrying the Ark — Hophni and Phinehas, the greedy sons of Eli — were killed, and the Philistines captured the precious treasure. A messenger ran to tell Eli what had happened. The priest was by now a very old man, and the news of the disaster so horrified him that he fainted, fell heavily and died.

The Philistines took the Ark to their city of Ashdod, where they placed it in the temple of Dagon, near to Dagon's statue. When they went to worship their god next day, they found that the statue had fallen on its face before the Ark. They hauled it back up, but the next day it had fallen again. This time Dagon was smashed to pieces. And that was not all: a few days later Ashdod was overrun with rats, and plague broke out among the people. So they took the Ark to the nearby city of Gath, but plague broke out there, too. When the same happened in Ekron, the people of the city begged their leaders to send the Ark back to Israel.

So the Philistines loaded the Ark on to a cart, along with some gold and valuable presents. Then they hitched two cows to the cart and let them pull it wherever they liked. If they took the road to Israel, the Philistines decided, it would show that the God of the Israelites was responsible for the disasters. And that is exactly what happened: the cows went straight to Israel, and the grateful Israelites thanked God for the Ark's safe return.

121

AND WHEN THEY AROSE EARLY ON THE MORROW MORNING, BEHOLD, DAGON WAS FALLEN UPON HIS FACE TO THE GROUND BEFORE THE ARK OF THE LORD; AND THE HEAD OF DAGON AND BOTH THE PALMS OF HIS HANDS WERE CUT OFF UPON THE THRESHOLD; ONLY THE STUMP OF DAGON WAS LEFT TO HIM.

(I Samuel 5.4)

SAMUEL THE KINGMAKER

Samuel led the Israelites for many years. When he was an old man, the elders of Israel came and asked him to appoint a new kind of ruler. The people wanted a king to lead them, like other nations. Samuel was unhappy at this, and he prayed to God for guidance. "They are rejecting me as their leader, not you," God said.

Samuel had already warned his people about the dangers of turning away from God. Now he also warned them that a king might treat his subjects unfairly, forcing them to fight in wars for bad reasons, or even making them slaves. But the people refused to listen: they wanted a king. When Samuel prayed again, God said, "Give them their king."

God told Samuel that he was to make a man named Saul king of the Israelites. Saul was a tall young man from the tribe of Benjamin. When God spoke to Samuel, Saul was wandering the countryside looking for his father's lost donkeys. He and a servant had been gone

from home for three days, but there was no sign of the missing animals. Saul thought it was time to give up the search, but the servant had heard that in a nearby town there was a man close to God. "Perhaps he will be able to tell us which way to go," the servant said.

The man close to God was Samuel. He told Saul that his father's donkeys had been found and, more importantly, that all the people of Israel were looking to him for leadership. Saul thought that Samuel must be mistaken. "I belong to a very small family in the smallest tribe of Israel," Saul protested. "Why do you say such a thing to me?"

"It is a message from God," Samuel replied. "He has chosen you to reign as king over the people of Israel." Then he took a horn full of olive oil and poured a few drops on Saul's head, to anoint him king. "When you leave here, you will meet two men who will tell you that your father's donkeys are safe. Next you will meet three men taking gifts to

The kings of Israel
Holy oil was used to anoint people who had been chosen by God for a special purpose. Kings and priests were anointed, and Israel's kings were often called "the Lord's Anointed". Right, Samuel anointing Saul as king of Israel, from the Nuremburg Bible of 1483.

God, and they will give you two loaves of bread. Then you will meet a group of prophets coming down a hill and you will become one of them. God will have changed you into a different person." Though Saul could scarcely believe it, when he left, everything happened exactly as Samuel had said it would.

Then Samuel called all the tribes of Israel together, to show them their king. Everyone wondered who it was that had been chosen. First Samuel selected the tribe of Benjamin. Then he picked out one small family. And finally he named one man. At first Saul was reluctant to come forward, but Samuel said, "This is the man that God has chosen to rule over you. There is no one like him in the whole of Israel." And when the people saw the tall figure of Saul, they all shouted, "Long live the king!"

Saul Disobeys God

S aul was a strong, brave warrior. The first thing he did as king was to save the Israelite town of Jabesh from attack by the Ammonites. After Saul had killed their enemies, the people thought that Samuel had certainly chosen the right king for them. Saul's son Jonathan was also a good soldier, and he helped his father by attacking Philistine outposts.

Though Saul was now a powerful king, Samuel still gave him God's commands and was concerned that Saul should carry them out. When Saul gathered his troops for an important battle against the Philistines at Michmash, Samuel told him to wait until he came personally to make a burnt offering and ask God for victory. Saul waited for seven days, but when Samuel didn't appear,

Saul and his men became impatient. The king did not want to risk losing the advantage against the Philistines.

At last Saul decided to wait no longer. He began to prepare the fire for the burnt offering, and when Samuel still did not turn up, he took a torch and lit it. Just at that moment Samuel arrived. "What have you done?" Samuel asked.

"I waited as long as I could," Saul replied firmly. "But when I saw the Philistines gathering, I had to make the offering myself to ask for God's help."

Samuel was very angry that the king had decided to act as a priest. His behaviour showed that he was not able to obey either Samuel or God. "You have acted very foolishly," said Samuel. "Since you have not kept the Lord's command, your kingdom will not last."

Not long afterward, there was another disagreement. Samuel told Saul that God had ordered the complete destruction of the Amalekites, to punish them for attacking the Israelites when they first came out of Egypt. "Do not spare a single one of them, not even one of their animals," Samuel told him. Saul's army attacked the Amalekites and wiped them out mercilessly. But Saul captured their king, Agag, and spared his life. Then he tried to please his own people by sparing the best of the Amalekites' sheep and cattle.

Saul claimed that he allowed the animals to live in order to sacrifice them to God. But Samuel replied that once again he had failed to obey God's orders. "You have rejected God's words, and he has rejected you as king of Israel," Samuel said. As he turned to leave, Saul tried to hold him back by catching hold of his robe. But the robe tore, and Samuel said to Saul, "God has torn the kingdom of Israel from you today, and has given it to another." Then Samuel had Agag brought to him, and he killed him, as God had commanded.

Samuel and Saul parted, never to meet again.

125

Philistine warriors
The Philistine soldiers (left, from an Egyptian relief) wore feathered helmets; they carried in battle a round shield, a long iron sword and two iron spears. They also rode in three-man chariots drawn by two horses. Only after fierce battles was king David able to defeat the Philistines and confine them to an area of land southwest of Judah.

GOD CALLS DAVID

God rejected Saul as king of Israel because he did not obey his commands. The prophet Samuel was very sad at this, even though he himself had fallen out with the king and found him obstinate. God had already chosen a new ruler, and he told Samuel that once again he would be the one to anoint him as the new king of the Israelites. "Fill your horn with oil," God told Samuel, "and go to Bethlehem. There you will find a man named Jesse. I have chosen one of his sons to be the next king."

Samuel was worried that Saul would hear of this and try to kill him, to stop him naming a new king. So God told Samuel to arrange a special feast in Bethlehem, so that Saul would think this was the reason for his visit. Then Samuel could invite Jesse and his family to the feast. Samuel did exactly as God ordered and went to Bethlehem. The elders of the town wondered why such an important person should choose to come to Bethlehem, but Samuel reassured them. "I come in peace," he said. "You are all invited to a special feast to honour God."

When Jesse came to the feast and introduced his sons to the prophet, the first in line was a tall, handsome young man named Eliab.

Samuel was sure that this must be the one chosen by God to be king. But God said to Samuel, "He is not the one. Human beings look at a person's outward appearance, but I look into their heart." The next son to be introduced was Abinadab, but God told Samuel that he had not chosen him either. The same was true of the third son, Shammah, and of four further sons who were presented.

Samuel began to wonder if he had made a mistake. "Are these all the sons you have?" he asked Jesse.

"There is one more, my youngest," Jesse replied. "But I did not bring him. He is looking after our sheep."

"Send for him," said Samuel. "The feast can wait until he arrives."

Jesse sent someone to fetch his youngest son, whose name was David. When the young man arrived, Samuel saw that he, too, was strong and handsome. Then God said to Samuel, "He is the one." So Samuel took his horn of oil and poured some drops on David's head to anoint him.

Samuel left Bethlehem after the feast. David went back to looking after his father's sheep, but now he knew that God had chosen him for a very special task. He was to be the second king of Israel.

DAVID AND GOLIATH

David the musician
Music and dance are an important part of David's story. He plays his harp to soothe Saul's bad moods, laments the deaths of Saul and Jonathan with a sad song and when the Ark of the Covenant is brought to Jerusalem, he dances in the street for joy. The Bible also describes how David organised an orchestra and choir "to sing and play joyful music" in the temple. Right: in this illumination from a medieval manuscript, David is shown playing an early instrument called a psaltery.

Although Saul was still king of Israel in the eyes of the people, he was very unhappy for he felt that God was no longer with him. Being king seemed a burden to him. He was never able to relax or think about things calmly, and his attendants were increasingly worried about him. One of the attendants suggested that sweet music might help Saul's mood, so the king asked him to find someone who could play the harp well.

The attendant had heard that Jesse of Bethlehem had a son who played the harp beautifully, was brave and strong, and looked after his father's sheep. The young man's name was David. So the attendant sent a messenger to David's father, Jesse, straight away.

Jesse sent David to the royal palace at once, and his youngest son entered the king's service. Whenever Saul felt troubled, he would ask David to take out his harp and play for him, and the music made him feel a little happier. Saul liked David so much that he made him one of his armour-bearers – his close personal attendants. When Saul was feeling better, David was able to go back to Bethlehem to help his father.

David's three oldest brothers joined Saul's army, which was often at war with the Philistines. The Israelite forces were camped on a hill beside the Valley of Elah, while the mighty Philistine army occupied the hill opposite. While the opposing armies faced each other and both waited for the other to make a move, a giant of a man suddenly came out of the Philistine camp. His name was Goliath. He was much bigger than any ordinary man, and his huge body was protected by armour. He wore a bronze helmet and carried a spear slung across his back. As his giant footsteps thudded across the valley, every Israelite soldier watched him attentively. Then Goliath stopped and shouted in a huge voice, "Servants of Saul, choose a man to come out and fight me! If he can beat me and kill me, we Philistines will become your subjects. But if I win, then you Israelites will serve us!"

An eerie silence fell across the valley as the giant waited. The Israelite soldiers looked at each other, but no one took up the challenge.

AND IT CAME TO PASS, WHEN THE
EVIL SPIRIT FROM GOD WAS UPON
SAUL, THAT DAVID TOOK A HARP, AND
PLAYED WITH HIS HAND; SO SAUL WAS
REFRESHED, AND WAS WELL, AND THE
EVIL SPIRIT DEPARTED FROM HIM.

(I Samuel 16.23)

Slings
Originally a shepherd's weapon for scaring away wild animals from their flocks, slings became common in warfare. Skilled soldiers could sling a stone over 200 metres and hit their targets accurately. Above, a 9th century BCE relief from Syria showing a man about to launch a stone from his sling.

Later that day Goliath came out and taunted the Israelites again, but once more there was no response. For forty days the same thing happened, morning and evening, as Goliath came out and roared at the Israelites. King Saul offered a rich reward to anyone who would kill the giant, but not one of his soldiers was brave enough to take up the challenge.

One day Jesse sent David to get news of his three brothers and take them food. Just as David was greeting his brothers, Goliath appeared across the valley and bellowed out his defiant challenge. "Who is this ignorant Philistine?" David asked.

"Nothing to do with you," his oldest brother Eliab answered angrily. "Anyway, what are you doing here? Who is left to look after father's sheep?"

Before David could say any more, he was called to Saul's tent. The king had heard that he was visiting his brothers. As soon as he saw the king, David said, "Do not be concerned about this Philistine. I will fight him."

"You cannot take on this giant," Saul replied, astonished. "He is a fighting man and you are just a shepherd boy."

"But I have fought off bears and even lions that have threatened my father's flock of sheep," said David. "The Lord who helped me then will certainly help me against this giant Philistine."

Saul insisted on giving him a heavy sword and full armour, but David was not used to them and could hardly walk. He took off the armour, put down the sword, and picked up the simple sling that he had brought with him. Then he chose five smooth stones from the stream in the valley and put them in his shepherd's bag. He was ready to face the giant.

Next time Goliath appeared, David walked bravely out of the Israelite camp. When he saw him, the giant roared with laughter. "Come on then," he bellowed. "I'll soon be feeding what's left of you to the birds and the beasts!"

David replied in a calm, strong voice. "You have just a sword and a spear," he said, "but I fight in the name of the Lord Almighty, the God of the armies of Israel, and he will hand you over to me."

This annoyed Goliath, who lumbered forward to attack David. But before he could reach him, David quickly took a stone from his bag, put it in his sling and hurled it at the giant. The stone struck Goliath on the forehead and he crashed to the ground, dead. David went and stood over him. Then he took the giant's own sword and cut off his head.

When they saw that their mighty champion was dead, the Philistines fled from their camp. The Israelites chased after them and killed many of their enemies on the roads from the Valley of Elah.

Saul Grows Jealous

While David lived at the palace of King Saul, he became a close friend of Saul's son, Jonathan. One day, as a sign of their friendship, the king's son took off the robe he was wearing and gave it to David, along with his favourite sword and bow. Jonathan knew that David was a fine soldier, and he soon had great success in Saul's army. When the king and his men returned from one of many battles with the Philistines, women lined the streets to celebrate their victory. They sang: "Saul has killed thousands of our enemies, but David has killed tens of thousands." The king grew jealous when he heard this.

One day when Saul was in a bad mood, he called for David to play the harp to him. The music usually made him feel better, but this time David's playing just made him angrier. When he could stand it no longer, Saul picked up a spear and hurled it at David. Fortunately David was quick enough to move out of the way as the spear whistled past him and crashed into the wall.

Saul became more and more jealous. When he discovered that his daughter, Michal, was in love with David, he said that David could marry her, for a small price – a hundred dead Philistines. The king hoped that this would be too much even for David to manage, but when David and his men went out and killed two hundred of the enemy, Saul had no choice but to allow him to marry his daughter.

Jonathan had noticed Saul's growing jealousy, and was horrified when his father told him that he intended to kill David. Jonathan warned his friend to be very careful. A few days later Saul sent men to David's house, but by then Michal was also suspicious. She helped her husband escape by rope from their upper window. Then she put an idol in their bed, covered it with a rug,

and put some goat's hair at the head. When the king's men arrived, Michal told them that David was ill in bed. The men rushed upstairs and went to kill David – only to discover that they and the king had been tricked.

David knew that he could not go back home, so he met Jonathan in secret and asked what he should do. Jonathan hoped that his father's anger would have passed and told David to hide while he went to find out. Jonathan agreed a signal with David. Next day he would fire an arrow at a rock they both knew, and then would send his servant to fetch it. If Saul's anger had died and David was safe, Jonathan would shout to the servant, "The arrow's right by you!"; but if David was still in danger, Jonathan would shout, "The arrow's a little farther off!"

Later, Jonathan spoke to his father about David, and Saul got angrier than ever. "You will never become king as long as the son of Jesse is alive," the king cried. "He must die!" Next day, Jonathan gave the agreed signal to David. He had no choice but to shout to his servant that the arrow was farther off. Jonathan was very sad that his best friend must go into hiding in order to stay alive.

David the warrior   *133*

David is shown in the Bible as a brave and clever soldier. He made daring raids against the Israelites' old enemy, the Philistines. As king, he led many military campaigns and built Israel's army into a strong fighting power. He also made the walls of towns stronger and built new forts to guard the southern borders. Above, a statue of David by the Italian sculptor Andrea del Verrocchio (1435–88). The young hero has cut off the head of Goliath, the Philistine giant.

AND JONATHAN SAID TO DAVID, GO IN PEACE, FOR AS MUCH AS WE HAVE SWORN BOTH OF US IN THE NAME OF THE LORD, SAYING, THE LORD BE BETWEEN ME AND THEE, AND BETWEEN MY SEED AND THY SEED FOR EVER. AND HE AROSE AND DEPARTED: AND JONATHAN WENT INTO THE CITY.

(I Samuel 20.42)

DAVID THE FUGITIVE

> DAVID THEREFORE DEPARTED THENCE, AND
> ESCAPED TO THE CAVE ADULLAM: AND WHEN HIS
> BRETHREN AND ALL HIS FATHER'S HOUSE HEARD IT,
> THEY WENT DOWN THITHER TO HIM.
> AND EVERYONE THAT WAS IN DISTRESS, AND EVERY
> ONE THAT WAS IN DEBT, AND EVERY ONE THAT WAS
> DISCONTENTED, GATHERED THEMSELVES UNTO HIM;
> AND HE BECAME A CAPTAIN OVER THEM: AND
> THERE WERE WITH HIM ABOUT FOUR HUNDRED MEN.
>
> (I Samuel 22.1–2)

Israel's priesthood
Priests led public worship and made sacrifices. They were all descendants of Jacob's son, Levi. They were supported by offerings from the people and by part of the offerings made to God. The High Priest had the greatest authority and was the only one who could enter the "Holy of Holies", once a year, during the solemn worship on the Day of Atonement. Above, a High Priest in a detail from a painting by Titian (1488–1576).

After leaving his friend Jonathan, David went to the priest Ahimelech and asked him for food. The priest helped David and gave him the sword of Goliath, which David himself had used to cut off the giant's head. David asked the priest to keep his whereabouts secret from King Saul, but his request was overheard by Doeg, the king's governor in the region.

Next David travelled to the Philistine city of Gath. When he heard people talking about his great victories at the head of the Israelite army, however, he was afraid that the Philistines would kill him. So he pretended to be mad, and then quickly escaped to a safe hideaway — a large cave at Adullam. Word of David's whereabouts reached his brothers, who went to join him, along with many other friends and supporters. Soon David was surrounded by hundreds of followers.

In the meantime, Doeg reported what he had heard to his master, Saul. The king was furious that Ahimelech had helped David, and decided to take revenge. He ordered his guards to kill Ahimelech and the other priests of the town. When the guards refused to harm men of God, Doeg himself carried out the command, killing eighty-five priests in one day. Then Saul and his army went in search of David.

David and his followers had moved to the barren hills of Judah. One day Saul got very close to finding the fugitive. He went into the mouth of a deep cave, little realising that David and his men were hiding in the cavern's dark depths. While Saul stood there with his back to him, David could easily have killed the king. He crept up to him unnoticed, but knew that he could not harm God's chosen ruler. Instead, he cut off a piece of Saul's robe.

A few days later, David had a second chance to kill the king. He and his nephew Abishai were out on patrol in the dead of night, when they came across Saul's camp. The two men crept up in silence, and found the king's guards asleep. Saul himself was lying nearby, with his spear stuck in the ground by his side. Abishai whispered to his uncle that he could kill the king with one thrust of his spear, but David would not allow it. Once again he could not harm God's anointed king. Instead, he took the king's spear and water jug, and when he and Abishai were some distance away, they shouted to wake the king's guards. Saul, seeing that his spear and jug were missing, realised that David had spared his life and said, "I will never harm you."

David knew, however, that the king's sorrow and forgiveness would not last for long. He decided it would be safer for him and his men to leave Israel and return to the land of the Philistines, where they were received well by Achish, the king of Gath. The Philistines were planning a new attack on the Israelite army, and Achish wanted David to be his own bodyguard and help him against Saul's army. But the Philistine commanders complained to their leader, reminding him that this was the man who was famed for killing

tens of thousands of Israel's enemies. Achish reluctantly agreed that David need not fight his own countrymen.

When Saul saw the size of the Philistine army, he was struck with fear. Feeling a terrible sense of coming disaster, he decided to consult a fortune-teller. In disguise, Saul visited the witch of Endor and asked her to call up the spirit of

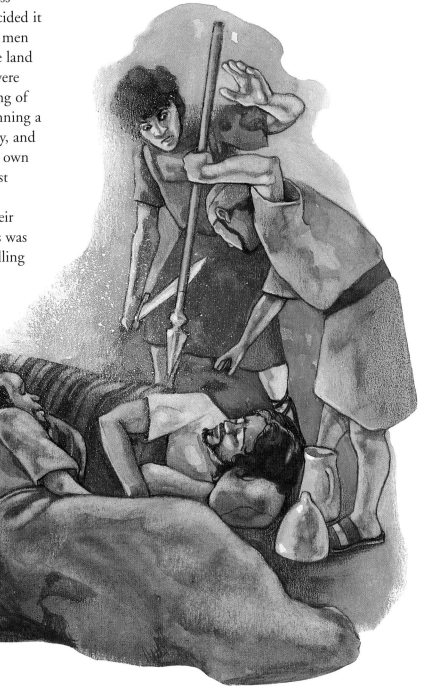

136

Samuel. The dead prophet's spirit said to Saul, "God has left you. Tomorrow the Philistines will win the battle and you and your sons will be killed." Saul collapsed to the ground. His worst fears were about to come true.

Next day a great battle was fought on the hills around Mount Gilboa. The Philistine army soon overcame their opponents, and the Israelites were defeated. Saul's three sons were killed, including his eldest, Jonathan. The fighting grew fierce around the king, and he was wounded by Philistine arrows. Saul saw that the end was near. Determined not to fall into the hands of the Philistines, he turned to his bodyguard. "Kill me!" he ordered. But the young man could not do it. So Saul took his sword and plunged it into his own body. Just as the spirit of Samuel had foretold, the king and his three soldier sons were all dead.

When David heard the news of Saul's death, he broke down in tears. Although Saul had treated him cruelly and unfairly, David had always respected him as God's chosen ruler. And Jonathan had been his closest, most loyal friend. David wrote a deeply sorrowful poem to lament their deaths and to remind people for ever of their lives.

DAVID AND ABIGAIL

While David and his men were fugitives, they often met shepherds out in the wilderness. Though food was short, David's men never harmed the shepherds or stole any of their animals. One day, David heard that a rich land-owner named Nabal, who had many thousands of sheep, was holding a feast. So he sent some young men to Nabal, to ask if he could kindly spare a little food and drink.

Nabal was a mean, bad-tempered man. "Who does this outlaw David think he is?" he sneered, as he sent the messengers away. When they arrived back, David was furious. "Buckle on your swords!" he ordered his best soldiers, and he set off with them at once.

Meanwhile, a servant had told Nabal's wife Abigail how rude her husband had been. Abigail lost no time. She loaded donkeys with food and wine and set off to find David. Meeting him on the way, she fell on her knees and begged his forgiveness. "Pay no attention to Nabal," she said. "His name means 'fool', and he behaved very foolishly. Please allow your men to accept my gifts." David was happy to accept her apology and her food.

When Nabal heard of this, he was so angry that his heart failed and days later he died. David's own wife, Michal, had been given by Saul to another man — so David married the beautiful, sensible Abigail.

137

DAVID BECOMES KING

King David
David established Israel's first royal house, or dynasty. During his reign (1000–961 BCE) he organised the state, gained more land and became an ally of the Phoenician king of Tyre. The Star of David, above, is a Jewish symbol of the protection given by God to David and his people, and it appears on the flag of Israel.

138

Jerusalem
Jerusalem was just a village at the time of its conquest, but because it was in the middle of the land of Israel, it soon became the religious and political heart of the community. By tradition, it was also the place where Isaac was nearly sacrificed. David made it the home of the Ark and built a fortress there for himself. His son Solomon enlarged the city (below) and added fine buildings.

After King Saul's death, David returned to Judah, the southern part of Israel. There, in the city of Hebron, David's fellow tribesmen made him king of Judah. David hoped that the whole of Israel could live in peace and unity, but at that time the northern part of the country was ruled by Ishbosheth, who was Saul's only remaining son. He was helped and guarded by Abner, his father's former army commander. For more than seven years Abner led his troops against Joab, David's nephew and greatest general. Eventually Abner fell out with his leader, and both men decided to make their peace with the kingdom of Judah. But first David insisted that Ishbosheth return his first wife Michal, the daughter whom Saul had given to another man.

Shortly after Ishbosheth was murdered by two of his own men, elders of all the tribes of Israel came to David at Hebron and proclaimed him king of the whole nation. David decided at once to move his capital north to Jerusalem, which was situated close to the boundary between the north and south regions. But Jerusalem was so strong a city that it

had never been captured from its original inhabitants, the Jebusites, since the Israelites came to Canaan. Nevertheless, it had a weakness which the Jebusites had not noticed – an unguarded water tunnel, through which water came into the city from a spring outside the walls. David sent soldiers in through the tunnel, and they captured Zion, the main fortress of the city. Jerusalem soon became known as the City of David. The king of Tyre sent David craftsmen to build him a palace, and plentiful supplies of wood.

David decided to bring the Ark of the Covenant to his new capital. He went with many men to Baalah, in Judah, and they carefully placed the sacred chest on a new cart, pulled by oxen. The Ark's journey to Jerusalem was accompanied by crowds of people singing and playing harps, tambourines, and cymbals. When one of the oxen suddenly stumbled and the cart swayed, one of the Ark's attendants put his hand on the chest to steady it. God struck the attendant dead for daring to touch the sacred chest, which made David very upset

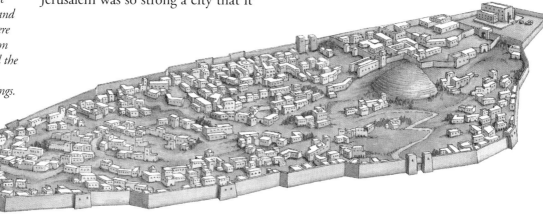

and angry. The king stopped the Ark's procession for three months, before eventually carrying on to Jerusalem.

When the Ark entered the city, a huge crowd escorted it, singing and playing pipes and tambourines. David threw off his priest's robes and danced for joy at the head of the procession. Michal was watching from a window. She hated to see her husband forget his dignity and behave in such a way before all the watching crowd. When he arrived home, she told him so. David was very angry. "I was celebrating before the Lord God, who chose me rather than any of your family to rule over Israel," he said. "Whatever you say, I shall dance for joy before the Lord." As a punishment from God, Michal was never able to give David children.

The Ark was placed in a tent, as it had been a long time earlier when the Israelites left Egypt seeking the Promised Land. David wanted to build God a temple in Jerusalem, but God told him through the prophet Nathan that he was not to do this – a son of David would build a temple in Jerusalem, for David's descendants were to be kings of Israel after him, and their kingdom would last for ever.

139

SO DAVID AND ALL THE HOUSE OF ISRAEL BROUGHT UP THE ARK OF THE LORD WITH SHOUTING, AND WITH THE SOUND OF THE TRUMPET. AND AS THE ARK OF THE LORD CAME INTO THE CITY OF DAVID, MICHAL, SAUL'S DAUGHTER, LOOKED THROUGH A WINDOW, AND SAW KING DAVID LEAPING AND DANCING BEFORE THE LORD; AND SHE DESPISED HIM IN HER HEART.

(II Samuel 6.15–16)

DAVID AND BATHSHEBA

One evening David sat on the roof of his palace, enjoying the cool breeze. As he looked down at the nearby courtyards, the king saw a young woman bathing. She looked very beautiful and David asked one of his attendants about her. He discovered that her name was Bathsheba, and that she was married to one of his army officers. Knowing that the army was away fighting the Ammonites, David sent for Bathsheba at once. That night he slept with her.

A few weeks later, Bathsheba sent a message to the king saying that she was going to have his baby. Knowing that he had broken one of God's commandments by sleeping with another man's wife, David decided to pretend that he was not the father. He ordered his commander Joab to send Bathsheba's husband, Uriah, back to Jerusalem. When Uriah arrived at the royal palace, David asked him how the war was going, and then sent him home to his wife. But the next day he was disappointed to discover that Uriah had spent the night on a mat near the palace gates.

David sent for Uriah and asked why he didn't go home. "My comrades are all sleeping rough in the field," Uriah replied. "So how could I go home and sleep in comfort with my wife?" David now had to think up another plan. He sent Uriah back to the army with a letter for Joab. In it he told his commander to put Uriah in the front line, and then retreat so that he would be killed by the enemy. Joab obeyed the king's orders, and Uriah was killed. When she was given the sad news, Bathsheba wept for her husband. But as soon as her period of mourning was over,

Nathan
David's selfish behaviour is strongly condemned by the prophet Nathan. In this picture from a Byzantine psalter, about 950 CE, Nathan is telling David, on the left, that he has done wrong. David is also shown on the right, repenting on his knees, while the prophet looks on.

140

David had her brought to his palace. Then he married Bathsheba, and she gave birth to a son.

But God was angry with David for what he had done, and he sent the prophet Nathan to tell him a story. "A rich man and a poor man lived in a village. The rich man owned whole herds of sheep and cattle, while the poor man had a single lamb, which he kept at home and treated like one of his children. One day, when the rich man had a visitor, he wanted to offer roast lamb. But instead of sending his servant for one of his many animals, he took the poor man's lamb and had it killed."

David was horrified. "That pitiless man deserves to die!" he cried.

"You are that man," said Nathan. "God made you a king and gave you everything you wanted, including wives and children. But you took from Uriah the woman he loved, and then you even had him killed. For this God is going to bring you misfortune: you are not going to die, but your baby son will." David prayed to God to save Bathsheba's child, but the baby fell ill at once and seven days later was dead.

In time, Bathsheba gave birth to another son by David, and they named him Solomon.

O My Son Absalom!

Hairstyles
The Israelites of Old Testament times usually wore their hair long. Beautiful hair was important to women, and wild, untidy hair was a sign of mourning or shame. Men wore beards and sometimes plaited their hair. Priests could trim but not shave their hair, and Nazirites like Samson, who were set apart in God's service, were forbidden to cut their hair at all. Above, two Assyrian noblemen with long hair and square-cut beards.

142

David had many children by different wives. His son Absalom and daughter Tamar were born to the princess of Geshur, a city in Syria. Absalom was a handsome young man, with a fine head of hair, which he cut only once a year. When his sister Tamar was raped by her half-brother Amnon, Absalom decided to take revenge. He invited all the king's sons to a feast, and ordered his men to kill Amnon.

Absalom then fled to Geshur. David missed his son, but would not send for him. Seeing his sadness, David's commander Joab sent a woman to tell the king a sad story that he had made up. "I am a widow and had two sons," the woman said. "But one son killed the other, and now everyone says I must hand over my remaining son, so that he can be put to death. How can I do this?" The king felt sorry for the woman and told her that he would protect her son. Then he realised that Joab had sent her to make him think about Absalom, and so at last he did send for his son.

Absalom soon made himself popular with the people of Jerusalem and began to plot against David. He took his followers south to Hebron. There he raised an army and gained the help of David's trusted adviser, Ahithophel. When David learned of this, he realised how serious the rebellion was. Fearing that Absalom's army would attack Jerusalem, David and his followers left the city and headed toward the River Jordan.

Then David had an idea. He told another of his close advisors, Hushai, to join Absalom's rebellion. Hushai could try to overturn the good advice that Ahithophel was bound to give his son. When Hushai arrived back in Jerusalem, he found Absalom acting as king and planning how best to defeat his father. Ahithophel advised his new master to send him with an army to attack David at once, while his men were tired after their march. Hushai knew this was good advice, but when he was also asked, he disagreed. "Your father and his men are fierce fighters," Hushai told Absalom. "You would do better to gather a vast army from all over Israel and then lead them yourself into battle." Absalom agreed.

Hushai secretly sent word of the plan to David, who crossed the River Jordan so his army could rest and prepare themselves. Joab and the other commanders persuaded David to stay out of the battle. As they got ready, David said to them, "Be gentle with Absalom, for my sake." When Absalom's army approached, David's men were too strong for their enemies. Absalom found himself surrounded by Joab's soldiers. As he turned his mule to make his escape, he rode into the overhanging branches of an oak tree and was caught by his hair. Joab rushed to the spot. He ignored David's plea and plunged his spear into Absalom's heart.

AND THE KING WAS
MUCH MOVED, AND
WENT UP TO THE
CHAMBER OVER THE
GATE, AND WEPT:
AND AS HE WENT,
THUS HE SAID,
O MY SON
ABSALOM, MY SON,
MY SON ABSALOM!
WOULD GOD I HAD
DIED FOR THEE,
O ABSALOM,
MY SON, MY SON!

(II Samuel 18.33)

David was grief-stricken when he heard of his son's death. "O my son Absalom!" he cried out. "If only I had died instead of you!" Such grief angered his soldiers. Joab had to wait for the right moment to approach the king and persuade him to stop mourning Absolom. After all, Absolom had plotted against the king's life. He advised David instead to thank the soldiers for their loyalty and for risking their lives for him.

THE PSALMS

The 150 psalms are songs and poems that praise and honour God. They were composed over a long period of time – from the days of King David until after the exile in Babylon – for use in worship in the Temple. Many may have been written by King David himself, the "sweet psalmist of Israel". The psalms express a wide range of feelings and ideas.

They praise God as the creator of everything, as in psalm 24:
The earth is the Lord's, and the fullness thereof; the world and they that dwell therein.

They recognise God as kind and forgiving, as in psalm 103:
The Lord is merciful and gracious, slow to anger, and plenteous in mercy.

Psalm 23 compares God to a loving shepherd looking after his people as a shepherd cares for his sheep:
The Lord is my shepherd; I shall not want.
He maketh me to lie down in green pastures; he leadeth me beside the still waters.
He restoreth my soul: he leadeth me in the paths of righteousness for his name's sake.
Yea, though I walk through the valley of

the shadow of death, I will fear no evil: for thou art with me; thy rod and thy staff they comfort me.
Thou preparest a table before me in the presence of mine enemies: thou anointest my head with oil; my cup runneth over.
Surely goodness and mercy shall follow me all the days of my life: and I will dwell in the house of the Lord for ever.

Psalm 121 also recognises God as a protector. It is one of several psalms called "Songs of Ascent", perhaps so-called because they were sung as people journeyed on a pilgrimage up to Jerusalem, located at the top of a steep hill:
I will lift up mine eyes unto the hills, from whence cometh my help.
My help cometh from the Lord, which made heaven and earth.
He will not suffer thy foot to be moved: he that keepeth thee will not slumber.
Behold he that keepeth Israel shall neither slumber nor sleep.
The Lord is thy keeper: the Lord is thy shade upon thy right hand.
The sun shall not smite thee by day, nor the moon by night.
The Lord shall preserve thee from all evil: he shall preserve thy soul.
The Lord shall preserve thy going out and thy coming in from this time forth, and even for evermore.

There are certain key words in the psalms that are often repeated: righteousness, faithfulness, steadfast love (of God), peace, salvation and blessing (that God gives). If we want to know what the Israelites felt about God, we can do no better than to read the psalms.

David's psalms
Many of the psalms are traditionally attributed to King David, shown here in a 15th century painting.

THE DEATH OF DAVID

When David was old and ill, his son Adonijah planned to take over as king of Israel. With the support of his father's commander Joab, Adonijah called all his followers to a celebration feast. He invited all the king's other sons, except for his half-brother Solomon.

As soon as the prophet Nathan heard about this, he went straight to Solomon's mother, Bathsheba. The prophet advised Bathsheba to go to David at once and remind him of his promise that Solomon would succeed him as king. Bathsheba did so, telling her husband that if Adonijah became king, she and Solomon would be treated as criminals.

David kept his promise. He told Nathan to take Solomon on the king's own mule to the spring at Gihon, where he and Zadok the priest should anoint him king of Israel. Nathan obeyed his king's orders, and after the ceremony all the people cried "Long live King Solomon!" as he rode back into the city. Adonijah and his supporters were just finishing their feast when they heard the news. They knew that their plans had been ruined.

David called Solomon to see him one last time. "Soon I shall no longer be here with you," David said. "Be strong, walk in God's ways, and always obey his laws and commands." David died shortly afterwards, and was buried in his royal city of Jerusalem.

AND ZADOK THE PRIEST TOOK A HORN OF OIL OUT OF THE TABERNACLE, AND ANOINTED SOLOMON. AND THEY BLEW THE TRUMPET; AND ALL THE PEOPLE SAID, GOD SAVE KING SOLOMON. AND ALL THE PEOPLE CAME UP AFTER HIM, AND THE PEOPLE PIPED WITH PIPES, AND REJOICED WITH GREAT JOY, SO THAT THE EARTH RENT WITH THE SOUND OF THEM.

(I Kings 1.39–40)

THE WISDOM OF SOLOMON

Solomon's wives
Solomon's marriage to the pharaoh's daughter was a proof of Israel's growing importance. Egypt, however, was less powerful than it had been, and was glad to have Israel as a friend. Solomon, like other eastern kings at that time, had many other foreign wives. Above, statue of an Egyptian queen.

Solomon's reign
Under Solomon, the Israelites began what was later regarded as a Golden Age of peace and wealth. Solomon began a building programme to make the cities larger. He also built temples, palaces and fortresses. Forcing people to work on his buildings and taxing everyone to pay for them, however, made him unpopular. Right, a gate from the city of Hazor, built during Solomon's rule.

Solomon, the new king of Israel, married the daughter of the Egyptian pharaoh. One night, God came to Solomon in a dream and told him that he could ask for whatever he wanted. "You have shown great kindness to my father and me by placing me on his throne," Solomon replied. "But I am young and do not know how to carry out my duties toward the people of Israel. Please give me the wisdom to tell right from wrong so that I can govern your people well."

God was pleased with this reply. "I will give you the wisdom for which you ask," he told Solomon. "And though you did not ask for anything more, I will also give you riches and honour. Furthermore, if you obey my laws as your father David did, you will enjoy a long life."

Solomon soon had the chance to put his new, God-given wisdom to the test. Two women came to their king in Jerusalem and asked him to settle a quarrel for them. "This woman and I live in the same house," one of them said. "Just a few days after my baby boy was born, she also gave birth to a son. Then one night her baby died, and she put him beside me and took my son from me while I was asleep. Next morning, I got up to feed my son and thought he was dead. But when I picked up the baby and looked at him closely, I saw that he wasn't my son at all."

"That's not true!" the second woman cried, holding the baby close to her. "This baby is mine. It is your baby that is dead!"

The two women looked at Solomon, wondering how he would settle the matter. They were surprised when the king asked a servant to fetch his sword. "Both these women say that the baby is theirs," said Solomon. "So cut the child in two and give half to one and half to the other."

The first woman was horrified and cried out at once: "Please don't kill him, my Lord! Please don't! Give the baby to her!"

AND GOD SAID UNTO HIM, BECAUSE THOU HAST ASKED THIS THING, AND HAST NOT ASKED FOR THYSELF LONG LIFE; NEITHER HAST ASKED RICHES FOR THYSELF, NOR HAST ASKED THE LIFE OF THINE ENEMIES; BUT HAST ASKED FOR THYSELF UNDERSTANDING TO DISCERN JUDGEMENT; BEHOLD, I HAVE DONE ACCORDING TO THY WORDS: LO, I HAVE GIVEN THEE A WISE AND AN UNDERSTANDING HEART; SO THAT THERE WAS NONE LIKE THEE BEFORE THEE, NEITHER AFTER THEE SHALL ANY ARISE LIKE UNTO THEE.

(I Kings 3,11–12)

The other woman disagreed: "Do as the king says, then neither of us will have the baby!"

Now Solomon knew which of the two women was the baby's real mother, because only she would care more about her baby than herself.

"Give the baby to the first woman," he ordered, "for she is his mother."

When the people of Israel heard what had happened, they knew that King Solomon was wise and would rule over them with good judgement and give them true justice.

BUILDING GOD'S TEMPLE

God kept his promise to Solomon by making him both wise and rich. Israel was a successful trading nation, at peace with its neighbours. Solomon knew that his father, David, had always wanted to build a temple for God in his own city of Jerusalem. But God had said that David's son would build the temple. In the fourth year of his reign, Solomon believed that it was time to put the plan into action.

So King Solomon sent a message to Hiram, king of the Phoenician city of Tyre, who had always been friendly with David. Solomon asked Hiram to supply him with cedar and pine wood from the great forests of Lebanon, in exchange for wheat and olive oil from Israel. Hiram was happy to agree.

Then Solomon sent thousands of workers to quarries in the hills of Israel. There they cut massive blocks of stone. The timber and stone were carried to Jerusalem, and work began on the temple. The outer walls were built out of cut and shaped stones, while the roof was made of the finest cedar. There were two rooms: a main hall and an inner sanctuary, or Holy of Holies, where the Ark of the Covenant was to be kept. Both rooms were lined inside with cedar panelling on the floor and walls, and the wood was overlaid with pure gold. On the walls all around the temple were carved palm trees, flowers and cherubim. A skilled craftsman from Tyre cast two bronze pillars to stand outside the main hall.

Once the building was complete, the inside of the temple was beautifully carved and decorated by the finest craftsmen and artists. Then Solomon had special items made of gold to go inside the temple, including an altar, a table, lampstands, dishes and incense-burners. At last the temple was ready to receive the Ark of the Covenant. Priests carried the sacred chest into the Holy of Holies, and placed it beneath the wings of two cherubim made of olive wood overlaid with gold. Altogether it took seven years for King Solomon to build God's temple in Jerusalem.

Cedars of Lebanon
These beautiful large trees once grew in vast forests in Lebanon. Today, few remain. Precious cedar wood, which is both strong and fragrant, was exported in great quantities from Tyre and used for carvings, buildings and ships.

149

AND, BEHOLD, I PURPOSE TO BUILD AN HOUSE UNTO THE NAME OF THE LORD MY GOD, AS THE LORD SPAKE UNTO DAVID MY FATHER, SAYING, THY SON, WHOM I WILL SET UPON THY THRONE IN THY ROOM, HE SHALL BUILD AN HOUSE UNTO MY NAME.

(I Kings 5.5)

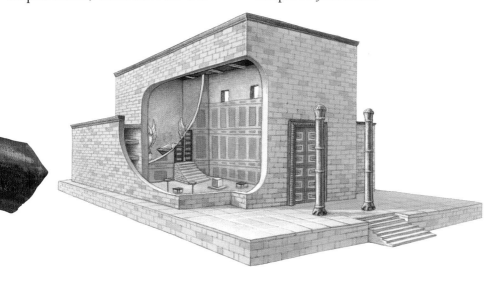

Solomon's temple
A reconstruction of the temple, as it may have looked. It was surrounded on three sides by a three-storey gallery, used by the priests for dressing, dining and storing sacred objects. The Holy of Holies, in the back, had no windows and was completely dark.

THE QUEEN OF SHEBA

Tales of King Solomon's wealth and wisdom spread far and wide. They soon reached a far-off land named Sheba, where the queen decided to find out for herself if what she had heard could possibly be true. She set out on the long journey to Jerusalem with a large caravan of camels loaded with gold, jewels and spices.

When she arrived at Solomon's palace, the Queen of Sheba saw that the tales of his wealth were not exaggerated. The palace itself was magnificent, and all the king's officials, courtiers and servants were dressed in the finest robes. She wanted to test the king's wisdom, so she asked him as many searching questions as she could. To her amazement, he answered every single one and nothing was too difficult for him to explain. It was clear to the queen that the stories of Solomon's wisdom were also true.

"I heard amazing reports of your wealth and wisdom," the queen told Solomon. "And I confess that I did not really believe these things until I saw them for myself. But if anything, your achievements are even greater than I had heard. How happy your people must be, and how lucky your officials are to be able to listen to your wise words every day. May your God be praised for placing you on the throne of Israel."

The queen then gave Solomon the presents of gold, jewels and spices that she had brought from Sheba. The king, in return, gave the Queen of Sheba expensive gifts, before she started out on the long journey back to her own land.

Trade
Solomon engaged skillful Phoenician shipbuilders and sailors to build up a merchant navy. Israel started importing goods and exporting metal and agricultural products. The Queen of Sheba may have wished to make a trade agreement with Solomon. Above, a merchant ship.

150

Sheba
Sheba may have been a state in the region of modern Yemen. The Queen of Sheba presented Solomon with quantities of incense and myrrh, which were produced in this area. Above, an amber and silver necklace from Yemen.

AND WHEN THE QUEEN OF SHEBA
HEARD OF THE FAME OF SOLOMON
CONCERNING THE NAME OF THE
LORD, SHE CAME TO PROVE HIM
WITH HARD QUESTIONS.
AND SHE CAME TO JERUSALEM
WITH A VERY GREAT TRAIN, WITH
CAMELS THAT BARE SPICES, AND
VERY MUCH GOLD, AND PRECIOUS
STONES; AND WHEN SHE WAS COME
TO SOLOMON, SHE COMMUNED WITH
HIM OF ALL THAT WAS IN HER HEART.

(I Kings 10.1–2)

A Kingdom Divided

The kings of Israel
Ten tribes made up the northern kingdom of Israel, which had Samaria as its capital. It was not a peaceful land and its royal dynasties changed many times. Right, the seal of an official who served Jeroboam II, one of the kings of Israel.

Israel and Judah
After Solomon's kingdom split into Israel and Judah, the two kingdoms spent years fighting each other over territory and over religion. These struggles weakened both kingdoms, and finally both were overrun by neighbouring enemies.

152

Solomon was a wise and wealthy king. He had many wives, in addition to the Egyptian pharaoh's daughter, and they came from many different countries. As the years passed, some of the royal wives persuaded Solomon to worship their own gods. He even built shrines to gods such as Chemosh, the chief deity of the Moabites, and Molech, the Ammonites' god of the dead.

God was angry with Solomon for failing to obey his command never to worship other gods. "Because of this I will take your kingdom away from you," God told Solomon. "But for the sake of David, your father, I will not do this in your lifetime, and I will leave a small part of the kingdom to your son."

God gave the future rule over most of Israel to one of Solomon's officials, a young man named Jeroboam. One day, as he was walking home, Jeroboam met the prophet Ahijah, who was wearing a new cloak. When Ahijah saw the young man, he tore the cloak into twelve pieces and gave ten of them to Jeroboam. "Take these pieces," Ahijah said. "They are the tribes of Israel that you will rule over after King

Solomon's death." But the prophet kept two pieces back. These represented the tribes and lands of Judah and Benjamin, which were to go to Solomon's son Rehoboam.

By the time of his death, Solomon had ruled over Israel for forty years. By then Jeroboam had gone to Egypt, where he waited for news of the king's death. Solomon's son Rehoboam took up the throne, but when he made it clear that he intended to rule strictly, the Israelites rebelled. When Jeroboam arrived from Egypt, the leaders of the northern tribes welcomed him and made him their king. Only the southern region of Judah, which included Jerusalem, remained loyal to King David's grandson Rehoboam. The country split into two kingdoms with two kings.

Jeroboam did not remain faithful to God for long, setting up golden idols to worship. His son, and many of the kings that followed, were murdered. One of these, named Omri, built a new capital for Israel and named it Samaria. But he also built shrines to pagan gods and worshipped idols. The people of the divided kingdom of Israel were once again turning against God.

SO WHEN ALL ISRAEL SAW THAT THE KING HEARKENED NOT UNTO THEM, THE PEOPLE ANSWERED THE KING, SAYING, WHAT PORTION HAVE WE IN DAVID? NEITHER HAVE WE INHERITANCE IN THE SON OF JESSE: TO YOUR TENTS, O ISRAEL: NOW SEE TO THINE OWN HOUSE, DAVID. SO ISRAEL DEPARTED UNTO THEIR TENTS.

(I Kings 12.16)

Elijah and the Ravens

When Omri, the king of Israel, died, his son Ahab became king. Ahab married a princess named Jezebel, from nearby Sidon. To please his wife, Ahab built shrines to Baal in Samaria, the capital of Israel. When he heard of this, the prophet Elijah went to see Ahab. He told the king that his heathen worship would lead to a long period of drought in the country.

God told Elijah how to survive the drought. He was to go to a stream named Cherith, near the River Jordan. "There you will have water to drink," God said, "and ravens will bring you food."

Elijah did as God told him. He stayed by the stream and drank when he was thirsty, and ravens flew down with bread and meat in their beaks. They fed Elijah so that he was able to stay alive, although there was no rain at all.

When the stream started to dry up, God told Elijah to go to Sidon. There the prophet would meet a widow, and when he asked her for food, her small jar of flour and jug of oil would never run out. Elijah did as God commanded, and everything happened exactly as he had been told. When the widow's son fell ill and died, Elijah prayed to God to bring the boy back to life. God granted Elijah's request and the boy's life was saved. The woman said to Elijah: "Now I know that you are a man of God."

Samaria
King Omri founded the new capital of Israel, Samaria, about 877 BCE. Once completed, it was a very strong fortress. It withstood a three-year siege by the Assyrians before falling in 722 BCE. Above, a winged sphinx from Samaria.

153

> So he went and did according unto the word of the Lord: for he went and dwelt by the brook Cherith, that is before Jordan. And the ravens brought him bread and flesh in the morning, and bread and flesh in the evening; and he drank of the brook.
>
> (I Kings 17.5–6)

ELIJAH AND THE PROPHETS OF BAAL

After no rain had fallen in Israel for three years, God told the prophet Elijah to go and find King Ahab. The king was out looking for water in the dried-up springs and streams. When he saw the prophet approaching, he looked angry. "Why are you causing us all this trouble?" the king demanded.

"It is you and your family who are making trouble for Israel," Elijah replied. "You have disobeyed God and turned to the idols of Baal. To settle the matter, come with me to Mount Carmel. Bring your prophets of Baal with you, and two bulls for us to sacrifice." The king was ready to try anything to end the drought, so he did as he was told.

On the mountain, Elijah invited Baal's prophets to build an altar to their god and put wood on top. Then he told them to put the meat of one of the bulls on the wood and ask their so-called god to create fire so that they could make a burnt offering. When they were ready, the prophets called on Baal to set their offering alight. They called for hours, "Baal, hear us,"shouting louder each time, but nothing happened.

Then Elijah built an altar to God, laid meat on the wood, and prayed: "O Lord, show these people today that you are God in Israel." Fire and smoke rose up from the altar at once, and the watching Israelites fell on their knees before the blaze and worshiped the true God.

154

> THEN THE FIRE OF THE LORD FELL, AND CONSUMED THE BURNT SACRIFICE, AND THE WOOD, AND THE STONES, AND THE DUST, AND LICKED UP THE WATER THAT WAS IN THE TRENCH. AND WHEN ALL THE PEOPLE SAW IT, THEY FELL ON THEIR FACES: AND THEY SAID, THE LORD, HE IS THE GOD; THE LORD, HE IS THE GOD.
>
> (I Kings 18.38–39)

A STILL, SMALL VOICE

Baal
Sometimes called "Rider of the Clouds," Baal was the chief Canaanite god. He was supposed to control the vital rainfall — if no rain fell in autumn, people could not plow or sow crops. Israelites were tempted to worship Baal, but the prophets warned them that to be disloyal to God was wrong. Left, a stone pillar showing Baal, from Phoenicia.

155

After sacrificing the bull on Mount Carmel, Elijah told the watching crowd of Israelites to kill the prophets of Baal. Then a cloud as small as a man's fist rose up from the sea, the sky grew dark, and at last the rains began to fall again in Israel.

When Queen Jezebel heard that Baal's prophets had been killed, she shouted in a fury that she would do exactly the same to the Lord's prophet. Elijah left at once for the land of Judah. He travelled for forty days through the desert, feeling utterly down-hearted, and was only kept alive by bread and water provided by an angel of God. When at last he arrived at Mount Sinai, he went into a cave to rest.

God spoke to Elijah in the cave and asked him what he was doing there. "The Israelites have turned away from you," Elijah replied wearily. "They have smashed your altars and killed your prophets. I am the only one left, and now they are trying to kill me, too."

As soon as Elijah had finished speaking, a great wind blew across the mountain. But God was not in the wind. Next the mountain was shaken by a violent earthquake. But God was not in the earthquake. Then a furious fire swept up the mountain. But God was not in the fire. Finally, there was the sound of a still, small voice. In awe and wonder, Elijah pulled his cloak over his face and went to stand at the mouth of the cave to listen to God's words.

Once again God asked his prophet what he was doing there, and Elijah gave the same reply. Then God told him that there were thousands of others in Israel who still worshipped their true Lord. And Elijah was not the last of the prophets: he was to find a ploughman named Elisha, who would be his helper and would one day take over from him.

NABOTH'S VINEYARD

Ahab's buildings
King Ahab was involved in many building projects in the cities of Israel. These included the building of water systems at Megiddo and Hazor, where he also made the fortress stronger. The Bible mentions his "ivory palace". Above, this fine ivory carving, found in Samaria, may be part of a decoration from Ahab's ivory palace.

Queen Jezebel
When Ahab became king, it was soon clear that the real ruler of Israel was Queen Jezebel. She wanted to stop the worship of God, and brought with her many prophets of Baal. She is described painting her face, a custom that shocked the people of Israel. Right, a painted carving of a Phoenician woman wearing make-up.

King Ahab had a palace in his second city of Jezreel, which lay to the north of Samaria. Next to the royal palace there was a vineyard, which belonged to a local man named Naboth. The king decided that he would like to take over Naboth's vineyard and use it as a vegetable garden for his palace. So the king approached Naboth and offered to buy his vineyard or exchange it for another plot in Jezreel, if he preferred. Naboth turned down the offer, saying that the land was part of his family inheritance. King Ahab was both disappointed and angry, and when he got back to his palace, he simply lay on his bed and sulked.

When Queen Jezebel saw this, she asked her husband what had upset him. He told her about Naboth's vineyard. The queen was astonished that her husband could sulk over such a thing. "Is this any way for the king of Israel to behave?" she scolded. "Now cheer up, I'll soon find a way to get this wretched vineyard for you." So Jezebel wrote letters to the elders and nobles of Jezreel, stamping them with the king's seal. She told the elders to arrange a public holiday, call all the townspeople together, and put Naboth in a prominent position among them. She also told them to find a couple of scoundrels, who must be seated near Naboth. The villainous men were then to swear that they had heard Naboth cursing both God and the king.

The elders and nobles did as they were ordered, and on the day in question the two villains gave their false evidence against Naboth. The people who heard the evidence were horrified, as Jezebel knew they would be, because cursing God was a most serious offence. The people wasted no

156

time, but took Naboth outside the city walls and stoned him to death. As soon as the news reached Jezebel, she went and told her husband that he could now take possession of the vineyard, as she had promised.

Ahab hurried out to the vineyard, delighted that he could turn it into a vegetable garden at last. But as he was walking around the plot, working out which plants he would put where, the prophet Elijah approached him. "Ah, so my enemy has found me again!" Ahab sneered.

"Yes, I have been sent by God to find you," Elijah said calmly, "because you have made him angry with your sinful ways. Urged on by your wife, you had a man murdered just to get your hands on his property. You killed Naboth, and in the place where dogs licked up an innocent man's blood, so they will lick up your blood. And those same dogs will tear your wife to pieces."

When King Ahab heard Elijah's harsh words, he felt ashamed. He took off his royal robes, and as a sign of his sorrow he changed them for rough garments made of goats' hair. He refused the fine meals served in his palace and ate only the humblest food. God saw this and decided that he would spare Ahab, but would bring disaster on his family in the days of his son.

AND IT CAME TO PASS, AS
THEY STILL WENT ON, AND
TALKED, THAT, BEHOLD, THERE
APPEARED A CHARIOT OF FIRE,
AND HORSES OF FIRE, AND
PARTED THEM BOTH ASUNDER;
AND ELIJAH WENT UP BY A
WHIRLWIND INTO HEAVEN.

(II Kings 2.11)

The Chariot and Horses of Fire

Elisha went everywhere with Elijah, who was now an old man. They both knew that the younger man was to be Elijah's successor, and Elisha refused to leave his master's side. When God sent Elijah to Bethel, Elisha insisted on going too. While they were there, the prophets of the town asked Elisha, "Do you know that the Lord is soon going to take your master from you?"

"Yes, I do," Elisha replied sadly, "but I don't want to talk about it." Then Elijah came up and said that God was sending him to Jericho. "I will come with you," Elisha said firmly.

While they were in Jericho, the prophets of the city asked Elisha, "Do you know that the Lord is soon going to take your master from you?" Once again he did not want to talk about it. Then Elijah said that God was sending him to the River Jordan. "I will come to the Jordan with you," Elisha said. "I will not leave you."

When the two men reached the banks of the River Jordan, Elijah took off his cloak, rolled it up and struck the water with it. To Elisha's astonishment, the water immediately divided to the right and left, leaving a pathway across the riverbed ahead of them. The two prophets walked across to the other side of the river.

When they reached the far side, Elijah asked Elisha, "What can I do for you before I leave?"

"Allow me to inherit your spirit," Elisha replied.

Elijah's ascent to heaven
According to the Book of Kings, when Elijah's work was finished, he was taken up into heaven without dying. Left, detail from an Orthodox Christian painting showing Elijah departing in a chariot of fire, watched by his successor, Elisha.

"You have asked a difficult thing," said Elijah. "But if you see me when I am taken from you, then you shall have your inheritance."

As the two prophets walked on, they suddenly saw a chariot and horses of fire come down between them. Elisha could only watch as Elijah was carried up to heaven in a whirlwind. "My father! My father!" Elisha cried, as Elijah disappeared from sight.

When Elisha looked down, he saw his master's cloak lying on the ground. He picked it up and went back to the River Jordan. Then he struck the water with the cloak. The water immediately divided to the right and left, just as it had done for Elijah. Elisha walked across the pathway to the other side of the river. When the prophets of Jericho saw this, they said: "Elijah's spirit has been passed on to Elisha." And they rushed to meet him again.

ELISHA'S MIRACLES

One day a woman came to the prophet Elisha and asked for his help. Her husband had died, and a man to whom he owed money wanted to take away her two sons as slaves.

"What do you have in your house?" Elisha asked the widow. "Only a little olive oil," she replied.

"Then go to your neighbours and ask for empty jars," Elisha said. "Collect as many as you can, and pour oil into the first jar. When it is full, put it to one side and fill another."

The woman did as the prophet said, and her oil miraculously kept pouring until all the jars were full. Then Elisha told her to sell the oil and pay her husband's debts. She and her sons could live on what was left.

Shortly afterward, Elisha visited the town of Shunem. Whenever he went there, a rich farmer's wife would offer him a meal and a bed for the night, which she made up on the roof of her house, so that he always had somewhere comfortable to sleep. Elisha wanted to thank the woman for her repeated kindness. Although she had wealth, the prophet knew there was one thing she did not have — a child. So he told the woman that in a year's time she would hold a baby boy in her arms. She hardly dared believe this was true, but it happened just as Elisha said.

The woman was overjoyed when she gave birth to a son. As the little boy grew up, he was able to help his father in the fields. But one day he fell ill and was carried home. There was nothing his mother could do to save him, and he died in her arms.

The woman sent for Elisha, who travelled at once to Shunem. When he reached the woman's house, the prophet went to her son's room, shut the door and prayed to God. Then he put his hands on the dead boy's hands and his mouth on his mouth. The boy's body grew warm and he slowly opened his eyes. Elisha called his mother to give her the good news – her son was alive!

NAAMAN IS HEALED

Naaman was a commander in the army of the king of Syria. He suffered from leprosy, a terrible skin disease. One day his wife's servant, who was an Israelite, told her mistress about the prophet Elisha. She was sure that he could cure Naaman. So Naaman went to the king, who at once agreed to send him to Israel. The king wrote a letter to the king of Israel, which Naaman took with him, along with gold and silver. But the king of Israel was angry when Naaman arrived, thinking that the Syrians were trying to make trouble. For how could he be expected to cure a man with leprosy?

When Elisha heard of this, he sent word to the king and asked to see Naaman. "Go and wash seven times in the River Jordan," Elisha told the Syrian. "Then you will be cured." This did not please Naaman, who had expected the prophet to cure him on the spot. Besides, he thought that the rivers of Syria were better than any of the waters of Israel. He was about to ride back to his own country, but his servant persuaded him to think again. "If the prophet had told you to do something amazing," the servant said, "would you not have done it? So surely you can just wash in a river."

Naaman went and dipped himself seven times in the Jordan. When he came out of the river, his skin was healed. The Syrian commander went to Elisha to thank him. "Now I know that there is only one God in the whole world," the Syrian said. He offered Elisha valuable gifts, but the prophet refused to accept them and sent Naaman home. "Go in peace," Elisha said.

161

JEHU AND JEZEBEL

The woman at the window
Above, an Assyrian carving in ivory, showing a woman at a window. It may show Jezebel, or it may represent the goddess Astarte.

One day Elisha called one of the younger prophets and told him that he had an important task for him. The young man was to go at once to the army camp and find an officer by the name of Jehu. He was a great commander and a fine charioteer. The young prophet was to take Jehu to one side and tell him that he was to destroy the descendants of Ahab and avenge the wickedness of Queen Jezebel. Then he was to anoint Jehu king of Israel.

The young prophet did exactly as Elisha had said. When Jehu returned to the other officers, they asked what the young man had wanted with him. To their amazement he told them that the prophet had anointed him king. The officers took off their cloaks, spread them on the ground before their fellow commander, and cried, "Jehu is king!"

Jehu took his troops and set out in his chariot to find Ahab's son Joram, who had been made king of Israel after his father's death. At that time Joram was in the city of Jezreel, recovering from wounds he had received in battle against the Syrians.

Joram's nephew Ahaziah, who was king of Judah, had fought with his uncle and was staying with him. When they heard that troops were approaching the city, the two kings sent a horseman to ask if they came in peace. "What do you know about peace?" Jehu replied. "Fall in behind my troops."

When the horseman failed to return, the kings sent out a second horseman, but Jehu answered in exactly the same way. Then he whipped his horses so that his chariot sped towards Jezreel. Seeing this, a lookout in the city tower sent an urgent message to King Joram. "The troops are still heading this way," the lookout said, "and I recognise their leader. Only a charioteer like Jehu would ride like that!"

Joram and Ahaziah hitched up their chariots at once and went out to meet Jehu. When Joram reached the commander, he asked, "Do you come in peace, Jehu?"

"How can there be peace," Jehu replied, "while you and your wicked mother Jezebel rule Israel?"

"This is treason!" Joram cried, quickly turning his chariot

Jehu
When Ahab's general, Jehu, became king, he got rid of the worship of Baal from Israel. Right, in this carving from the Black Obelisk of Shalmaneser III, Jehu is shown bowing low before the Assyrian king. This is the only contemporary portrait of an Israelite king that we know of.

AND WHEN JEHU WAS COME TO
JEZREEL, JEZEBEL HEARD OF IT; AND
SHE PAINTED HER FACE, AND TIRED HER
HEAD, AND LOOKED OUT AT A WINDOW.
AND AS JEHU ENTERED IN AT THE
GATE, SHE SAID, HAD ZIMRI PEACE,
WHO SLEW HIS MASTER?.

(II Kings 9.30–31)

round so that he could go back to the safety of the city. Jehu drew his bow and shot Joram in the back as he rode away. Seeing this, Ahaziah fled, but Jehu's men soon caught up with him and killed him, too.

News quickly reached Jezreel that King Ahaziah and King Joram were dead. When Queen Jezebel heard what had happened to Joram, she went upstairs in her palace, put make-up on her face and arranged her hair. Then she went to the window to watch for Jehu. When he came riding past, Jezebel cried out, "Do you come in peace, you murderer?"

Jehu looked up at Jezebel's window and saw her servants standing behind her. "If you are on my side, throw her down!" he ordered. The servants grabbed the queen and threw her down from the window. Her body was trampled by the soldiers' horses. Later, Jehu sent men to bury Jezebel's body, but all they found of her were bits of flesh and bones. Queen Jezebel had been torn to pieces by dogs, just as the prophet Elijah had foretold.

Joash the Boy King

When she heard that her son Ahaziah had been killed by Jehu's men, Athaliah decided to rule Judah herself and teach the people to worship Baal. Just like her mother Jezebel, Athaliah was a ruthless woman, and she soon set about murdering the rest of the royal family. One royal prince escaped, however. Athaliah's baby grandson Joash was rescued by an aunt, who hid him away in a temple with his nurse. The priest of the temple, Jehoiada, was the little boy's uncle.

When Joash was seven years old, Jehoiada decided that his nephew was old enough to be crowned king. The priest called together the temple guards and other armed soldiers, who all stood around Joash when he was brought out of hiding. Then Jehoiada put a crown on the little boy's head and anointed him king. The crowd that had gathered around the temple cried: "Long live the king!" Queen Athaliah heard the cry and rushed to the temple. When she saw her grandson, she was horrified and yelled: "Treason! Treason!" But no one moved against the new boy king. Then Jehoiada ordered the guards to seize the queen, take her out of the temple and kill her.

The people of Judah were glad that Queen Athaliah's reign was over. Joash and Jehoiada ordered that all the shrines to Baal throughout the land should be destroyed. The young king raised money so that the temple of the Lord could be repaired. Once again the people of Judah had a good king on the throne.

HEZEKIAH AND THE ASSYRIANS

The powerful Assyrian empire had been threatening the northern kingdom of Israel for a long time. During the reign of the Israelite king Hoshea, an Assyrian army marched through Israel to the capital, Samaria. Under the direction of their king, Shalmaneser, the Assyrians laid siege to the city. The people of Samaria held out for three years, but the city finally fell. King Hoshea was captured, and all his people were driven out of their country. The ten tribes of Israel had failed to listen to God and his prophets and now they were forced to go and live as prisoners in Assyria, far away across the desert.

The people of the southern kingdom of Judah had not behaved much better, but now they had a good, strong king in Hezekiah, the great-great-grandson of Joash. Hezekiah followed God's laws, and he was successful in defending his walled cities against invading neighbours. He defeated the Philistines and refused to give in to the Assyrians. Hezekiah held out for many years, but the new king of Assyria, Sennacherib, was determined to conquer Judah, just as Shalmaneser had captured Israel. Eight years after the fall of Samaria, the Assyrians invaded Judah once again and captured the walled cities near its borders.

Hezekiah felt he had no choice but to try and reach an agreement with Sennacherib. He offered to pay whatever the Assyrians demanded if they would only withdraw from Judah. The Assyrian king took the opportunity to demand a very great sum, and Hezekiah was forced to empty the royal treasury and even strip the temple of gold in order to try and satisfy him. But it was not enough. Sennacherib sent a vast army along with his three chief commanders to Jerusalem, with orders to persuade Hezekiah to give up Judah. Hezekiah sent his three chief advisers to talk to the Assyrians at the walls of the city.

The Assyrian commanders called out in Hebrew, the local language, "Resistance is useless! The people of Jerusalem must surrender at once, or starve!" Hezekiah's advisers were worried that their own people near the wall would hear this and believe it, so they asked the Assyrians to speak to them in Aramaic, the language of the court, which only they understood. The commanders refused, thinking that the people of

165

The Assyrians
The plains beside the Tigris River, in what is now northern Iraq, were the Assyrian homeland. From there the Assyrian Empire began its expansion to the east and west. From about 900 BCE, a series of powerful kings conquered much of the Middle East, including Israel and Egypt. The Assyrian Empire eventually became too big to defend, and in 612 BCE fell to the Babylonians, who destroyed its capital, Nineveh. Above, an Assyrian warrior, about 750 BCE.

166

Lachish
Lachish was one of the cities of Judah captured by the Assyrians. A carving in Sennacherib's palace at Nineveh shows the siege. The detail above shows some of the defeated people of Judah being sent into exile.

Jerusalem would listen to them. "Do not let Hezekiah deceive you," they shouted in Hebrew. "Do not listen to him when he tells you that your God will deliver you. Surely you have heard what we have done to other countries? Make peace with us and choose life, not death!"

There was silence on the walls. Hezekiah did not know how to answer, so he sent his officials to the prophet Isaiah, who had always helped him and given him good advice in the past. Isaiah gave the officials a message for their king:

"God says that the Assyrian king will not enter Jerusalem or shoot a single arrow here. The Assyrians will return by the way they came. God will defend and save this city."

That night an angel of the Lord visited the Assyrian camp outside Jerusalem and put to death one hundred and eighty-five thousand Assyrian soldiers. When the people of the city woke up next morning, they saw that they had indeed been saved. Sennacherib, the king of Assyria, went back to his capital of Nineveh, leaving Judah in peace.

JOSIAH AND THE SCROLL OF THE LAW

Hezekiah's great-grandson Josiah was just eight years old when he became king of Judah. The boy's father and grandfather had disobeyed God's laws and worshipped foreign idols. During their reigns as king, the people of Judah had even sacrificed their own children to pagan gods.

When Josiah grew up, he decided that it was time to repair God's temple in Jerusalem. Masons and carpenters began their work. While they were clearing out the temple, one of them found a dusty scroll. The man took the scroll to Hilkiah, the High Priest of the temple, who saw at once how important it was. Hilkiah had the scroll taken to King Josiah, and when the royal scribe read from it, the king tore his robes in despair. He knew that the people ruled by his father and grandfather had not obeyed the commands laid down by God in this Scroll of the Law.

Josiah sent the High Priest to consult the prophetess Huldah about the scroll. She told him that a terrible fate lay in store for Judah. "God says that he is going to bring disaster on Judah's people because they have not obeyed his laws," Huldah said. "But because the king has been loyal, Judah will be spared during his lifetime."

When he heard this, Josiah called his people to the temple. The king of Judah read out the commands that were written in the Scroll of the Law, and all the people promised to obey them. After ordering the destruction of all remaining shrines to idols, the king told his people that they would celebrate the Passover. It was the first time that this important feast had been held for hundreds of years.

Sacred scrolls
Before the invention of books, Bible texts were handwritten onto scrolls made of papyrus or leather sheets glued or sewn together and rolled up on rods. Above, in Jewish synagogues today, Bible readings are still made from large scrolls.

167

AND THE KING WENT UP INTO THE HOUSE OF THE LORD, AND ALL THE MEN OF JUDAH AND ALL THE INHABITANTS OF JERUSALEM WITH HIM, AND THE PRIESTS, AND THE PROPHETS, AND ALL THE PEOPLE, BOTH SMALL AND GREAT: AND HE READ IN THEIR EARS ALL THE WORDS OF THE BOOK OF THE COVENANT WHICH WAS FOUND IN THE HOUSE OF THE LORD.

(II Kings 23.2)

WORDS OF THE PROPHETS

The prophets
Seventeen books of the Old Testament are devoted to the teachings of the prophets. They include Isaiah, Jeremiah, Amos (shown above), Hosea and Micah. In the Jewish Bible, there are some important differences in the order of these books.

> THEREFORE TURN THOU TO THY GOD; KEEP MERCY AND JUDGMENT AND WAIT ON THY GOD CONTINUALLY.
>
> (Hosea 12.6)

Micah
Right: a painting of Micah, by Jan van Eyck (1390–1441). Micah preached at the same time as Isaiah, about 730 BCE. He was the first prophet to warn the Israelites that one day the city of Jerusalem would be destroyed because of its people's lack of faith in God.

Amos was a shepherd from Tekoa, near Bethlehem. To sell his wool, he had to travel to the market at Bethel, in the northern kingdom of Israel. This was during the reign of King Jeroboam II, who had made Israel strong and rich. But there were still many poor Israelites, and Amos was shocked and distressed when he saw how much the poor suffered. He told the rich traders in the market that they must mend their ways and obey God's laws, or disaster would fall upon Israel. "May justice roll down like water, and righteousness like an everlasting stream," said Amos. Many people were not happy to hear the prophet's words. But the disaster he spoke of came true when Israel was conquered by the Assyrians.

Hosea was an Israelite who suffered great sorrow in his life. His wife Gomer was unfaithful to him, and one day she left him and their children. This hurt Hosea deeply, but God told him to find his wife and take her back. "Love her as I love the Israelites," God said, "though she has turned to other men as my chosen people have turned to other gods." So Hosea searched for Gomer and took her away from the wicked man who now owned her. He realised from his own experiences how deeply God loved Israel, and spent the rest of his life preaching this message to his fellow countrymen.

Micah was another prophet who warned people of the disaster that would strike Israel and Judah if they did not change their ways and obey God's laws. Like Amos, he was angry at the way in which poor people were treated in Israel, especially labourers who worked on the land. Micah also told his fellow Israelites that one day there would be peace in the world. "Nation will no longer take up sword against nation," Micah said, "and people will stop training for war."

THE LAST DAYS OF JUDAH

During the reign of Josiah, king of Judah, God chose a young man to become a prophet and spread his word among the people. He was the son of Hilkiah, the High Priest of the temple, and his name was Jeremiah. God told the shy young man that more enemies were about to attack Jerusalem, and that he would speak to his people through him. The people would not like what they heard. "They will fight against you," God told Jeremiah, "but I will always be with you."

Jeremiah knew that the Assyrians had been powerful enough to destroy Samaria and force the Israelites into exile. King Josiah had tried to turn his people back to the ways of God and had fought to defend his country. When he heard that the Egyptian pharaoh was on his way to help the king of Assyria, he marched out to stop him. But the Egyptians won the battle and King Josiah was killed.

Josiah's son Jehoiakim became king of Judah and was forced to pay silver and gold to Egypt. During his reign, a new invader – Nebuchadnezzar, king of Babylon – threatened Judah. The Babylonians had to be bought off with heavy taxes. At the same time, the prophet Jeremiah warned the Judaeans of what would happen if they did not obey God's laws. "An army will come from a distant land," Jeremiah said, "and will destroy Judah's fortified cities with the sword." But the people

169

thought that Jeremiah was a prophet of doom, and would not listen to him.

God then sent Jeremiah to a potter's house to give him a further message. As Jeremiah watched the potter at work, something went wrong and the clay pot he was shaping was ruined. The potter started again, and this time shaped the pot well. Then God spoke to Jeremiah. "The people of Judah are in my hands, just as the clay is in the potter's hands," he said. "I can destroy and remake them. And if they repent of their evil, I will not bring

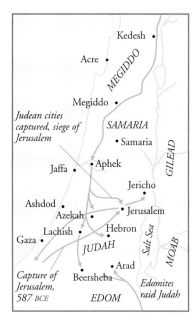

Map labels: Kedesh, Acre, MEGIDDO, Megiddo, Judean cities captured, siege of Jerusalem, SAMARIA, Samaria, GILEAD, Jaffa, Aphek, Jericho, Ashdod, Azekah, Jerusalem, Lachish, Gaza, Hebron, JUDAH, Salt Sea, MOAB, Arad, Capture of Jerusalem, 587 BCE, Beersheba, EDOM, Edomites raid Judah

Nebuchadnezzar's campaign

The Babylonians launched a military campaign against Judah in 588 BCE, and within two years had completely devastated the region. The siege of Jerusalem lasted eighteen months. When the city finally fell, the Babylonians destroyed Solomon's Temple and took its treasures as war booty.

the disaster on them that I had planned."

Despite the warnings Jeremiah gave, the people of Judah still did not change their ways. Nebuchadnezzar's army laid siege to Jerusalem, and it was only a matter of time before the city-dwellers were forced to give in. The Babylonians captured the king of Judah and took all the army officers and skilled workers to Babylon. Jeremiah stayed in Jerusalem and warned the new king, Zedekiah, that the Babylonians would soon come to destroy the city completely. This angered the king's officials, who thought that the prophet was discouraging the few Judaean soldiers they had left. They seized Jeremiah and threw him into a deep, muddy well. One of the courtiers who saw this thought it was wrong to leave Jeremiah to starve to death, so he went to the well, lowered a rope and pulled him to safety.

When King Zedekiah finally rebelled against the Babylonians, Nebuchadnezzar again besieged Jerusalem. The people held out for as long as they could, but eventually the Babylonians broke in and set fire to all the important buildings, including the temple and the royal palace. Many people were marched out of the city in chains and taken into exile in Babylon. The conquerors left only the poorest people behind. Jeremiah stayed with them. King Zedekiah attempted to escape, but was captured. His sons were killed in front of him, then he was blinded and made to march in chains like a slave to Babylon.

Just like the Israelites, the people of Judah had failed to listen to God and his prophets. Now most of them were rounded up and taken to live as prisoners in Babylon.

170

SO THEY TOOK THE KING, AND
BROUGHT HIM UP TO THE KING OF
BABYLON TO RIBLAH; AND THEY
GAVE JUDGEMENT UPON HIM.
AND THEY SLEW THE SONS OF
ZEDEKIAH BEFORE HIS EYES, AND PUT
OUT THE EYES OF ZEDEKIAH, AND
BOUND HIM WITH FETTERS OF BRASS,
AND CARRIED HIM TO BABYLON.

(II Kings 25.6–7)

Ezekiel and the Exiles in Babylon

The exiles from Judah had no choice but to settle in the foreign land of Babylon, near the southern waters of the River Euphrates. The Babylonians allowed them to build simple houses, and the exiles dug canals and used them to water the dry land so they could farm. They built their own altars to God and soon began to elect their own priests, but they never forgot that they were far from their homeland.

Sometimes at the end of a hard day the exiles would sit down and sing songs in praise of God. One of their favourite songs told of their sadness at being in a faraway land. "By the rivers of Babylon," they sang, "we sat and wept when we remembered Jerusalem." The words went on to describe how the singers never forgot that they were captives. "Our masters ask us for songs and they demand songs of joy, but how can we sing such songs in a foreign land? We will never forget Jerusalem, and we will always know that Babylon is doomed to destruction!"

The prophet Jeremiah, who had stayed behind in Jerusalem, sent a letter to the elders and priests among the exiles. It contained a message

> THUS SAITH THE LORD GOD UNTO THESE BONES; BEHOLD, I WILL CAUSE BREATH TO ENTER INTO YOU, AND YE SHALL LIVE: AND I WILL LAY SINEWS UPON YOU, AND WILL BRING UP FLESH UPON YOU, AND COVER YOU WITH SKIN, AND PUT BREATH IN YOU, AND YE SHALL LIVE; AND YE SHALL KNOW THAT I AM THE LORD.
>
> (Ezekiel 37.5–6)

Babylon was an ancient city on the Euphrates River. After Assyria's defeat, it became the magnificent capital of the Babylonian Empire. Its many monuments are still famous today, like the tower of Babel, the Royal Palace and the Ishtar gate (right).

of hope. "Remember that God says your people must spend seventy years in exile," Jeremiah wrote. "Then he will carry out his promise to bring you back to Judah. When you seek him with all your heart, you will always find him. When the time comes, he will gather you from all the places where you have been banished and bring you back."

Among those who had been taken to Babylon was a young man named Ezekiel. At home he had wanted to be a priest in the temple. In exile, God called him to be his prophet. God told Ezekiel that he would be his messenger, and would have to tell the exiles things that they might not want to hear. The new prophet did as God commanded, warning his fellow exiles that there were hard times ahead. But he also gave them hope, reminding them that God had promised to give them their homeland back.

Sometimes Ezekiel had visions, when certain things became clear to him. One day he was walking through a valley when he saw a great scattering of human bones. Then he heard God's voice speaking to him. "Do you believe these dry bones can come to life again?" God asked his prophet.

"Only you know the answer to that," Ezekiel replied.

"Tell these bones that God says he will bring them back to life," God said. "Then you will know that I am the Lord."

Ezekiel did as God commanded. As he spoke to the dry bones, there was a rattling sound and they started moving. The bones came together to make skeletons, and then flesh and skin began to cover them. But still they were not alive. Then God said to Ezekiel: "Tell breath to come from the four winds and make these bodies live."

Again Ezekiel obeyed, and watched as the bodies started to breathe and then stood up. God said: "The exiled people of Judah are like these bones. Tell them that I will breathe new life into them, so that they can settle again in their own land." When God had spoken these words, the vision faded away.

Ezekiel knew that God had given him the task of making sure that God's people were always ready to return home.

Old Jeremiah
Below: Jeremiah grieves for the capture of Jerusalem in this painting by Rembrandt (1606–69). Everything that Jeremiah had warned came true, but he saw that although the nation could be conquered and Jerusalem destroyed, the people could still have faith in God.

173

NEBUCHADNEZZAR'S DREAM

Nebuchadnezzar, the king of Babylon, gave an order that the best young noblemen of Judah should be trained to become advisers at his court. One of those chosen was an intelligent young man named Daniel.

One day Nebuchadnezzar called on his Babylonian astrologers to interpret a dream that was troubling him. But when they asked what the dream was about, the king ordered that they both tell him the dream and interpret it. "No one on earth can do that," the astrologers replied.

The king flew into a rage and ordered that all his advisers be executed, including the young Judaean noblemen. When Daniel heard this, he asked the king for a little time to think. The king reluctantly agreed. That night Daniel and his three friends – Shadrach, Meshach, and Abednego — all prayed to God and the dream's meaning came to Daniel in a vision.

Next morning Daniel told the king that God had explained everything to him. "In your dream you saw a huge statue," Daniel began. "Its head was made of gold, its body of silver, bronze and iron, and its feet of clay. But a rock struck the statue and smashed it to pieces."

"That was my dream," the king said. "Now tell me what it means."

"It means that you are the king of kings," Daniel said, "for you are the head of gold. After you, there will be other kingdoms – the parts made of other metals. But the rock is the kingdom of God, which will crush all others and last for ever."

Nebuchadnezzar was so pleased to have his dream explained that he gave Daniel a high position at court.

The Golden Statue

King Nebuchadnezzar decided to have an enormous statue made of solid gold, and he had it set up outside the city of Babylon. Then the king called on all the officials of Babylonia to attend the dedication of the statue, including those exiled from Judah who had been accepted into his court. The king had special music written for the celebration, and the governors, judges, treasurers and other officials from all over the kingdom were told that they were to bow down before the statue when they heard the music strike up. Anyone who failed to bow down would be punished by being thrown into a blazing furnace.

When the crowds of officials were assembled before the statue, the silence was suddenly broken by the beautiful sound of horns, flutes and zithers. The dedication had begun, and the officials at once got down on their knees and bowed their heads low to the ground before Nebuchadnezzar's enormous golden statue. Some of the officials noticed, however, that a few of their number did not bow down. The officials recognised them at once as the three young noblemen from Judah — Shadrach, Meshach and Abednego. The shocked officials rushed off to inform the king.

Nebuchadnezzar was angry when he heard that the young men had disobeyed his order. He had them brought before him and reminded them of his command. "If you do not worship the golden statue," the king commanded, "I will have you thrown at once into a blazing furnace."

176

Nebuchadnezzar watched all this from a safe distance, but could scarcely believe his eyes when he saw four men walking around in the fire, unbound and unharmed. "Did the guards not throw three men into the furnace?" the king asked his attendant.

"Certainly, your majesty," the attendant replied.

"Yet now I see four men walking in the fire," said Nebuchadnezzar, "and the fourth man looks like a son of the gods." Then he ordered Shadrach, Meshach and Abednego to come out of the furnace.

The three young men walked out of the fiery flames, and the king and his attendants could all see that they were totally unharmed. Their robes were not scorched and not a hair on their heads was even singed. "Praise be to your God, who sent an angel to save you," said King Nebuchadnezzar. "You were prepared to give up your lives rather than worship any other god. I therefore command that anyone who says a word against your God be cut to pieces, for no other has the power to save in this way."

Then Nebuchadnezzar gave the three young men important positions in his kingdom.

AND THE PRINCES, GOVERNORS, AND CAPTAINS, AND THE KING'S COUNSELLORS, BEING GATHERED TOGETHER, SAW THESE MEN, UPON WHOSE BODIES THE FIRE HAD NO POWER, NOR WAS AN HAIR OF THEIR HEAD SINGED, NEITHER WERE THEIR COATS CHANGED, NOR THE SMELL OF FIRE HAD PASSED ON THEM.

(Daniel 3.27)

But the three men were not afraid. "We will never worship anyone but our God," they said. "And even if you do throw us into a furnace, the God we serve will save us."

This made Nebuchadnezzar even more furious, and he ordered his guards to prepare the furnace and make sure that it was hotter than it had ever been before. Then the guards seized and bound Shadrach, Meshach and Abednego and took them to the blazing furnace. It was so hot that the guards themselves were scorched to death as they threw the three young men in.

BELSHAZZAR'S BANQUET

One day Belshazzar, who had succeeded his father Nebuchadnezzar as king of Babylon, decided to hold a great banquet. He ordered his servants to serve wine in the gold and silver goblets that his father had taken when he sacked the temple in Jerusalem. He and his nobles raised the sacred goblets and drank to the gold, silver and bronze idols of their own Babylonian gods.

Suddenly, a hand appeared and wrote words on the wall of the banqueting hall. King Belshazzar was frightened, and called at once for his advisers and astrologers to tell him what the words meant. But although they were offered great rewards, none of the advisers could understand the writing. Then the king's wife remembered how Nebuchadnezzar's dream had been interpreted by the young Judaean named Daniel. So Belshazzar sent for Daniel and offered him the same rewards.

Daniel refused to accept any gifts, but said that he could indeed explain the writing on the wall, which came from a hand sent by God. "'Mene' means number, meaning that the days of your reign are numbered," Daniel said. "'Tekel,' means weighed, meaning that you have been weighed on the scales and failed the test. And 'Upharsin' means

divided – your kingdom will be divided between Medes and Persians."

That very night Babylon was invaded. As the writing on the wall foretold, Belshazzar was killed and his kingdom was taken over by King Darius the Mede.

> IN THE SAME HOUR CAME FORTH FINGERS OF A MAN'S HAND, AND WROTE OVER AGAINST THE CANDLESTICK UPON THE PLAISTER OF THE WALL OF THE KING'S PALACE: AND THE KING SAW THE PART OF THE HAND THAT WROTE.
>
> (Daniel 5.5)

Medes and Persians
The Medes and their Persian neighbours lived in what is now Iran. In 549 BCE, King Cyrus of Persia overthrew the Medes and made their kingdom into part of his empire. Ten years later he conquered Babylon. Cyrus was a tolerant, wise king, and he allowed the Jews to return to Israel. Above, relief statue of a Persian palace guard, from Susa.

177

DANIEL IN THE LIONS' DEN

King Darius planned to put Daniel in complete charge of the governors of his empire. When they heard this, the governors and other advisers became jealous and decided to get rid of Daniel. They first asked the king to pass a new law. It said that any person found praying to anyone except Darius would be thrown into a den of lions. The king had no idea that this was a trap for Daniel, and signed the new law.

Daniel soon heard about the new law, but he went on praying to God three times a day, as he had always done. A group of his enemies found him in his house, kneeling before a window that faced Jerusalem and asking God for help. They went straight to King Darius and told him what they had seen. The king knew that he could not change the law and though it upset

him to do so, he gave orders for Daniel to be thrown into the lion's den.

The king said to Daniel, "May your God rescue you." A large stone was placed over the entrance to the den. King Darius returned to his palace, but he could not sleep that night. At the first light of dawn, he hurried straight to the lions' den. "Daniel," he called out, "has your God kept you safe from the lions?"

Darius was amazed to hear Daniel reply, "Your Majesty, God sent an angel to shut the lions'

> THEN THE KING AROSE VERY EARLY IN THE MORNING, AND WENT IN HASTE UNTO THE DEN OF LIONS.
> AND WHEN HE CAME TO THE DEN, HE CRIED WITH A LAMENTABLE VOICE UNTO DANIEL: AND THE KING SPAKE AND SAID TO DANIEL, O DANIEL, SERVANT OF THE LIVING GOD, IS THY GOD, WHOM THOU SERVEST CONTINUALLY, ABLE TO DELIVER THEE FROM THE LIONS?
>
> (Daniel 6.19–20)

Asiatic lions
Lions are referred to more often than any other wild animal in the Bible. Lion hunting was a popular sport with the Assyrians, who lived to the east of the River Jordan. The last lion in Iraq (part of the old Assyria) was killed in 1920 CE. Above, leaping lion from an Assyrian carving.

178

mouths. They have not hurt me because I am innocent and have done you no wrong." The king was delighted and had Daniel lifted out of the den. There was not a scratch on him.

King Darius had the governors who had accused Daniel brought to him. He ordered that they be thrown into the lions' den. The hungry lions attacked and killed them at once.

THEN SAID I UNTO THEM, YE
SEE THE DISTRESS THAT WE
ARE IN, HOW JERUSALEM
LIETH WASTE, AND THE
GATES THEREOF ARE BURNED
WITH FIRE: COME, AND LET
US BUILD UP THE WALL OF
JERUSALEM, THAT WE BE NO
MORE A REPROACH.

(Nehemiah 2.17)

180

HOME TO JERUSALEM

Return from exile
After Cyrus' decree of 538 BCE, the Jewish people started to move back to their homeland. The first large group to return was guided by Zerubbabel, who laid the foundation of a new temple. In the following century, Ezra and Nehemiah led more people home. Above, Hebrews on their way to Israel.

When Cyrus came to the throne as king of Persia, he ordered that the different nations within his vast kingdom be allowed to follow their own ways and beliefs. He also decided that the exiled people of Judah should be allowed to return from Babylon to their homeland.

King Cyrus ordered his treasurer to give back the gold dishes and other valuable objects that had been removed from the temple in Jerusalem when it was sacked almost seventy years earlier. The family heads of the tribes of Judah and Benjamin called their people together and prepared for the long journey back to Israel. Not everyone returned, however, because many Judaean families had settled well in Babylonia and built good lives for themselves.

After their long journey westward, some people went straight

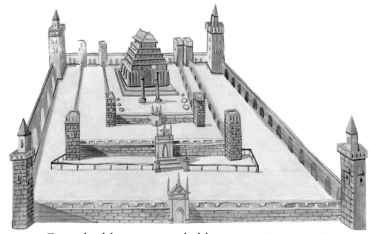

to Jerusalem, while others returned to their own towns and villages. Jerusalem had been almost destroyed during the Babylonian invasion, and the city was still in ruins. Outsiders had moved into Judah from the northern region where the Israelites had lived before their exile to Assyria. Nevertheless, many people were determined to put things right as quickly as possible, and the elders set up a fund for the urgent rebuilding of the temple in Jerusalem.

A descendant of David named Zerubbabel and the priest Jeshua led the work on the temple. The priests called the people together, and they began by building an altar to God. Then they celebrated their first harvest back in the homeland with a Feast of Tabernacles. Some of the descendants of the poor people who had been left behind in Jerusalem during the exile had forgotten the importance of following the ways of God. Two prophets, Zechariah and Haggai, reminded them of God's commands. Zechariah also told the two leaders that God would always help them to rebuild the temple.

After some years and many delays and difficulties, the rebuilding of the temple was at last completed. It was less splendid than Solomon's original temple, but no less important. The priests and all the people celebrated its dedication with burnt offerings, including the sacrifice of twelve male goats – one for each of the tribes of Israel.

There was still a great deal of work to be done in restoring Jerusalem, including rebuilding the defensive walls around the city. By now Cyrus had been succeeded by King Artaxerxes, and he allowed his cup-bearer, Nehemiah, to visit the Persian province of Judah to see for himself how the rebuilding work was going. When Nehemiah saw the walls still in ruins, he asked the Persian king for permission to rebuild them. Though many of the people were only too willing to help Nehemiah, there was opposition from the governor of Samaria and other Persian officials. Some opponents even suggested that Nehemiah was planning a rebellion. Nevertheless, the people of Jerusalem all played their part in the work, and the walls were rebuilt in less than two months. Guards and gatekeepers were appointed, and at last Jerusalem was a fortified city once more. The people celebrated by dancing and singing in thanks to God.

Now that the people felt safer within their city, a priest and scholar named Ezra reminded them once again of God's commands. Ezra stood on a high wooden platform and read from the scroll known as the Book of the Law. He did this hour after hour, day after day, until those who had turned away from God saw that they had done wrong. At last the people of Jerusalem gave their promise to Ezra that they would keep God's laws.

The Second Temple
Above, an 18th century depiction of how the Second Temple in Jerusalem may have looked. Built by the returning exiles, it was not as splendidly decorated as Solomon's Temple. In 20 BCE, King Herod began to replace it with a finer building. This was destroyed by the Romans in 70 CE.

181

Nehemiah
In 445 BCE Nehemiah was appointed governor of Judah by the Persian emperor. He managed to get the walls of Jerusalem rebuilt in spite of his enemies' efforts to stop him. A just governor, he helped Judah to grow prosperous again. Above, Nehemiah directs the work.

AND THE KING
SAID UNTO
ESTHER AT THE
BANQUET OF
WINE, WHAT IS
THY PETITION?
AND IT SHALL BE
GRANTED THEE:
AND WHAT IS
THY REQUEST?
EVEN TO THE
HALF OF THE
KINGDOM IT
SHALL BE
PERFORMED.

(Esther 5.6)

THE QUEEN OF PERSIA

Esther was the beautiful young wife of Xerxes, king of Persia. She and her cousin Mordecai belonged to a family that was exiled from Judah, but Xerxes did not know that his queen was Jewish. One day Mordecai heard two Persian officials plotting to assassinate their king at his winter palace in Susa. When the king was informed, the plotters were executed.

Not long afterward, an official named Haman became chief minister of Persia, and all the royal officials bowed down before him. The only exception was Mordecai, who said that he would bow only before God. Haman was furious at this insult and persuaded the king to agree that people who did not obey Persian customs could be executed. The chief minister then issued an instruction, on the king's command, that all Jews were to be killed. When he heard this, Mordecai sent word to Esther, asking her to speak to the king. Esther arranged a banquet for the next evening and invited Haman to attend.

That very same day, Xerxes realised that he had not rewarded Mordecai for uncovering the assassination plot against him. So the king called for Haman and asked his advice on honouring someone for a special act of loyalty. Thinking the king was referring to himself, Haman advised that the fortunate person be given a royal robe and horse. When Xerxes gave this honour to Mordecai, Haman was horrified.

At her banquet, Queen Esther asked her husband to spare her life. At first the king did not understand. Then Esther explained that her family had come from Judah and that Haman had condemned all Jews to death. Xerxes was furious with his chief minister and ordered his immediate execution. Then at Esther's request, the king not only overturned his first order against the Jews, but from that day on gave them the right to defend themselves with arms against an attack from anyone.

Purim
Esther is celebrated in the Jewish festival of Purim. A day's fast is followed by a day of feasting. A scroll of the book of Esther, like the one above, is read aloud in synagogues, and when Haman's name is mentioned, people boo and hiss and children shake rattles.

THE SUFFERING OF JOB

Job was a wealthy man who owned thousands of sheep, oxen, camels and donkeys. He had seven sons and three daughters, and led a good, honest life. Job worshipped God and was a happy man.

Then suddenly Job met with a series of disasters. First his animals were carried off by raiders. Then his children all died when a whirlwind destroyed the house where they were feasting. Job was devastated at the loss of his sons and daughters, and soon sores broke out all over his body. He had lost his children, his wealth, and his health, and his wife encouraged him to curse God for such misfortune. But Job refused. "We accept good from God," he said, "and so we must also accept trouble."

Some of Job's friends heard of his suffering and went to try and comfort him. When they saw him, they hardly recognised their old friend. He was sitting on the ground in rags, and didn't even greet them. After a long silence, the friends offered their advice. One said that Job must have done wrong to suffer such misfortune. Another said that his suffering would do him good in the end. And the third said that suffering was a mystery that no man could understand. Yet Job knew that he had done nothing wrong in his life, and his friends were no comfort to him.

Job finally asked God why he had been singled out for such misfortune. God's reply simply reminded him that he was the creator of the whole world and everything in it. Who was Job to question almighty God? Then Job realised that there were things he could not possibly understand. Despite his troubles, he still had faith in God.

From then on things went well for Job. God healed him, and in the course of time he had another seven sons and three daughters. Job became wealthy again and lived to a very old age.

> THEN JOB ANSWERED THE LORD, AND SAID, I KNOW THAT THOU CANST DO EVERY THING, AND THAT NO THOUGHT CAN BE WITHHOLDEN FROM THEE. WHO IS HE THAT HIDETH COUNSEL WITHOUT KNOWLEDGE? THEREFORE HAVE I UTTERED THAT I UNDERSTOOD NOT; THINGS TOO WONDERFUL FOR ME, WHICH I KNEW NOT.
> (Job 42.1–3)

Jonah and the Great Fish

Nineveh

The Assyrian kings grew rich through trade and taxes, and built splendid temples and palaces in their cities. Sennacherib's capital city, Nineveh, had stone walls over six miles round, set with 15 gates. Above: slaves at work building Sennacherib's palace in Nineveh.

The story of Jonah

Jonah was God's most reluctant prophet. God told him to go to Nineveh, but instead he took a ship sailing in the opposite direction, for Tarshish. Below, a medieval mosaic shows Jonah emerging from a sea monster's mouth.

God spoke to the prophet Jonah and told him to go to the Assyrian capital of Nineveh, where he was to speak out against the people's wicked ways. But fearing what the Assyrians might do to him, Jonah disobeyed and took a ship bound for the faraway city of Tarshish.

God sent a violent storm so that Jonah's ship got into difficulties. The sailors realised that they were in serious trouble, and thought that someone must be to blame for this. They cast lots to find out who it could be, and it turned out to be Jonah. When they questioned him, Jonah admitted that he had disobeyed God. He told his shipmates that the only way to save themselves was to throw him overboard. Although they felt sorry for Jonah, the sailors did as he said.

The raging seas at once grew calm, but Jonah was sinking fast into the ocean depths. Then suddenly a huge shape loomed out of the darkness, and Jonah was swallowed whole by a great fish. He stayed safe inside the fish for three days, until at last it swam close to land and threw him up on the shore. Then

God spoke to Jonah a second time and told him to go to Nineveh.

This time Jonah obeyed. When he reached the city, he warned the people that Nineveh would be destroyed in forty days if they did not give up their wicked ways. The people listened to him and asked for God's forgiveness. Even the king took off his royal robes and put on rough clothes.

When God saw this, he forgave the people and spared their city. But this made Jonah angry, because he did not like the Assyrians and thought they did not deserve God's kindness and love. So Jonah went and sat down outside the city. God made a vine grow over his head to give him shade, and Jonah was pleased. But next day God sent a worm to chew the vine and it withered away. Then Jonah was angry again.

"Do you have a right to be angry?" God asked him.

"Yes, I do, and I am miserable enough to die," Jonah replied.

"You are angry about losing a single plant, though you did not make it grow," God said. "Yet this city has thousands of people. Should I not care about and spare them?"

> AND HE SAID UNTO THEM, TAKE ME UP, AND CAST ME FORTH INTO THE SEA; SO SHALL THE SEA BE CALM UNTO YOU; FOR I KNOW THAT FOR MY SAKE THIS GREAT TEMPEST IS UPON YOU.
>
> (Jonah 1.12)

THE NEW TESTAMENT

THE FOUR GOSPELS

Augustus Caesar
Above, a portrait of the first emperor of the Roman empire, Augustus Caesar. The burden of Roman rule became more and more intolerable to the Jews.

A map of the Holy Land
Jesus grew up and spent most of his life in Galilee, a hilly area in the centre of which is a large lake, the Sea of Galilee. To travel to Jerusalem for major festivals, Jesus and his family and friends would have journeyed down the fertile Jordan valley. The Sea of Galilee is where he called his first disciples. Capernaum, a thriving fishing village on the seashore, became his base. Here he taught in the synagogue and preached his Sermon on the Mount, on the hillside overlooking the lake.

At the time of the birth of Jesus — probably in 4 BCE — Palestine was ruled by Herod the Great. It was not a free country, for the Romans had conquered it, and it was the Roman Emperor Augustus who had set Herod in place as its king. When Herod died in 4 BCE, most of the kingdom went to his son, Archelaus, but he was incompetent and disloyal to Rome. The emperor deposed him, placing his lands of Judea, Samaria, and Idumea under a Roman governor, Pontius Pilate. Perea, to the east of the River Jordan, and Galilee were ruled by Herod Antipas. This was the country where Jesus lived and taught.

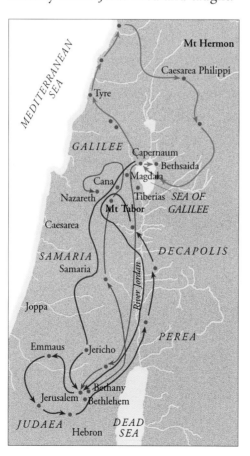

We know what he said and did, because the story of his life, and what followed, is written down in a collection of books that we call the New Testament.

The New Testament contains 27 books: four books, the gospels, describe the life and message of Jesus; one book, the Acts of the Apostles, tells the story of the first Christians; 21 contain letters written by the apostles to the faithful; and there is one book of visions.

In Bible times, people heard news by word of mouth. So news about Jesus was told and not written down. When Jesus left his disciples with an instruction to teach everyone the things that he had taught them, they went around "talking" about Jesus. Their "eye-witness" accounts told the same stories in a slightly different way — just as newspapers do.

As the disciples grew older, Christians wanted a written account of all that Jesus had said and done, to give them courage to face persecution.

The first written record of the life of Jesus was probably what we call the gospel of Mark. (The word "gospel" comes from an Anglo-Saxon word meaning "good news".) Mark wrote down what the apostle Peter recalled of Jesus's life. His gospel is the shortest of the four, and is action-packed, but somewhat abrupt. One can almost hear Peter hurrying Mark along!

Some years later, a Jewish Christian, Matthew, wrote a longer account of the life of Jesus. (Matthew may not have been the apostle

Matthew, the tax-collector.) One of his purposes was to show to Jewish Christians that Jesus was the expected Messiah, the son of David.

Luke's gospel was the first part of a two-volume book written for a friend named Theophilus. (The second volume is the Acts of the Apostles.) Luke set out to show that Jesus came not just for the Jews, but for people of every race, and especially for the poor and most disliked people in society. According to tradition, Luke was a doctor and an artist. His gospel contains a full account of Jesus's birth and childhood.

Because they contain so many similarities, the gospels of Mark, Matthew and Luke are sometimes printed in parallel columns and are known as the "synoptic" gospels ("synoptic" comes from a Greek word meaning "things can be seen together".) All four gospels emphasise the dramatic events of the last week of Jesus's life and his resurrection.

It is uncertain who wrote John's gospel (it may have been the apostle John). This gospel is quite different from the other three. It is not so much concerned with telling a story or setting down what Jesus said, but tries to get at the true meaning of the things that Jesus taught.

From the gospels we learn that after returning from Egypt, Jesus and his family settled in Nazareth, a hill village in Galilee. There, Jesus learned his father's trade: carpentry. He was educated in the local synagogue and began his public ministry when he was about 30. He chose the thriving fishing town of Capernaum as his base.

Jesus's teaching was based on the Old Testament (the Hebrew Bible). His methods were similar to those of the rabbis — he told many parables. The pharisees (the strict upholders of Jewish law) opposed Jesus because his teachings criticised the narrow way that they interpreted the law. Jesus thought that their strict ritual distorted God's purpose for humankind.

The synagogue
During New Testament times, every town had a synagogue — the place where Jews met. (The word "synagogue" comes from the Greek for "place of assembly".) Synagogues developed after the temple in Jerusalem had been destroyed in 587 BCE; the Jews in exile met in each other's houses to worship God and study the Torah (the first five books of what Christians call the Old Testament). Synagogues were also schools. Jesus was certainly educated in a synagogue — a Greek or Roman education would have involved worshipping heathen gods.

189

The gospels
The first four of the 27 books of the New Testament are the gospels, a word meaning "good news". They were written by Matthew, Mark, Luke and John. They are traditionally symbolised as a winged man, a winged lion, a winged ox and a winged eagle. Left, this illustration from a Byzantine gospel shows the four gospel-writers in front of summaries of their gospels, with their symbols above.

A Son for Elizabeth and Zechariah

Zechariah was a priest during the reign of Herod, king of Judea. He and his wife Elizabeth were good people who lived according to God's laws. They had always wanted children, but Elizabeth had never become pregnant. Now the couple were sad to think that they were too old to become parents.

One day, when Zechariah was burning incense in the temple, an angel suddenly appeared beside the altar. The priest was startled, but the angel said to him: "Do not be afraid, Zechariah. Your prayers have been answered, and your wife will soon give birth to a son. You are to call him John, and he will bring great joy to you and your wife. Others will also rejoice at his birth, for he will have the spirit and power of the prophet Elijah. He will be able to turn people's hearts and will bring many of the people of Israel back to their Lord."

"How can I be sure of this?" Zechariah asked the angel in disbelief. "My wife and I are surely too old to have a child?"

"My name is Gabriel," the angel replied, "and I have been sent by God to give you this good news. You should not doubt my words, but because you have done so, you will not be able to speak again until the day that all I have said comes true."

The worshippers who were waiting outside the temple wondered why the priest was so long burning incense. When at last Zechariah came out, he made signs to them that he could not speak, and the people realised that he must have had a vision. When he had finished serving in the temple, Zechariah went home to his wife.

Shortly afterwards, Elizabeth became pregnant, just as the angel Gabriel had said. Though Zechariah was not able to tell his wife what the angel had told him, she knew in her heart. "The Lord has made this happen," Elizabeth said happily.

Burning incense
It was a great honour for Zechariah to have been chosen to offer incense, for this allowed him to enter the temple sanctuary or "holy of holies". Below, a four-horned, stone altar like the one Zechariah would have used for burning incense.

191

AND THERE APPEARED UNTO HIM AN ANGEL OF THE LORD STANDING ON THE RIGHT SIDE OF THE ALTAR OF INCENSE. AND WHEN ZECHARIAH SAW HIM, HE WAS TROUBLED, AND FEAR FELL UPON HIM. BUT THE ANGEL SAID UNTO HIM, FEAR NOT ZECHARIAH: FOR THY PRAYER IS HEARD; AND THY WIFE ELIZABETH SHALL BEAR THEE A SON, AND THOU SHALT CALL HIS NAME JOHN. AND THOU SHALT HAVE JOY AND GLADNESS; AND MANY SHALL REJOICE AT HIS BIRTH.

(Luke 1.11–14)

WONDERFUL NEWS FOR MARY

A few months after the angel Gabriel appeared to Zechariah, God sent his angel to visit a young woman in the town of Nazareth, in Galilee. Her name was Mary, and she was a cousin of Zechariah's wife Elizabeth. Mary was promised in marriage to a man named Joseph, a carpenter who was a descendant of the family of King David, the beloved king of long ago.

Mary was busy with her household chores when the angel Gabriel suddenly appeared before her. Mary was frightened by this, but the angel greeted her with astonishing news. "God has chosen you and blessed you," the angel said. "Do not be afraid, Mary, for you have found great favour with God. You will soon give birth to a son, and you are to give him the name Jesus. The child will be very special and will be called Son of the Highest. God will give him the throne of David, and his kingdom will last for ever."

"But how can I have a child?" Mary asked. "I am a virgin and have no husband?"

"You will be filled with the Holy Spirit," the angel replied. "God's power will take you over, and your child will be called the Son of God. Your cousin Elizabeth is also going to have a child, though she was sure that she was too old. God makes everything possible."

"I am God's servant," Mary said to Gabriel. "May everything happen as you have said." Then the angel disappeared, and Mary was left to think about the wonderful news that she had received.

AND THE ANGEL SAID UNTO HER, FEAR NOT MARY: FOR THOU HAST FOUND FAVOUR WITH GOD. AND, BEHOLD, THOU SHALT CONCEIVE IN THY WOMB, AND BRING FORTH A SON, AND SHALT CALL HIS NAME JESUS. HE SHALL BE GREAT, AND SHALL BE CALLED THE SON OF THE HIGHEST.

(Luke 1.30–32)

193

Joseph
Mary's husband, Joseph, was the foster-father of Jesus, and therefore his legal father. Descended from King David's family line, he worked as a humble carpenter, and may have died before Jesus was grown up. Above, detail of a painting of Joseph in his workshop by the Dutch painter Robert Campin (c.1375–1444).

The Annunciation
The angel Gabriel brings news to Mary that she will become the mother of the Messiah, God's promised saviour. This event — a popular subject in religious art — is known as the Annunciation. Left, in this detail from a 15th-century German painting by the Master of Liesborn (1435–95), Gabriel's words of greeting appear on the twisting scroll.

Mary Visits Elizabeth

194

Naming a baby
Jewish babies were usually named eight days after birth. Boys were circumcised (their foreskins were removed) as a sign of the agreement, or covenant, made between God and his Jewish people in the time of Abraham. Above, a covenant bag is used to carry a child to its naming or circumcision ceremony.

Shortly after she had been visited by the angel Gabriel, Mary made herself ready for a journey. She left Nazareth and set out for a town in the hilly region of Judea. Mary had decided to visit her cousin Elizabeth, to tell her that now they had both received wonderful and astonishing news.

When Mary arrived at Zechariah's house, Elizabeth was very pleased to see her. As the cousins embraced one another, Elizabeth's baby leapt in her womb. She was filled with happiness and said to Mary: "God has chosen you among women, and blessed is the child that you will give birth to. As soon as I heard your voice, my baby leapt for joy. I am honoured that the mother of such a special child should visit me!"

Mary felt so happy that she sang a song of praise to God, telling how her spirit rejoiced in the Lord her saviour: "From this day on, future generations will bless my name."

Mary stayed with her cousin for three months, and the two women enjoyed each other's company. Not long before it was time for Elizabeth to have her baby, Mary went back to her home town of Nazareth.

The Gezer calendar is written on a clay tablet. It lists the agricultural tasks for the year. Zechariah may have written his message on such a tablet, or he may have written it on paper made of the papyrus plant.

Elizabeth gave birth to a son, as the angel Gabriel had said. Everyone who knew Elizabeth and Zechariah was delighted for them, and the new mother's relatives and neighbours all came to congratulate her. They all knew how much Zechariah and his wife had wanted a baby. After eight days, it was time to name the baby, according to custom. Everyone expected that he would be named after his father. But Elizabeth surprised them all when she said, "No, he is to be called John."

"But there's no one in our family by that name," one of the relatives said. Then they all turned to Zechariah, who still could not speak, to see what he thought.

Zechariah asked for a writing tablet, and to everyone's astonishment he wrote: "His name is John."

As soon as he had done this, Zechariah found that he could speak again, and he at once praised God. Then he picked up the baby John, and said: "You, my child, will be called a prophet of the Lord. You will prepare the way for him, giving people a message of salvation because of our Lord's tender mercy. Then the Sun will shine on those who live in darkness and in fear of death, guiding their feet along the path of peace."

Jewish homes
Homes changed little throughout the centuries. Below, a large house belonging to a wealthy Jewish family, from about the 3rd century CE.

195

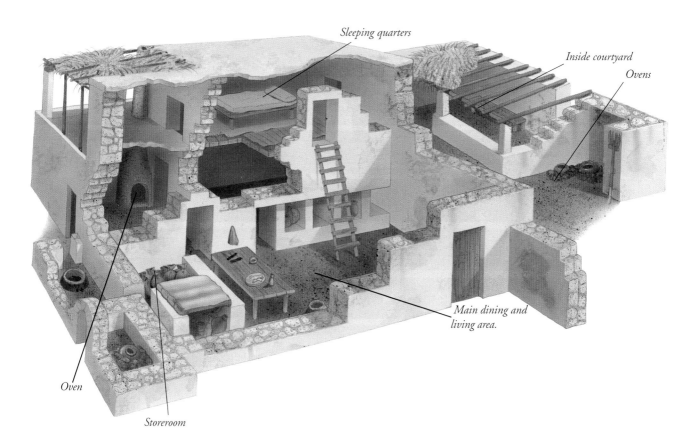

Sleeping quarters

Inside courtyard

Ovens

Main dining and living area.

Oven

Storeroom

JESUS IS BORN

When Joseph discovered that Mary was expecting a baby, he was worried that people would think badly of her. But an angel appeared to him in a dream. "Do not be afraid to take Mary home as your wife," the angel said. "For her baby was conceived by the Holy Spirit. She will give birth to a son, and you are to name him Jesus."

At that time Emperor Augustus ordered every man in the Roman empire to return to his home town and register for a census. The emperor wanted everyone counted so that he could work out how much tax was due to him. So Joseph left Nazareth and travelled to Bethlehem, his home town.

196

AND IT CAME TO PASS, AS THE ANGELS WERE GONE AWAY FROM THEM INTO HEAVEN, THE SHEPHERDS SAID ONE TO ANOTHER, LET US NOW GO EVEN UNTO BETHLEHEM, AND SEE THIS THING WHICH IS COME TO PASS, WHICH THE LORD HATH MADE KNOWN UNTO US. AND THEY CAME WITH HASTE, AND FOUND MARY, AND JOSEPH, AND THE BABE LYING IN A MANGER.

(Luke 2.15–16)

Mary and Jesus
The theme of the Madonna and Child has been an important inspiration for artists. According to legend, Luke was the first to paint a picture of the Virgin Mary. Right, this 15th-century stained-glass window depicts Mary with Jesus.

The Shepherds
A shepherd watching his flock by night probably wore a warm sheepskin coat like this one (above), worn by present-day shepherds. The crook's hook could be used to catch a sheep or lift a lamb out of danger. The rod with nails could be used to ward off wild animals.

Mary went with him, riding on a donkey.

When they reached Bethlehem, Mary felt that it was time for her baby to be born. Joseph quickly took her to the inn, but the inn was full. They knew that there was no time to lose, and Joseph was glad when they were allowed to stay the night in a stable. It was just a rough cave where a farmer kept his animals, but at least it would give them shelter and somewhere to rest.

That night, Mary's baby was born in the stable. She wrapped her tiny son in bands of cloth and laid him in a manger, which was normally used as a feeding trough for the animals. Then at last Mary rested, happy that her son was safe and well.

In the fields outside the town, shepherds were watching over their flocks of sheep. They were frightened when an angel suddenly appeared to them. "Do not be afraid," the angel told the shepherds. "I bring you good news of great joy for everyone. A saviour, Christ the Lord, has been born to you in the town of David. You will find him wrapped in cloths and lying in a manger." Then a whole host of angels appeared in the night sky. "Glory to God in the highest," they sang.

The shepherds decided at once to go to see this newborn child. They hurried to Bethlehem and soon found Mary and Joseph, with the baby lying in a manger. Then they knew that the angel's words were true. The shepherds praised God for all they had heard and seen, while Mary thought about the wonderful things that had happened to her.

The Nativity, or birth of Jesus
Jesus's birth has been the inspiration of many great works of art. Although not mentioned in the gospel account, an ox and an ass are often depicted in the stable adoring the newborn baby Jesus.
Right, this painting on wood dates from the 13th century and is in the Museum of Catalan art, Barcelona.

THE VISIT OF THE WISE MEN

After Jesus was born in Bethlehem, a group of wise men from the East travelled to Jerusalem. In their homeland, astronomers had seen a special star shining brightly in the night sky, and the wise men believed this was a sign that an important king had been born. They prepared their camels at once and followed the special star, which led them to Jerusalem.

The wise men thought that the capital city, Jerusalem, must be the birthplace of the new king. When they arrived in the city, they asked local people: "Where can we find the one who has been born king of the Jews? We have come to worship him."

The wise men's gifts
The wise men, or magi, brought with them gifts of gold, frankincense, and myrrh. By tradition, gold honoured Jesus as a king, frankincense as a god and myrrh (the spice used in burials) as a human who would suffer and die. Above, a mosaic of the magi from Ravenna, Italy.

Epiphany
The feast of the Epiphany (a word meaning "showing") on 6th January recalls the day when the wise men arrived in Bethlehem, were shown the baby Jesus and offered their gifts to him. In some countries, people exchange gifts on this day rather than at Christmas. In Germany, children dress up as kings. Right, detail from the 15th-century altarpiece Adoration of the Magi *by Gentile da Fabriano (1370–1427).*

✴ But no one knew what they were talking about.

When news of the strangers reached Herod, king of Judea, he was very worried. He at once called together all the chief priests and scholars of Judea and asked them if any of their scriptures foretold where a special king was to be born. "Yes," one of the religious teachers replied. "The prophet Micah said that the town of Bethlehem is a special place. He wrote that a ruler of all the people of Israel would come from there."

Herod's worst fears were coming true. Who was this new king who had been born in his own land? He decided to use the wise men from the East to find out. The king had the wise men brought to his palace and asked them all about this special star that they had followed. Then he told them that they should continue on their journey to Bethlehem, which was not far to the south of Jerusalem.

"Search carefully for this child," he told the wise men. "When you have found him, come back and tell me so that I too may go and worship him."

So the wise men went on their way. The special star still shone brightly and led them to the town of Bethlehem. When the wise men reached a simple house in the town, the star stopped overhead, and they were overjoyed. They knew that this was where they would find the newborn king. When they stepped inside the house, they saw the baby Jesus in the arms of his mother, Mary. The wise men bowed before the child and worshipped him. Then they presented Jesus with the special gifts of gold, frankincense and myrrh that they had brought for him from their distant homeland.

The wise men intended to go back to Jerusalem the next day, as Herod had asked. But that night God warned them in a dream not to go back that way, and so they returned home by another route.

JESUS IS PRESENTED TO GOD

When Mary's baby was eight days old, he was circumcised and given the name Jesus, as the angel had instructed. Then Mary and Joseph took the baby to the temple in Jerusalem, to present him to God.

The new parents also followed the usual custom of making a thanksgiving offering of a pair of doves. While they were in the temple, a devout old man named Simeon came up to Joseph and Mary and took the baby Jesus in his arms. Simeon had been promised by God that he would not die before he had seen the Lord's Messiah, and he now praised God for sending this baby into the world. "Your servant can now die in peace, Lord,"

Simeon said in his song of praise. "For at last my eyes have seen the salvation that will come to everyone and bring glory to your people of Israel." Then Simeon blessed the baby's parents.

When Simeon had finished speaking, an old prophetess named Anna approached. She worshiped in the temple day and night, and she too knew that she was in the presence of the Messiah. She gave thanks to God for sending his saviour.

When Simeon and Anna had finished their songs of praise, Mary took Jesus back in her arms. She and Joseph were amazed at all these wonderful things that had been said about their special baby.

201

THEN TOOK HE HIM UP IN HIS ARMS, AND BLESSED GOD AND SAID, LORD, NOW LETTEST THOU THY SERVANT DEPART IN PEACE, ACCORDING TO THY WORD: FOR MINE EYES HAVE SEEN THY SALVATION, WHICH THOU HAST PREPARED BEFORE THE FACE OF ALL PEOPLE; A LIGHT TO LIGHTEN THE GENTILES, AND THE GLORY OF THY PEOPLE ISRAEL.

(Luke 2.28–32)

Escape to Egypt

Journey to safety
Right, detail from an Italian fresco showing Joseph taking Mary and Jesus to Egypt, to escape Herod.

Massacre of the Innocents
The killing of the babies in Bethlehem by soldiers sent by King Herod is known as the Massacre of the Innocents. Below, detail of a painting of this event, by Fra Angelico (1400–55).

 King Herod realised that he was wasting his time waiting for the return of the wise men from the east. He was furious that they had tricked him and gone home by a different route, avoiding Jerusalem altogether. Herod decided that he would have to take the matter into his own hands. He was determined to make sure that the newborn king he feared would never grow up. The wise men had told Herod that they had first seen the special bright star in the sky some months before. So Herod called his guards and ordered them to go out and kill all baby boys under the age of two in Bethlehem and the surrounding area.

That very night an angel appeared to Joseph in a dream and warned him that his family was in danger. "Get up at once," the angel told Joseph, "and take Jesus and his mother to the land of Egypt. Stay there until I tell you that it is safe to return, for Herod wants to kill the baby." Joseph wasted no time. He woke Mary, and they left at once, carrying the little boy Jesus.

Not long afterwards, while the family were safe in Egypt, King Herod died. The angel appeared again to Joseph, to give him the good news. "You may take Jesus and his mother back to the land of Israel," the angel said, "for those who were trying to kill the child are dead." Joseph and Mary

THEN HEROD, WHEN HE SAW THAT HE WAS
MOCKED OF THE WISE MEN, WAS EXCEEDING
WROTH, AND SENT FORTH, AND SLEW ALL THE
CHILDREN THAT WERE IN BETHLEHEM, AND IN
ALL THE COASTS THEREOF, FROM TWO YEARS AND
UNDER, ACCORDING TO THE TIME WHICH HE HAD
DILIGENTLY ENQUIRED OF THE WISE MEN.

(Matthew 2.16)

were pleased to be able to return to their homeland, and they left Egypt at once. But when Joseph learned that Herod's son, Archelaus, was now ruler in the southern region of Judea, he decided not to go there. Instead, the family went back to the town of Nazareth, in the northern region of Galilee, where Mary and Joseph had lived before Jesus was born. There the baby was safe. Looked after and loved, he grew into a strong, wise child.

204

AFTER THREE DAYS THEY FOUND HIM IN
THE TEMPLE, SITTING IN THE MIDST OF
THE DOCTORS, BOTH HEARING THEM, AND
ASKING THEM QUESTIONS. AND ALL THAT
HEARD HIM WERE ASTONISHED AT HIS
UNDERSTANDING AND ANSWERS.

(Luke 2.46–47)

The Boy Jesus in the Temple

Every spring, Joseph and Mary travelled to Jerusalem to celebrate the great feast of Passover. When Jesus was twelve years old, his parents took him with them. The celebrations in Jerusalem went on for about a week, and then Joseph and Mary — along with many other families — began making their way back home. They thought that young Jesus was with them, but after they had travelled for a whole day, they suddenly realised that they had not seen their son on the return journey. Mary rushed from one friend to another and asked all her relatives, and Joseph did the same. But no one had seen Jesus.

Joseph and Mary hurried back to Jerusalem, hoping that they might find Jesus on the way. But there was no sign of him, so when they got back to the city, they began a long search through the many narrow streets. They searched for three days without success, until at last they reached the temple. Mary and Joseph had almost given up hope of finding their son, but there he was, sitting in the temple court surrounded by teachers and other wise men. As they approached, they saw that Jesus was discussing things with the teachers, asking them questions and answering theirs. They were too relieved to notice how amazed the wise men were at the wisdom and understanding shown by this twelve-year-old boy.

"How could you treat us like this?" Mary said tearfully to Jesus. "Your father and I have been searching for you everywhere. Didn't it occur to you how worried we would be? What are you doing?"

"Why were you searching for me?" Jesus replied calmly. "Surely you knew that I had to be in my Father's house? Where else could I be?"

Mary and Joseph did not understand what Jesus meant, but they were very glad when the boy got up to go with them. They left the temple together and set off again on their journey home to Nazareth. Jesus was obedient to his parents and did as he was told, but his mother thought hard about what had happened at the temple in Jerusalem.

Bar-Mitzvah
When a Jewish boy is 13 years old, he has a bar mitzvah ceremony to mark his entry into adulthood. The boy is called up in synagogue to read from the Torah for the first time. Friends and relatives attend to hear him read, and a celebration usually follows.

205

Herod's temple
Herod rebuilt the temple in Jerusalem, the centre of Jewish religious life, on a grand scale. Of his splendid temple only the base of the western wall, the "wailing wall". remains. Left, a reconstruction of Herod's temple.

JESUS IS BAPTISED

Baptism
Baptism is practiced by Christians all over the world as a sign of entry into the Christian faith. In some churches, baptism takes place soon after a child is born. Above, a priest baptises a baby, sprinkling water on the child's head.

John, the son of Elizabeth and Zechariah and cousin of Jesus, grew up into a strong, independent young man. The angel Gabriel had told his father that John would have the spirit and power of the prophet Elijah. Once he became a man, John wore rough clothes made of camel's hair. He left home and went out into the desert lands of Judea, where he lived a hard, simple life, surviving on locusts and wild honey.

John preached to the people he met, telling them to turn from their wicked ways and repent, and that the kingdom of heaven was coming. His message soon spread beyond the desert, and people flocked to him from Jerusalem, to confess their sins and be baptised by him in the waters of the River Jordan. When John the Baptist dipped people in the water, it was a sign that God had forgiven their sins, so that they were clean once more and were given a fresh start. John told everyone that he was only preparing the way for someone who was much greater than himself. "I baptise you with water," John said, "but I am not fit to undo the sandals of the one who will come after me. He will baptise you with the Holy Spirit and with fire."

One day Jesus went to the desert to hear his cousin preach and to be baptised by him. John was troubled by this, and tried to put Jesus off. "You have come to me," John said, "but it is I who need to be baptised by you."

"This is the way it should be now," Jesus replied, and so John agreed to baptise him. The two cousins went into the river, and John dipped Jesus under the water. At the very moment when Jesus came up from the water, he had a vision of the Holy Spirit flying down to him like a dove. Then he heard a voice from heaven: "This is my beloved son, with whom I am well pleased."

Baptismal bath
Right, this 6th-century baptismal bath would have been filled with water and used to baptise people by totally immersing them in water — a sign of their entering into the Christian faith. Some church groups, such as Baptists, only baptise older people, and still use total immersion.

AND IT CAME TO PASS IN THOSE DAYS, THAT JESUS CAME FROM NAZARETH OF GALILEE, AND WAS BAPTISED OF JOHN IN JORDAN. AND STRAIGHTWAY COMING UP OUT OF THE WATER, HE SAW THE HEAVENS OPENED, AND THE SPIRIT LIKE A DOVE DESCENDING UPON HIM: AND THERE CAME A VOICE FROM HEAVEN, SAYING, THOU ART MY BELOVED SON, IN WHOM I AM WELL PLEASED.

(Mark 1.9–19. *See also* Matthew 3.13–17, John 1.29)

Jesus in the Wilderness

In the wilderness
The jackal was despised by the Jews, largely because animal gods such as Anubis, the dog or jackal, were worshipped by people in neighbouring lands.

When he had been baptised by his cousin John, Jesus left the River Jordan and went out into the desert wilderness on his own. He wanted time to think and pray to God. He stayed alone in the bare, rocky desert for forty days. It was fiercely hot by day and bitterly cold at night, and Jesus had only wild desert animals for company.

Jesus ate nothing for all that time, and after forty days he was exhausted and desperately hungry. Seeing an opportunity, the devil suddenly appeared and said to him: "If you are the Son of God, tell these stones to turn into bread."

Despite his terrible hunger, Jesus was not so easily tempted. "It is written in the scriptures that people do not live by bread alone," he said, "but by all the teachings of God."

Since he was getting nowhere in the desert, the devil led Jesus to Jerusalem and got him to stand at the highest point of the Temple roof. "If you are the Son of God," the devil sneered, "throw yourself down from here. You will surely be safe, because your God has said that his angels will always guard you and look after you so that you never hurt yourself."

But Jesus answered calmly: "It says in the scriptures, 'Do not put the Lord your God to the test.'"

The devil did not give up easily, however. He led Jesus to the top of a rocky hill and showed him a vision of all the kingdoms of the world. "I could give you power over all the world's splendour," the devil said. "If you agree to worship me alone, all this will be yours."

Once again Jesus turned down the devil's temptations. "I will not listen to you, Satan," he said firmly. "For it says in the scriptures, 'Worship only the Lord your God, and serve no one else.'"

The devil had offered his strongest temptations, and in resisting them Jesus showed that he would not turn away from what God wanted of him. He had to tell people what God was really like and, more than that, by his life he also had to show them.

The devil
This 13th-century French stained-glass window depicts the devil tempting Jesus to turn stones into bread. The devil is a spiritual being who opposes God's purposes by tempting people to disobey him.

AND WHEN THE TEMPTER CAME TO HIM, HE SAID, IF THOU
BE THE SON OF GOD, COMMAND THAT THESE STONES BE
MADE BREAD. BUT HE ANSWERED AND SAID, IT IS WRITTEN,
MAN SHALL NOT LIVE BY BREAD ALONE, BUT BY EVERY
WORD THAT PROCEEDETH OUT OF THE MOUTH OF GOD.

(Matthew 4.3–4 *See also* Luke 4.3–4)

Jesus Chooses his Disciples

After his forty days in the wilderness, Jesus went back to Galilee to preach to people and tell them about God. "The kingdom of heaven will soon be here," he said, "so confess your sins and listen to God's good news."

One day, a crowd of people listened to Jesus as he walked beside the Sea of Galilee. Near the shore

Jesus saw a couple of fishermen, Simon Peter and his brother Andrew, who were cleaning their nets. Jesus stepped into Simon Peter's boat and asked to be rowed a little way from the shore. Then he sat down in the boat and talked to the crowd standing along the water's edge. When he had finished speaking, Jesus said to Simon Peter: "Row us out to

deeper water and let your nets down for a catch."

"My brother and I have been fishing all night," Simon Peter replied, "and we have caught nothing. But I will do as you ask." When he let down his nets, they were filled at once with such a huge catch of fish that the nets started to break. Andrew quickly came to help his brother. They pulled in the nets as fast as they could and soon filled both boats with fish. The catch was so heavy that the boats began to sink, and the brothers were both amazed and frightened.

"Don't be afraid," Jesus told them. "Follow me and from now on you will catch men." Simon Peter and Andrew rowed Jesus to the shore, pulled up their heavy boats, left them, and followed their new leader.

A little farther on, Jesus saw James and John, who were sitting beside their boat mending nets with their father, Zebedee. When Jesus called them, the two brothers dropped the nets, left their father, and followed him at once.

Jesus and his four new disciples travelled the countryside near the Sea of Galilee, preaching the word of God. One day Jesus saw a man named Matthew sitting in a tax collector's hut. "Follow me," Jesus said, just as he had done to the fishermen. Matthew got up and followed him at once. Later that day Matthew invited Jesus and the other disciples to have dinner at his house. He wanted all his friends to meet them, so other tax collectors came along too. When the Pharisees, who were religious leaders, saw this, they asked the disciples: "Why does your master sit down to eat with tax collectors and other rascals?"

Jesus overheard this and replied: "It is not healthy people who need a doctor, but the sick. I have not come to look for good people who have done nothing wrong, but to help those who have sinned."

Jesus went through all the towns and villages, preaching the good news and healing the sick. Crowds followed him. He said to his disciples, "The harvest is good, but the workers are few." So he chose another seven disciples to help in his work. Their names were Philip, Bartholomew, Thomas, James son of Alphaeus, Thaddaeus, Simon the Zealot and Judas Iscariot.

Then Jesus called together these twelve apostles, or messengers, and gave them the power and authority to drive out evil spirits and heal every kind of sickness. "Go and look for the lost sheep of Israel," Jesus told the apostles. "As you go, preach the message that the kingdom of heaven is near. Drive out demons and heal the sick. Just as you have received freely from me, so you must give freely to others."

Fishing
Fishing was widely practised along the coastlines and in the inland rivers and lakes. At least four of Jesus' disciples were fishermen. Above, the fish in the Sea of Galilee were an important source of food for the people of Canaan.

211

The symbol of a Christian
Above, the fish was an early Christian symbol. The Greek word for fish, Ichthus, is made up of the first letters of the Greek words for Jesus Christ, God's son, Saviour.

WATER INTO WINE

Jesus and his disciples were invited to a wedding feast at Cana, a village in the hills of Galilee. Mary, Jesus's mother, was also present at the feast.

Before the end of the feast the wine ran out, and Mary came and told Jesus. "What has that to do with me?" he asked. "My time has not yet come to act." But his mother quietly told the servants to do whatever Jesus said.

At the feast there were six large water pots, which were used for ceremonial washing. Jesus told the servants to fill them with water. Then he said, "Pour some into a jug and take it to the master of the feast." The servants did as they were told, and the master of the feast poured from the jug. Amazed, the servants saw that the water had turned into rich red wine.

The master of the feast did not know where the wine had come from, and said to the bridegroom, "You have saved the best wine till last!"

This was the first miracle that Jesus performed, and his disciples put all their faith in him.

> WHEN THE STEWARD OF THE FEAST TASTED THE WATER THAT WAS MADE WINE, AND KNEW NOT WHENCE IT WAS (BUT THE SERVANTS WHICH DREW THE WATER KNEW) THE STEWARD OF THE FEAST CALLED THE BRIDEGROOM, AND SAITH UNTO HIM, EVERY MAN AT THE BEGINNING DOTH SET FORTH GOOD WINE; AND WHEN MEN HAVE WELL DRUNK, THEN THAT WHICH IS WORSE: BUT THOU HAST KEPT THE GOOD WINE UNTIL NOW.
>
> (John 2.9–10)

Containers

Above, two amphorae — large, ceramic, two-handled jars. The one on the left is from Mount Sinai, the one on the right from Carthage. Both date from the 5th to 4th centuries BCE. They were used for transporting and storing liquids such as olive oil or wine.

212

Ceremonial washing

The six large water pots at the wedding were kept to be used for ceremonial washing. It was a Jewish ritual for tableware to be washed before a meal was served. Guests also used the water to wash their hands. Right, ivory sculpture of the 6th century CE, from Ravenna, Italy.

THE DEATH OF JOHN THE BAPTIST

John the Baptist
The cousin of Jesus, John the Baptist preached to people and told them to turn away from sin. In doing so, he prepared them for the life and teachings of Jesus. Those who accepted John's message, he baptised. John was beheaded by Herod Antipas because he spoke out against Herod's marriage to Herodias, the wife of Herod's brother Philip. Above, this painted and gilded wooden statue of John the Baptist was carved in 1438 by the Italian sculptor Donatello (1386–1466).

John the Baptist was an honest man who always spoke the truth plainly. As he went around preaching and baptising people, however, John learned that there were many people who did not like to hear the truth about themselves. One such person was Herod Antipas, one of the sons of the old King Herod, who had tried to kill the baby Jesus.

Herod Antipas had been appointed governor of the region of Galilee on behalf of the Roman Empire. He had heard a great deal about John the Baptist, and was fascinated by his teachings. But he feared the power of such a good and holy man, and was worried about the influence John had over the people of Galilee. One day, John the Baptist's plain speaking got him into serious trouble with Herod. John told the governor that it was not right that he had married Herodias, the former wife of Herod's own brother, Philip.

When Herodias heard what John the Baptist had said, she was furious and decided to do everything she could to have him killed. She complained about him to her husband, but Herod was too frightened of John to do anything about him. Herodias was a very determined woman, however, and would not give up. She kept on at Herod, telling him how upset she was at having her marriage described as unlawful. At last Herod gave in and had John the Baptist arrested, bound and thrown into prison.

John was used to a rough, simple life, but he also loved the freedom he had always enjoyed. As he lay bound in the dark, damp prison, he thought more and more about his cousin Jesus, whom he had baptised. When one of John's followers managed to find out where he was and speak to him through his prison bars, John asked him to go and find Jesus. "Ask him whether he is really the Messiah," John said. "Or are we still waiting for someone else?"

John's messenger found Jesus busy healing the sick. When he heard John the Baptist's question, Jesus replied: "Go back and tell John what you have seen here. The blind can see again, the deaf can hear and the poor have hope." After John's disciple had left, Jesus spoke to those around him. "There is no greater man than John," he said. "He is more than a prophet, he is a messenger who was sent ahead to prepare the way."

But at that moment, John the Baptist was in great danger. It was Herod's birthday, and he had decided to hold a banquet for his officials, army commanders and the leading men of Galilee. After they had eaten and drunk a great deal, Herod's guests looked forward to some entertainment, and they were not disappointed. Salome, the beautiful young daughter of Herodias from her first marriage, came into the banqueting hall. Music struck up as Salome began a wild, graceful dance. The men were all delighted by Salome. When she finished and the music died down, Herod called her over. After congratulating his stepdaughter on her dancing, Herod offered her a gift. "Ask for anything you want," he said. "I will give you anything you desire, up to half my kingdom, so choose well!"

Salome thanked her stepfather. "May I think for a moment?" she asked. Then she ran to find her mother, asking, "What shall I say?" Herodias realised that this was the opportunity she had been waiting for. "Ask for the head of John the Baptist," she replied. When Salome went back into the banqueting hall, silence fell. All the guests wanted to know if she really had chosen half the kingdom. Salome went straight up to Herod, bowed before him, and said: "I would like you to give me John the Baptist's head on a dish, at once."

Herod Antipas was not at all pleased when he heard this. He still feared John and respected him for his holy way of life. But he had made a firm promise in front of all his dinner guests and he did not want to look a fool. So Herod called his chief guard and ordered him to go immediately to the prison and behead John the Baptist. The guard did as he was ordered, and shortly afterward returned with John's head on a big dish. This was presented to Salome, as she had asked. The girl gave it to her mother. Herodias was pleased to see the head of the man who had dared to criticise her.

When they heard the terrible news, John the Baptist's followers came to collect his body and gave it a proper burial in a tomb.

> AND IMMEDIATELY THE KING SENT AN EXECUTIONER, AND COMMANDED HIS HEAD TO BE BROUGHT: AND HE WENT AND BEHEADED HIM IN THE PRISON, AND BROUGHT HIS HEAD IN A CHARGER, AND GAVE IT TO THE DAMSEL: AND THE DAMSEL GAVE IT TO HER MOTHER.
> (Mark 6.27–28. *See also* Matthew 14.10–11)

Salome
In the time of Jesus, rich people often hired beautiful women to entertain them with dancing. Salome, the daughter of Herodias, pleased her stepfather and his drunken guests so much with her dancing that he foolishly promised to give her anything she wanted. Above, a bronze figure of a veiled and masked dancer, made in Greece in the 3rd century BCE.

215

BLESSED ARE THE POOR IN SPIRIT: FOR
THEIR'S IS THE KINGDOM OF HEAVEN.

BLESSED ARE THEY THAT MOURN: FOR
THEY SHALL BE COMFORTED.

BLESSED ARE THE MEEK: FOR THEY
SHALL INHERIT THE EARTH.

BLESSED ARE THEY WHICH DO
HUNGER AND THIRST AFTER
RIGHTEOUSNESS: FOR THEY SHALL
BE FILLED.

(Matthew 5.3–6. *See also* Luke 6)

THE SERMON ON THE MOUNT

As Jesus went through Galilee, large numbers of people began to follow him to listen to his words. Some of the religious leaders, such as the Pharisees, did not want Jesus to preach in their synagogues. They thought that his teachings did not stick closely enough to the laws they had inherited from Moses.

One day, when Jesus saw that a large crowd of people wanted to listen to him, he climbed up on to a hillside so that everyone could see and hear him. Jesus began his special sermon with a series of blessings for people who live their lives in the right way. "Blessed are the gentle," he said, "for they will inherit the earth. Blessed are the merciful, for they will be shown mercy. Blessed are the peacemakers, for they will be called the children of God."

Jesus told his followers: "You are the light of the world. But there is no point in covering a light and hiding it. You must let your light shine out so that others will also praise our Father in heaven."

Then Jesus had special words for those who were concerned about the laws of Moses. "I have not come to abolish the laws or go against the sayings of the prophets, but to carry them out. Those who practise and teach God's commandments will be called great in the kingdom of heaven. The law says 'You must not commit murder,' but anyone who has murderous thoughts against others or who is angry with a brother or sister will also be judged severely. You have heard it said, 'An eye for an eye and a tooth for a tooth.' But I say, if someone strikes you on one cheek, turn the other cheek so that they can strike that one, too. Or if someone wants to take your tunic, hand over your cloak as well. You have heard it said, 'Love your neighbour and hate your enemy.' But I say, love your enemies too, and pray for those who persecute you. And when you do good, such as giving to the poor, don't announce it to everyone, but keep it to yourself. Your Father in heaven sees everything and will reward you.

"It is the same when you pray. You do not need to stand in a synagogue or a public place, to be seen by others. Simply go into your room, close the door, and pray:

"Our Father in heaven, hallowed be your name, may your kingdom come, may your will be done on earth as well as in heaven. Give us today our daily bread, and forgive us our sins, as we forgive those who do wrong to us. Help us

217

Jesus and Moses
Like Moses, Jesus preached from a mountainside to the crowds that followed him. The site of the Sermon on the Mount may have been Mount Tabor. Below, a medieval miniature of Moses on Mount Sinai.

Jesus teaching
Above, a detail from an Italian fresco showing Jesus speaking to his disciples on a mountainside. He is sitting, the usual Jewish position for teaching. In Luke's much shorter account, Jesus stood on a level plain to preach his "Sermon on the Plain".

to avoid temptation and keep us away from evil. For the kingdom, the power, and the glory are yours for ever. Amen."

Then Jesus told a story that he knew would be a lesson to some of those listening to him, including the Pharisees. "Two men went to the temple to pray. One was a Pharisee, and the other was a tax collector. The Pharisee stood and prayed about himself: 'God, I thank you that I am not like other people, such as criminals, thieves, or that tax collector. I fast twice a week and give a tenth of my wealth to the poor.' The tax collector simply hung his head in shame and said, 'God, have mercy on me, for I am a sinner.' Now I can tell you, it was the tax collector rather than the Pharisee who made his peace with God. People who think highly of themselves will be brought down, while those who are humble will be praised."

Jesus finished his Sermon on the Mount with some more important lessons. "Do not store

valuable things on earth, but store up treasures in heaven, where rust cannot destroy them and thieves cannot steal them. You cannot serve God and money, because no one can serve two masters. And remember, you will be judged in the same way that you judge others. It's no good looking at a speck of sawdust in another person's eye when you have a large splinter in your own. Always deal with others as you would like them to deal with you. Just ask, and things will be given to you. Seek, and you will find. The door will be opened to everyone who knocks.

"Watch out for false prophets, who are like wolves in sheep's clothing. You can recognise how good a tree is by its fruit. A good tree cannot bear bad fruit, and a bad tree cannot bear good fruit. And trees that do not bear good fruit are cut down and thrown on the fire. Those of you who put my words into practice will be like a wise man who builds his house on rock. Rain may beat down and winds howl, but the house will not fall. But those who do not follow my words will be like a foolish man who builds his house on sand. When rain beats down and winds howl, that man's house will come crashing down.

"Don't worry about what you are going to eat or wear. Look at the birds flying overhead. God takes care of them — and he cares much more about you."

The crowd watched as Jesus came down from the hill. Everyone was amazed at what he had said, because his words were very different from those spoken by the religious teachers.

Jesus Cures the Sick

The Man with Leprosy

When Jesus came down from the hillside, a large crowd of people followed him. A man with leprosy — a terrible skin disease — made his way through the crowd and fell down on his knees before Jesus. The sick man bowed low. "Lord, if you are willing," he begged, "you can make me well again."

Jesus looked down at the man and felt great pity for him. He reached out his hand and touched the man gently. "I am willing," Jesus said. "Be well again." At once the man was cured of his illness. Then Jesus said to him, "Do not tell anyone about this, but go to a priest and offer the sacrifices that Moses commanded as thanks for your cure."

But the man found it impossible not to tell people of his miraculous cure. As a result, even more people flocked to see Jesus to hear what he was teaching.

The Centurion's Servant

The Roman legions
There were about 6,000 soldiers in a legion. Legions were made up of smaller units of about 100 soldiers, commanded by a centurion. The efficiency of the Roman armies was what made the Roman Empire great. Above, a stone carving of some Roman soldiers in full armour.

When Jesus reached Capernaum on the shores of the Sea of Galilee, the elders of the town came out to meet him. "We have been sent by a Roman centurion," one of the elders said. "He begs you to come and heal his faithful servant, who is very ill and in great pain." Another elder told Jesus that the centurion deserved help because he loved the Jewish nation and had built them a synagogue. So Jesus agreed to go with them.

Before they reached the Roman's house, however, the centurion himself came to meet Jesus. "Lord, I do not deserve to have you under my roof," the centurion said. "You have only to say the word and my servant will be healed. I can recognise authority. I myself have soldiers who report to me, and if I tell a man to go, he goes. And when I order my servant to do something, he does it."

Jesus was amazed when he heard these words, and turned to those who were following him. "I have not found such great faith among the people of Israel as this man has shown," he said. "Go home," Jesus told the Roman, "and everything will be just as you believed." When the centurion reached home, he found that his servant was cured.

> FOR I AM A MAN UNDER AUTHORITY, HAVING SOLDIERS UNDER ME: AND I SAY TO THIS MAN, GO, AND HE GOETH; AND TO ANOTHER, COME, AND HE COMETH; AND TO MY SERVANT, DO THIS, AND HE DOETH IT. WHEN JESUS HEARD IT, HE MARVELLED, AND SAID TO THEM THAT FOLLOWED, VERILY I SAY UNTO YOU, I HAVE NOT FOUND SO GREAT FAITH, NO, NOT IN ISRAEL.
>
> (Matthew 8.9–10. *See also* Luke 7.8–9)

The Paralysed Man

Religious teachers
Great care is needed to read Hebrew. A rabbi (above) — a teacher of Jewish law — uses a pointer called a yad to pick out the words as he reads the Torah from a scroll.

While Jesus was in Capernaum, people flocked to hear him speak. Great crowds gathered around the house where he stayed, and soon it was impossible even to open the door. Four men brought a Paralysed man to Jesus, hoping that he would cure him. They carried the sick man on a mat, but as they had no hope of pushing their way through the door, they decided to enter the house by a different route. The men made a hole in the roof and carefully lowered the invalid to the ground inside the house.

When Jesus saw the faith that the men had in him, he said to the Paralysed man, "Son, your sins are forgiven." Some of the religious teachers present were shocked by these words, because they thought that God alone had the power and the right to forgive sins. How dare this man speak so disrespectfully? Although they said nothing, Jesus

knew what the teachers were thinking. "Why do you think so badly of me in your hearts?" he asked the teachers. "Is it easier to say to this man 'Your sins are forgiven' or to tell him 'Get up and walk'? Now I will show you that the Son of Man has the power to forgive sins."

Then Jesus turned to the Paralysed man: "Get up," he said, "take your mat, and go home." At once the man did as Jesus said. No one had seen anything like this before, and all those present were astonished. They praised and thanked God for such a miracle.

AND WHEN THEY COULD NOT COME NIGH UNTO HIM FOR THE PRESS, THEY UNCOVERED THE ROOF WHERE HE WAS: AND WHEN THEY HAD BROKEN IT UP, THEY LET DOWN THE BED WHEREIN THE SICK OF THE PALSY LAY.

(Mark 2.4)

Jairus's Daughter

A large crowd was waiting at the shore as Jesus crossed the lake by boat. One man in particular was longing to speak to him. His name was Jairus and he was one of the synagogue elders. As Jesus approached, Jairus fell at his feet. "My daughter is dying," he told Jesus. "She is just twelve years old. Please come to my house, for I know that if you touch her, she will live." So Jesus and his disciples went with Jairus.

As they hurried along, the crowd followed them. Suddenly a woman stepped out as Jesus passed by and touched the hem of his cloak. "Who was that who touched me?" Jesus asked. None of the disciples had seen the woman, and Peter assured his master that it must have been the crowd pushing against him. But Jesus replied: "I know that someone touched me because power has gone out of me."

Then the woman threw herself on the ground before Jesus and confessed in a trembling voice that it was she who had touched him. "I have been suffering from a terrible disease of the blood for twelve years," she said, "and no one has been able to help me. But I knew that if my hand just touched your cloak, I would be cured."

Jesus looked down at the woman for a moment. He said: "Be happy, my daughter, for your faith has healed you. Go in peace, your suffering has come to an end."

Just as Jesus spoke these words, a messenger arrived from Jairus's house. "There is no need to bother the teacher any more," he told Jairus. "Your daughter is dead."

Hearing the messenger's words, Jesus said to Jairus: "Don't be afraid. Just believe, and your daughter will be healed."

But when they arrived at Jairus's house, they could hear people weeping and wailing. "Stop your mourning," Jesus said at once. "The girl is not dead, but asleep." At that the people laughed scornfully in disbelief, so Jesus told everyone to leave the house. He took Peter, John, and James with him, and they led Jairus and his wife into the room where their child was lying.

Jesus bent over the girl, took her by the hand, and said, "Get up, my child." The girl rose from her bed at once and walked across the room.

Her parents were astonished by this miracle. Jesus told them to give their daughter something to eat and to tell no one about what had happened. But the miraculous news soon spread around the whole region.

AND HIS DISCIPLES SAID UNTO HIM, THOU SEEST THE MULTITUDE THRONGING THEE, AND SAYEST THOU, WHO TOUCHED ME? AND HE LOOKED AROUND TO SEE HER THAT HAD DONE THIS THING. BUT THE WOMAN FEARING AND TREMBLING, KNOWING WHAT WAS DONE IN HER, CAME AND FELL DOWN BEFORE HIM, AND TOLD HIM ALL THE TRUTH.
(Mark 5.31–33)

Evil spirits
Demons were regarded as evil spirits that joined with the devil to oppose God's purposes. It was also believed that demons entered humans and caused mental illness. Above, a sculpture of the Mesopotamian winged demon, Pazuzu.

The Boy and the Evil Spirit

One day Jesus saw his disciples arguing with some teachers of the law. He went up to them and asked what the argument was about. The answer came from a man in the crowd. "I brought my son here," the man said, "hoping that your disciples would be able to drive out the evil spirit that possesses him. When the spirit takes hold of my boy, it throws him to the ground and holds him in its grip till he grinds his teeth and foams at the mouth. Your friends tried to cast it out, but they couldn't get rid of it."

Jesus told the man to bring his son to him. But as they came near, the evil spirit threw the boy into a terrible fit. As he lay writhing on the ground, Jesus asked his father how long the boy had suffered like this. "Since he was a baby," the man replied. "The demon must want to kill him, because it sometimes throws him into the river or even into the fire. If there is anything you can do,

please have pity and help us."

"If you truly believe and put your faith in me," said Jesus, "then everything is possible."

"I do believe," the man said. "Help me to overcome my doubts."

People came rushing up to see what Jesus would do. "Evil spirit," he commanded, "come out of the boy and never enter him again." The spirit made a screaming noise, threw the boy into another fearful fit, and then suddenly left him. The boy lay on the ground without moving a muscle, and all the crowd thought that he was dead. But Jesus took the boy by the hand and lifted him to his feet. He was alive and well.

Later, when they were on their own with Jesus, the disciples asked him why, although they had tried to help the man, they had not been able to drive the demon out. "This kind of evil spirit can only be driven out by prayer," Jesus replied.

AND, BEHOLD A MAN OF THE COMPANY CRIED OUT, SAYING, MASTER, I BESEECH THEE, LOOK UPON MY SON: FOR HE IS MINE ONLY CHILD. AND, LO, A SPIRIT TAKETH HIM, AND HE SUDDENLY CRIETH OUT; AND IT TEARETH HIM AND HE FOAMETH AGAIN, AND BRUISING HIM HARDLY DEPARTETH FROM HIM.
(Luke 9.38–39 See also Matthew 17.14, Mark 9.17-20)

224

The Blind Beggar

Jesus and his disciples passed a beggar who had been blind from birth. One of the disciples asked Jesus: "Who sinned, this man or his parents, for him to be born blind?"

"Neither the man nor his parents sinned," Jesus replied. "It happened so that God's work could be shown in the man's lifetime. While it is day, we must do the work of the one who sent me. For when darkness comes, no one can work. As long as I am here, I am the light of the world." Then Jesus spat on the ground, mixed some soil with his spittle, and dabbed the paste that he had made onto the blind man's eyes. "Go and wash in the pool of Siloam," he told the man.

After the man had washed in the pool, he opened his eyes and could see. When he came back, the people who had known him as a beggar thought he must be someone else. "No, it really is me!" the man said.

"Whoever was it who made you see?" someone in the crowd asked.

The man replied that Jesus had cured his blindness. But when the people demanded to know more about this miracle-worker, he could tell them nothing. When the Pharisees heard what had happened, they too questioned the man. They thought that whatever Jesus had done, he had committed a sin by doing it on the Sabbath day, which was a day of rest.

But all the man could tell them was that he had been blind, and now he could see. "This Jesus is a prophet," the man said. "No one has ever been able to cure the blind before. He must come from God." The man who had been blind was full of belief, but still the Pharisees did not trust Jesus.

At the Pool of Bethesda

225

One day Jesus went to Jerusalem for a Jewish festival. Near the city's sheep market he passed a pool named Bethesda, and saw many blind, lame and Paralysed people sheltering there. They were all waiting for the water to move, because they believed that at certain times an angel would come down to the pool and stir up the water. It was said that the first person who then went into the pool would be cured of disease.

One man who was lying there had been an invalid for thirty-eight years. When Jesus saw the man, he asked him: "Do you want to be cured?"

"Sir," the invalid replied, "I have no one to help me get into the pool when the water is stirred. So someone else always gets there before me."

Jesus said to the man: "Get up, take your mat and walk." At once the man was cured. He stood and was able to walk.

This happened on the Sabbath, a day on which it was forbidden for people to carry loads. So the man got into trouble with the religious authorities for carrying his mat. When they came to Jesus, he said to them: "My father has never stopped his work, and I, too, am working." This made them even angrier. Jesus was breaking the law. But worse, he seemed to be making himself out to be God's equal.

> JESUS SAITH UNTO HIM, RISE, TAKE UP THY BED AND WALK. AND IMMEDIATELY THE MAN WAS MADE WHOLE, AND TOOK UP HIS BED, AND WALKED: AND ON THE SAME DAY WAS THE SABBATH.
>
> (John 5.8–9)

JESUS WALKS ON THE WATER

The Sea of Galilee
Jesus spent most of his life and the years of his public ministry in the Galilee countryside. Many of his best-known miracles took place in this region.
Right, St Peter and St Andrew fishing on the Sea of Galilee, a detail from an early Christian mosaic in Ravenna, Italy.

One late afternoon, Jesus told his disciples to leave the crowds and sail across the Sea of Galilee. Their boat had gone out a long way when a fierce storm blew up. Huge waves tossed it about, and the disciples were afraid it would sink. They turned to Jesus for help, but found that he was fast asleep in the stern. In their panic, they shook Jesus awake, shouting: "Lord, save us, or we'll all drown!"

"Why are you so afraid?" Jesus asked calmly. "Do you have no faith?" He stretched out his hand over the lake and ordered the wind and waves to be still. At once the storm died down. The disciples watched this in amazement and asked one another, "Who is this man? Even the wind and the waves obey him!"

On another occasion, after Jesus had spent time preaching to some great crowds, he went up into the hills to pray. He wanted to be alone, so he sent his disciples across the lake to Bethsaida. Hours later, when Jesus looked down at the lake, he saw that it was dark and stormy. The disciples' boat was making little headway against the wind, and it looked as if they needed help to survive the storm. So Jesus went down the hillside and began to walk across the lake toward the boat. When the disciples saw a figure walking on the water, they were terrified. As he drew closer, they were sure it must be a ghost.

"Don't be afraid," Jesus called. "It is I!"

"If it really is you, Lord," Peter cried out, "tell me to come to you on the water."

"Come!" Jesus said.

Peter climbed out of the boat and walked across the water to Jesus. Suddenly a strong gust of wind caught him, his fear returned, and he began to sink. "Lord, save me!" he cried.

At once Jesus reached out, took his disciple by the hand, and pulled him from the foaming water. "You have little faith, Peter," Jesus said. "Why did you doubt me?" As soon as they climbed into the boat, the wind died down and the lake was calm once more. All those in the boat worshipped Jesus, saying, "Truly, you are the Son of God."

227

AND IMMEDIATELY JESUS STRETCHED FORTH
HIS HAND, AND CAUGHT HIM, AND SAID UNTO
HIM, O THOU OF LITTLE FAITH, WHEREFORE
DIDST THOU DOUBT? AND WHEN THEY WERE
COME INTO THE SHIP, THE WIND CEASED.

(Matthew 14.31–32 *See also* Mark 6.48–51,
John 6.19–21)

FEEDING THE FIVE THOUSAND

Bread
Bread was a main food throughout the Bible lands. To make bread, first the wheat (or barley, if the family was poor) had to be ground into flour. The flour was mixed with water and salt, then with yeast from the previous day's baking, to make it rise. After the dough had been kneaded, it was shaped into loaves and left to rise. The loaves were baked in an outdoor oven. Above, grinding grain into flour.

The miraculous feeding
Right, this mosaic in the 5th-century church of St Apollinare Nuovo in Ravenna, Italy, shows a scene from the miracle of Jesus feeding the five thousand on the shores of Lake Galilee. Jesus is shown blessing the bread and fish, which his disciples then shared out among the huge, hungry crowd.

Jesus and his disciples had been preaching to crowds of people all day. No one had had time to eat, because the people had stayed near Jesus all day, hoping to see him perform one of the miracles they had all heard about. Jesus knew that his disciples were tired and hungry, so he said to them, "Come with me to a quiet place where you can rest."

They got into a boat and rowed along the shore for a while, until they found a place to land. As soon as Jesus stepped out of the boat, he was surrounded by people who had followed him around the lake on foot. Jesus took pity on them because he saw that without him, the people were like sheep without a shepherd. So once again he let them crowd around him and began teaching them again.

Some time later the disciples asked Jesus to send the people away so that they could go to their villages and get something to eat. But Jesus said: "There's no need to send these people away. You can give them food here." The disciples were confused. How could they possibly feed such a large crowd? There were at least five thousand people, and they had very little to offer them.

"We have only five loaves of bread and two fish," the disciples said. Jesus told them to ask the people to sit down on the grass, and to bring the bread and fish to him. When the huge crowd was seated, Jesus looked up to heaven, thanked God for the food and broke the loaves. He gave the bread to his disciples to share among the people, and did the same with the fish. As the disciples gave out the food, they found to their amazement that there was more than enough for everyone. In fact, afterwards, twelve baskets were filled with the food that was left over.

AND JESUS TOOK THE LOAVES; AND
WHEN HE HAD GIVEN THANKS, HE
DISTRIBUTED TO THE DISCIPLES, AND
THE DISCIPLES TO THEM THAT WERE SET
DOWN; AND LIKEWISE OF THE FISHES AS
MUCH AS THEY WOULD. WHEN THEY
WERE FILLED, HE SAID UNTO HIS
DISCIPLES, GATHER UP THE FRAGMENTS
THAT REMAIN, THAT NOTHING BE LOST.

(John 6.11–12 *See also* Matthew 14.18–20)

JESUS IN HIS RADIANT GLORY

When Jesus was on his own with his disciples on one occasion, he asked them, "Who do people say that I am?"

"Some say you are John the Baptist, and others say Elijah," they replied. "Some think you are Jeremiah or one of the prophets."

"But what about you?" Jesus asked. "Who do you say I am?"

Peter answered at once. "You are the Christ, the Son of God," he said. Hearing these words, Jesus blessed Peter. "This truth was revealed to you by my Father in heaven," Jesus told him. "And I tell you, Peter, whose name means 'rock,' you are the rock on which I will build my church. I will give you the keys to the kingdom of heaven."

Then Jesus warned his disciples not to tell anyone else about who he really was. He explained that he must go to Jerusalem and suffer many things. "The elders, chief priests and teachers of the law will turn against me," Jesus said. "They will arrest me and kill me. But three days after my death, I will rise again."

"Never!" Peter cried. "That will never happen to you!"

Jesus told the disciples that human concerns were not important, and that only God's wishes counted. Then he called all the people together and told them and his disciples: "If you want to follow me, you must live through times of suffering. Those who are ready to do everything for me will be saved."

Some days after Jesus had spoken about his own death, he led Peter, John and James up a high mountain. As Jesus prayed to God on top of the mountain, his face shone like the Sun. His clothes became dazzling white, as bright as a flash of lightning. His disciples saw two men appear beside Jesus and talk with him. They recognised the men as Moses and Elijah, symbols of the law and the prophets, and they knew that they were seeing Jesus in all his radiant glory. "Lord, let us put up three shelters," Peter said, "one for you, one for Moses and one for Elijah."

But before Peter finished speaking, a bright cloud came down all around them. And a voice spoke from the cloud: "This is my Son, whom I love. Listen to him!"

Trembling with fear, the disciples fell to the ground and

St Peter's church
The largest Christian church in the world today is St Peter's church in Rome. It replaced the original church (shown below) in the 17th century. Like this first church, today's St Peter's stands above a crypt (underground vault), which is believed to contain the body of St Peter, who is traditionally thought of as the first bishop (pope) of Rome.

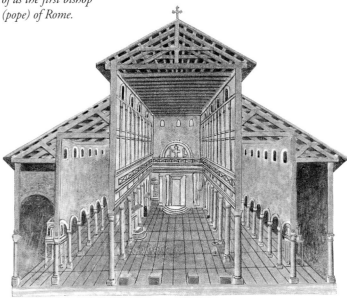

covered their faces. Then a hand touched each of them. "Do not be afraid," Jesus said. They looked up and saw that Jesus was alone again.

As they made their way down the mountain, Jesus told Peter, James and John not to talk to anyone about what they had seen.

BEHOLD, A BRIGHT CLOUD OVERSHADOWED THEM: AND BEHOLD A VOICE OUT OF THE CLOUD, WHICH SAID, THIS IS MY BELOVED SON, IN WHOM I AM WELL PLEASED; HEAR YE HIM. AND WHEN THE DISCIPLES HEARD IT, THEY FELL ON THEIR FACE, AND WERE SORE AFRAID.

(Matthew 17.5–6. *See also* Mark 9.7, Luke 9.34–35)

JESUS TEACHES AND TELLS MANY PARABLES

The Wise and Faithful Servant

Servants
During the time of Jesus, both men and women worked as servants. They were either slaves or hired workers, paid for their services. Above, a Roman relief shows a mother bathing her baby with the help of a servant.

One day Jesus told his disciples, "You must always be ready, for the Son of Man will come when you least expect him."

Then Jesus asked: "Who is the wise and faithful servant who is chosen by his master to look after the other servants while he is away? A wise servant will always do what he is asked. So when his master comes back and finds things as they should be, he will happily put the faithful servant in charge of everything he owns.

"But if the master stays away for a long time, the servant who has been put in charge may decide not to follow his orders any longer. He may grow lazy and start treating the other servants badly. When his master returns unexpectedly, he will beat the head servant and throw him out.

"The servant who knows his master's wishes will be punished for his wrongdoing more severely than one who does not know what the master wants. This is because much more is asked of people who are given a great deal and have a position of trust."

> BLESSED ARE THOSE SERVANTS, WHOM THE LORD WHEN HE COMETH SHALL FIND WATCHING: VERILY I SAY UNTO YOU, THAT HE SHALL GIRD HIMSELF, AND MAKE THEM TO SIT DOWN TO MEAT, AND WILL COME FORTH AND SERVE THEM.
>
> (Luke 12.37 *See also* Matthew 24.45–47)

The Wise and Foolish Bridesmaids

Once there were ten bridesmaids waiting to be called to join a wedding celebration. As it was getting dark, the girls all took their lamps to go out and meet the bridegroom, but five of them were wise and the other five were foolish. The wise ones took jars of extra oil for their lamps, while the foolish ones didn't bother.

The bridesmaids had to wait a long time for the bridegroom, and fell asleep. At midnight the call came: "Here comes the bridegroom!" The ten girls all woke up at once and quickly turned up their lamps. The five foolish girls soon realised their mistake, however, because their lamps were about to go out. They asked the others to give them some oil, but the wise bridesmaids refused. "We haven't got enough oil for you as well," they said. "If yours has run out, you'll have to go and buy some more."

The foolish girls rushed off to buy more oil, but while they were away, the bridegroom arrived. The wise bridesmaids followed the bridegroom into the wedding hall, and the door was shut behind them. When the foolish girls got back, they knocked on the door. "Sir, sir," they cried, "please let us in!" But the bridegroom replied, "I don't know you," and sent the foolish girls away.

After telling this story, Jesus told his followers that they should be like the wise girls and keep watch. Then they would always be ready for the coming of the kingdom of heaven.

Oil lamps
Oil was the main fuel used for lamps in the Bible lands. Above, a pottery oil-burning lamp from the Roman city of Caesarea.

> AND THE FOOLISH SAID UNTO THE WISE,
> GIVE US OF YOUR OIL; FOR OUR LAMPS ARE
> GONE OUT. BUT THE WISE ANSWERED,
> SAYING, NOT SO; LEST THERE BE NOT
> ENOUGH FOR US AND YOU: BUT GO YE
> RATHER TO THEM THAT SELL, AND BUY FOR
> YOURSELVES. AND WHILE THEY WENT TO
> BUY, THE BRIDEGROOM CAME; AND THEY
> THAT WERE READY WENT IN WITH HIM TO
> THE MARRIAGE: AND THE DOOR WAS SHUT.
>
> (Matthew 25.8–10)

Parables about the kingdom of God

The word parable means the placing of two things side by side for the sake of comparison. For instance, to explain what the kingdom of heaven is like, Jesus says that it is like … a mustard seed … treasure hidden in a field … a man who sowed good seed in his field, and so on.

The Mustard Seed

Another time, Jesus told his followers: "The kingdom of heaven is like the mustard seed that a man took and planted in his field. Although it is the smallest of seeds, mustard turns into the largest plant in the whole field. When the man planted his mustard seed, it first grew into a plant and then into a tree, large and strong enough for birds to perch in its branches and build their nests." God's kingdom is like that — growing and growing.

In another parable Jesus told his followers that the kingdom of heaven is like the yeast that a woman mixed with flour until it changed all her heavy dough into good bread.

Workers in the Vineyard

One morning the owner of a vineyard went to the marketplace to hire some workers for the grape harvest. He agreed to pay them each a cent for the day's work and sent them off to gather the grapes in his vineyard.

Three hours later the man went back to the marketplace and hired more workers, promising to pay them a fair wage. The man went on doing this throughout the day. When he went to the marketplace for the last time, there was just an hour left before the end of the working day. On this last visit, the man still found people standing around. "Why have you stood here all day doing nothing?" the man asked. "Because no one has given us any work," they replied. So he hired these last workers to pick his grapes.

Later, the man called all the workers together to pay them. The ones hired last were paid first and were given a cent each. When it came to the turn of the workers who had

Harvest time

Right, a Roman mosaic from the mausoleum of Saint Costanza, 350 CE, showing workers harvesting grapes and treading on them to press out the juice.

started early, they expected more pay, but they too received a cent each. "That's not fair," they complained. "We've been working all day. The people you hired last only had to work for an hour. We should get more than them."

The owner of the vineyard reminded them that they had agreed to work for a cent each. "I can do what I want with my own money," the man said. "It is up to me if I want to be generous and pay the others the same as you. Why be jealous? Take your pay and go!"

Jesus explained to his listeners why he had told this story. "It shows that the last will be first, and the first will be last," he said. In the kingdom of God, those people who come late to God are loved as much as those who have always been close to him.

> WHEN THE FIRST CAME, THEY SUPPOSED THAT THEY SHOULD HAVE RECEIVED MORE; AND THEY LIKEWISE RECEIVED EVERY MAN A PENNY. AND WHEN THEY HAD RECEIVED IT, THEY MURMURED AGAINST THE GOOD MAN OF THE HOUSE, SAYING, THESE HAVE WROUGHT BUT ONE HOUR, AND THOU HAST MADE THEM EQUAL UNTO US, WHICH HAVE BORNE THE BURDEN AND HEAT OF THE DAY.
>
> (Matthew 20.10–12)

The Sheep and the Goats

Giving to the poor
This detail from a 13th-century fresco (wall-painting) by the Italian painter Giotto (1266–1337) in the cathedral of Assisi, Italy, shows St Francis giving his coat to a poor man.

AND HE SHALL SET THE SHEEP ON HIS RIGHT HAND, BUT THE GOATS ON THE LEFT. THEN SHALL THE KING SAY UNTO THEM ON HIS RIGHT HAND, COME, YE BLESSED OF MY FATHER, INHERIT THE KINGDOM PREPARED FOR YOU FROM THE FOUNDATION OF THE WORLD: FOR I WAS AN HUNGERED AND YE GAVE ME MEAT; I WAS THIRSTY AND YE GAVE ME DRINK; I WAS A STRANGER AND YE TOOK ME IN.

(Matthew 25.33–35)

Jesus said: "When the Son of Man comes with the angels in all his glory, he will sit on his throne and all the people will stand before him. Then he will divide them just as a shepherd separates the sheep from the goats. He will put the sheep on his right and the goats on his left.

"From his throne, the King will say to those on his right: 'You who are blessed by my Father will come and share God's kingdom. When I was hungry you gave me food, and when I was thirsty you gave me drink. I was a stranger and you invited me into your house. When I needed clothes you gave them to me, when I was sick you looked after me, and when I was in prison you came to visit me.'

"Then those on the right will answer: 'Lord, when did we see you hungry or thirsty and give you food or drink? When did we invite you in, clothe you, look after you, or visit

you?' And the King will reply that whatever they did for any one of his brothers or sisters, they did for him.

"Then he will say to those on the left: 'You who are wicked will burn for ever in the fire prepared for the devil. When I was hungry you gave me no food, and when I was thirsty you gave me nothing to drink. I was a stranger and you did not invite me in. When I needed clothes you gave me nothing, and when I was sick and in prison you did not look after me.'

"Then those on the left will answer: 'Lord, when did we see you hungry or thirsty? When did we see you in need and did not help you?'

"And the King will reply: 'Whenever you failed to do any of these things for one of the least important of my brothers or sisters, you failed to do it for me.' Then they will be sent away to be punished for ever, while those who did good things and were kind will have eternal life."

The Royal Wedding Banquet

There was once a king who prepared a wedding banquet for his son. He sent his servants to tell all those who had been invited that everything was ready. But when the servants passed on the king's message, no one paid any attention. So the king sent more messengers to those invited to the banquet, but they just ignored the message and went about their own business. Some even insulted the king's servants.

This made the king very angry. "The banquet is ready," he told his servants, "but those I invited do not deserve to come. Go onto the streets and invite anyone you can find." The servants did as they were told and the wedding hall was soon filled with all sorts of people.

When the king came to greet his guests, he noticed that one of them was not wearing proper wedding clothes. "My friend," the king said, "how did you manage to get in here without wedding clothes?" The man did not know what to answer. So the king ordered his servants to tie up the man and throw him back out into the street.

Jesus explained this parable to the people around him who were listening: "For many are invited, but few are chosen."

The Wheat and the Weeds

Wheat
Wheat made the best flour and was used to make the bread offered to God by priests. Barley produced a poorer-quality flour, used by peasants to make bread. Barley was also brewed to make beer.

Jesus told his followers: "The kingdom of heaven is like the farmer who sowed good seeds of wheat in his field. That night, when everyone was asleep, someone who hated him came and sowed weeds among the wheat. Weeks later, when the wheat started to grow, weeds also began to appear among the shoots.

"When the farmer's workmen saw this, they went and told him. Then they asked the farmer: 'Sir, if you sowed good seed, where did all these weeds come from?'

"'An enemy of mine must have done this,' the farmer replied.

When his workmen offered to pull up the weeds, he said: 'No, if you pull the weeds out now, you may uproot the wheat at the same time. Let both grow together until harvest time. Then we will first collect the weeds, bundle them up, and burn them, before gathering the wheat and taking it into the barn.'"

SO THE SERVANTS OF THE HOUSEHOLDER CAME AND SAID UNTO HIM, SIR, DIDST NOT THOU SOW GOOD SEED IN THY FIELD? FROM WHENCE THEN HATH IT TARES? HE SAID UNTO THEM, AN ENEMY HATH DONE THIS...

(Matthew 13.27–28)

238

The Pearl of Great Value

MATTHEW 13.45

In one of his parables, Jesus compared the kingdom of God to a precious pearl. "There was once a merchant, a dealer in fine pearls," Jesus said to his followers. "One day the merchant saw a perfect pearl of great value. Though he did not have enough money to buy it, the merchant knew that the pearl was more valuable than anything else in the world. So he sold everything that he had in order to buy that pearl."

The Rich Man and Lazarus

BUT ABRAHAM SAID, SON, REMEMBER THAT THOU IN THY LIFETIME RECEIVEDST THY GOOD THINGS, AND LIKEWISE LAZARUS EVIL THINGS; BUT NOW HE IS COMFORTED, AND THOU ART TORMENTED.

(Luke 16.25)

There was once a rich man who had a big house. He dressed like a king and lived a life of luxury. Outside his gates lay a poor beggar named Lazarus, who was covered in sores and only longed to eat the scraps of food that were left over from the rich man's table.

When Lazarus died, angels carried him up to heaven to sit next to Abraham. But when the rich man died, he was taken to suffer the torments of hell. From there he could see Abraham and Lazarus far off in the distance, so he called out: "Have pity on me, Father Abraham, and send Lazarus to dip his finger in water and cool my burning tongue."

But Abraham replied that the rich man had received good things in

Heaven and Hell
The Jews in Bible times pictured heaven as the place where God ruled in majesty. No one, they believed, knew what heaven was like, except that people there knew God completely and there was no more suffering or evil. It was believed that the fate of the wicked was to be eternally separated from the face of God. Hell was originally seen as a pit (sheol), a place out of God's sight, where the wicked were imprisoned and punished.

239

his lifetime, while Lazarus had had nothing. "Now Lazarus knows comfort, while you have to suffer," Abraham said. "Besides, the gap between heaven and hell is so great that no one can ever cross it."

When the man heard that there was no hope for him, he begged Abraham to send Lazarus back to warn his five brothers, who were still alive, so they would not end up in the same torment. "All they have to do is listen to the words of Moses and the prophets," Abraham replied.

"But if someone comes back from the dead to warn them," begged the man, "they will surely listen."

"If they do not listen to Moses and the prophets, nothing will convince them," said Abraham.

The Good Samaritan

The Samaritans
At the time of Jesus, Samaritans lived in central Palestine. They were descended from people who lived in Israel after the Assyrian conquest in 722 BCE. Samaritans accept only the Torah (above) as the word of God. They had been worn enemies of the Jews for centuries.

> BUT A CERTAIN SAMARITAN, AS HE JOURNEYED, CAME WHERE HE WAS AND, WHEN HE SAW HIM, HE HAD COMPASSION ON HIM. AND HE WENT TO HIM, AND BOUND UP HIS WOUNDS, POURING IN OIL AND WINE, AND SET HIM ON HIS OWN BEAST, AND BROUGHT HIM TO AN INN, AND TOOK CARE OF HIM.
>
> (Luke 10, 33–34)

240

A teacher of the scriptures asked Jesus, "What must I do to gain eternal life?"

"What do the scriptures say?" Jesus asked in return.

"Love God with all your heart," the man said, "and love your neighbour as yourself. But who should I regard as my neighbour?"

Jesus answered with a story. "Once a man on his way from Jerusalem to Jericho was attacked by robbers. They beat him, stole his clothes and left him for dead by the roadside. Soon a priest came down the same road, but when he saw the man, he passed by on the other side. Later, a Levite, one of the temple officials, came along, but he too hurried on past. Then a Samaritan came by, and he at once took pity on the man. He cleaned and bandaged his wounds, lifted him onto his donkey and took him to the nearest inn. Then he gave the innkeeper money and said, "Look after him. If you need more money for his care, I'll pay you when I return this way shortly."

"Now which of these three do you think was a true neighbour to the man?" Jesus asked.

"The one who was kind to him," the teacher replied. "Then go and do the same," said Jesus.

The Wicked Servant

Peter asked Jesus: "Lord, how many times should I forgive someone who has done me wrong? Up to seven times?"

"Not just seven times, but seventy-seven times," Jesus replied. "I will tell you a story to show you the importance of forgiveness. There was once a servant who owed his king a huge sum of money. When the man could not repay his debt, the king demanded that he sell everything he had, including his wife and children. The servant fell to his knees and begged the king to give him a little more time, promising that he would pay back every cent he owed. The king felt sorry for the man and let him off his debt.

"That same day the man happened to bump into one of his fellow servants who owed him a small sum of money. He threatened the other man and demanded to be paid back at once. The servant fell to his knees and begged for more time to raise the money. But the man showed no pity and had his fellow servant thrown into prison for not repaying his debt.

"When the other servants heard about this, they were shocked and went to inform the king. He was angry and ordered that the servant be brought to him at once. 'You are a wicked man,' the king told him. 'When you begged me, I felt sorry for you and let you off your debt. Why could you not do the same and have mercy on your fellow servant?'

"The king had his servant thrown into prison, and ordered that he be tortured until he had paid back every cent of the sum he owed.

"This is how my heavenly Father will treat each of you unless you forgive one another's wrongdoing from your heart," Jesus said to them.

Parables about loving and forgiving
Many of the parables that Jesus told teach that it is essential to love and value your neighbour. One of the most memorable — the Good Samaritan — addresses the question: "Who is my neighbour?"

241

BUT THE SAME SERVANT WENT OUT, AND FOUND ONE OF HIS FELLOW SERVANTS, WHICH OWED HIM AN HUNDRED PENCE: AND HE LAID HANDS ON HIM, AND TOOK HIM BY THE THROAT, SAYING, PAY ME THAT THOU OWEST. AND HIS FELLOW SERVANT FELL DOWN AT HIS FEET, AND BESOUGHT HIM, SAYING, HAVE PATIENCE WITH ME, AND I WILL PAY THEE ALL.

(Matthew 18.28–29)

The Good Shepherd

Jesus as the Good Shepherd
God's care of the Israelites in the Old Testament is often compared to a shepherd looking after his sheep. Jesus calls himself the Good Shepherd. Above, a Roman statue of a shepherd boy.

Jesus told the people: "I am the good shepherd. And the good shepherd will risk his life for every single one of his sheep. Someone who is only a hired hand, paid to look after sheep, does not really care what happens to them. If he sees a wolf coming, he forgets about the sheep and runs away.

"But the good shepherd knows every one of his sheep, and his flock all know and trust him, just as my Father knows me and I know my Father. I will lay down my life for my sheep. And I have many other sheep, who have not yet joined my flock. I must bring them into the flock, too. They will listen to my call, so that there will be just one flock and one shepherd to look after them."

The people who heard these words were divided in their opinions. Some said that these were the words of someone possessed by demons. "Why listen to him?" they asked.

But others said: "He cannot be possessed. Could a demon perform miracles and open the eyes of men who have always been blind?"

> I AM THE GOOD SHEPHERD, AND KNOW MY SHEEP, AND AM KNOWN OF MINE. AS THE FATHER KNOWETH ME, EVEN SO KNOW I THE FATHER: AND I LAY DOWN MY LIFE FOR THE SHEEP. AND OTHER SHEEP I HAVE, WHICH ARE NOT OF THIS FOLD....
>
> (John 10.14–16)

The Lost Son

Lost and Found
Three parables in Luke's gospels have the theme of something lost and then found. The lost sheep is found because of the love and care shown by the shepherd; the lost coin is found through the owner's careful sweeping through her house; and the lost son is welcomed home by his father.

The Pharisees and religious teachers were outraged to see Jesus surrounded by people they thought were sinners. So Jesus told them another story.

"There was once a man who had two sons," he began. "The younger son asked for his share of the family inheritance. The father gave this to him, and the young man set off for a faraway land. There he squandered all his inheritance on wild living. To make matters worse, there was a famine in the land. When he had no money left at all, the young man got a job feeding pigs. He was so hungry that he would gladly have eaten all the pig-food himself.

"At last the young man came to his senses. 'Here I am starving,' he said to himself, 'while at home my father's servants have more than enough food. I will go back, and perhaps my father will take me on as his servant.' With that he set off.

"The young man's father saw him coming from a long way off. He ran to his son, threw his arms around him and kissed him. The son said, 'Father, I have sinned against heaven and against you. I am not worthy to be called your son.' But the father told his servants: 'Bring fresh clothes! Kill the fattened calf for a feast!'

"Later, the older son came back from working in the fields and heard music and dancing. He asked what was going on, and learned that his brother had returned. He was angry about the feast and refused to go in. Finding his father, he said to him: 'All these years I have slaved away and always obeyed you. But you never gave me even a young goat to have as a feast with my friends. And now that your son who has squandered your money has come back, you kill the fattened calf for him!'

"'My son,' his father replied. 'You are always with me, and everything I have is yours. It was right to celebrate, for your brother was dead and is alive again. He was lost and has been found.'"

SON, THOU ART EVER WITH ME, AND ALL THAT I HAVE IS THINE. IT WAS MEET THAT WE SHOULD MAKE MERRY, AND BE GLAD: FOR THIS THY BROTHER WAS DEAD, AND IS ALIVE AGAIN; AND WAS LOST, AND IS FOUND.

(Luke 15.31–32)

243

The Lost Coin

LUKE 15.8

Jesus said to his listeners, "Suppose a woman has ten silver coins and loses one. She would not just forget about the lost coin and make do with the other nine. No, she would light a lamp, sweep the house carefully and search every corner until she found the lost coin. And when she found it, she would invite all her friends to celebrate and share her happiness at finding it.

"In the same way," Jesus said, "the angels in heaven celebrate over one single sinner who repents."

The Lost Sheep

The Pharisees and teachers of law complained that Jesus welcomed sinners and ate with them. Jesus knew what they were thinking, and told this parable to the crowds who listened to him.

"If a shepherd has a hundred sheep and one goes missing, would he just forget about the lost sheep? No, he would leave the other ninety-nine sheep in the field and go and search for the lost one. And when he found the lost sheep, he would happily put it over his shoulders and carry it home. Then he would call all his friends and neighbours together to celebrate and share his happiness at finding the sheep that was lost."

"In the same way," Jesus said, "there is more happiness in heaven about one sinner who repents than about ninety-nine good people who have never done anything really wrong in the whole of their lives."

244

AND WHEN HE HATH FOUND IT, HE LAYETH IT ON HIS SHOULDERS, REJOICING. AND WHEN HE COMETH HOME, HE CALLETH TOGETHER HIS FRIENDS AND NEIGHBOURS, SAYING UNTO THEM, REJOICE WITH ME; FOR I HAVE FOUND MY SHEEP WHICH WAS LOST.

(Luke 15.5–6 *See also* Matthew 18.12)

The True Vine

I AM THE VINE, YE ARE THE BRANCHES: HE THAT ABIDETH IN ME, AND I IN HIM, THE SAME BRINGETH FORTH MUCH FRUIT: FOR WITHOUT ME YE CAN DO NOTHING.

(John 15.5)

Jesus said: "I am the true vine, and my Father is the gardener. He cuts off all the branches that do not have any fruit and prunes those with grapes so that they will produce even more. But the good branches can only produce fruit if they stay attached to the stem.

"I am the vine and you are the branches. If you stay with me, you will be strong and be like a branch with fruit. But without me you can do nothing. If you cut yourself off from me, you will be like a branch that withers and dries up.

Withered branches are picked up, thrown on the fire and burned. But if you listen to my words and stay with me, you can ask for whatever you wish and it will be given to you.

"If you show yourselves to be my disciples, you will produce much fruit. I love you just as my Father loves me. No one can show greater love than by giving up his life for his friends. You are all my friends, and if you do as I teach you, you will produce plentiful fruit for the vine. So my command is this: love each other as I love you."

The Sower of Seeds

A crowd gathered at the Sea of Galilee to hear Jesus speak. Jesus climbed into a boat and pushed it out into the lake, so that everyone could see and hear him.

"A farmer went out to sow seeds," Jesus began. "As he scattered the seeds, some fell on the path and birds pecked them up. Others fell on rocky ground. Seedlings sprang up quickly there, but because the soil was thin, they soon died in the hot sun. Some seeds fell among thorns, which choked the seedlings as they grew. And some seeds fell on good soil, where they grew tall and produced a wonderful harvest of grain."

Later, the disciples asked Jesus what his story meant. "The seeds stand for the words of God," Jesus replied. "Some people have hard hearts, like the hard path. When God's message comes to them, Satan swoops down and snatches it away. Others are delighted to hear the words, but they are like rocky ground and the delight does not last. At the first sign of trouble, they ignore the message. Others hear, but let their own worries and desires act like thorns to destroy God's words. But people who have good hearts act like the good soil. They listen to the message and act on it, producing a wonderful harvest for God."

MATTHEW 13.3–23

The Wise and Foolish Builders

MATTHEW 7.24

Jesus said: "Everyone who listens to me and puts my words into practice is like the wise man who built his house on solid rock. The rains came down, the rivers flooded and storms beat against his house, but it did not fall because it stood on rock.

"But those of you who hear my words and do not put them into practice are like the foolish man who built his house on sand. The rains came down, the rivers flooded and storms beat against his house and it soon fell down with a great crash."

The Rich Young Man

The needle's eye
A needle's eye was a small door in a city gate that allowed people to go in and out of the city at night, when the main gate was closed. It would be a very tight squeeze for a camel to get through.

One day, when Jesus was out walking with his disciples, a young man of great wealth came up and asked: "Master, what must I do to gain eternal life?"

"You must obey God's commandments," Jesus told him. "Do not murder, do not commit adultery, do not worship idols, do not steal or give a false account of things, always honour your father and mother and love your neighbour."

The young man said that he had always followed these rules, but was there anything else he needed to do?

"If you want to be perfect," Jesus replied, "you must sell all your possessions and give the money to the poor. Then you can come and follow me." The young man was sad when he heard this, because he was very rich and did not want to give everything away.

"It is hard for the rich to enter the kingdom of heaven," Jesus told his disciples. "Indeed, it is easier for a camel to go through the eye of a needle than it is for a rich man to enter God's kingdom."

The disciples were puzzled when they heard this. "Who then can be saved?" they asked.

"With God, all things are possible," Jesus replied. "When the Son of Man sits on his glorious throne, you who have followed me will also sit on twelve thrones. Everyone who has given things up for my sake will receive a hundred times as much and will gain eternal life in the world to come."

> IT IS EASIER FOR A CAMEL TO GO THROUGH THE EYE OF A NEEDLE, THAN FOR A RICH MAN TO ENTER INTO THE KINGDOM OF GOD. AND THEY WERE ASTONISHED OUT OF MEASURE, SAYING AMONG THEMSELVES, WHO THEN CAN BE SAVED?
>
> (Mark 10.25–26)

246

Jesus on his Throne
Christians believe that on the day of judgement, we shall all stand before the throne of God and Jesus will separate those who will enter heaven and those who will be sent for ever to the desolation of hell.

The Rich Fool

A man in the crowd called out to Jesus: "Master, tell my brother to share his inheritance with me."

Jesus did not want to judge between brothers. "Make sure you are not being greedy," he told the man. "Worldly possessions are of no importance. This story will show you what I mean:

'One year a rich farmer had a bumper harvest. His workers gathered more grain than the farmer could store, and so he decided to pull down his barns and build bigger ones. The farmer was pleased with himself. 'Now I have enough grain to last me for years,' he said. 'I can take life easy and enjoy myself.'

'But God said to him: 'You fool! Tonight your life will be taken away from you, and who will get all you stored up for yourself?'

"This is what will happen to those who think only about getting rich instead of serving God," Jesus said.

LUKE 12.16–20

Zacchaeus the Tax Collector

LUKE 19.1–10

A large crowd turned out to welcome Jesus when he arrived in Jericho. Among them was the chief tax collector, a rich man named Zacchaeus. He wanted to see Jesus but, as he was a short man, he had trouble seeing over the heads of the crowd. So he ran ahead and climbed a tree to get a better view.

As Jesus walked under the tree, he looked up and said to the tax collector: "Come down, Zacchaeus. I would like to stay at your house today." The tax collector was overjoyed that Jesus had chosen his house and climbed down at once. The people nearby began to mutter: "Why is Jesus staying with Zaccheus? He will be the guest of a crook."

Hearing this, Zacchaeus spoke up. "Lord," he said, "Here and now I give half of my possessions to the poor. And if I have ever cheated anyone, I promise to pay them back four times the amount." Jesus said: "This man, too, is a son of Abraham. And I have come to find and save those who were lost."

247

The Widow's Offering

LUKE 21.1–4

One day, after Jesus had been teaching in the temple court, he watched people making their offerings. Many rich people put lots of silver coins into the collection bowls. Then a poor widow came along and put in two small copper coins, which were not worth much.

Jesus called his disciples over and told them what he had just seen. "The poor widow put more into the collection bowl than any of the others," he said. "The rich people gave only a tiny part of their wealth, but the widow put in all the money she had to live on."

Poor widows
Unless they remarried, widows had no place in society. Without a husband to support them, they were often poor and ignored by people. Jesus showed them special concern.

The Three Servants

A man had to go away on a long journey. So he called his three servants and asked them to look after his money while he was away. He divided it between them according to how well he thought they would manage it. He gave five talents of money to the first servant, two talents to the second, and one talent to the third. Then he left on his journey.

The servant who had five talents put the money to work and used it in such a way that it soon doubled. The one with the two talents did the same. But the servant who was given only one talent buried it.

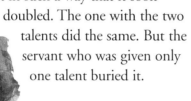

When the man returned from his journey, the servant with five talents proudly presented his master with five more coins. The man was delighted and praised his servant. "You are a good and faithful servant," he said. "You have done well with a few things, so from now on I will put you in charge of many things."

Then the servant with two talents showed that he had made two more. "You too are a good and faithful servant," the man said. "You have done well with a few things, so from now on I will put you in charge of many things."

Finally it was the turn of the servant who had been given one talent. "Master," he said, "I know that you are a hard man, eager to make as much money as you can. So I didn't dare risk your money, but hid it in a hole in the ground. Now you can have back what is yours."

This made the man very angry. "You lazy good-for-nothing!" he said to the third servant. "If you knew I wanted to make as much money as I could, you should have put my money in the bank. At least then I would have had it back with interest." With that the man took the single talent and gave it to the servant with the ten coins. "Those who have much will be given more," the man said, "and they will be even better off. Those who have little will have even less, because the little they have will be taken from them. Throw out that useless servant!"

We must make the most of whatever God gives us.

Taxes for Caesar

The chief priests and teachers of the law sent spies to Jesus, hoping to catch him out by getting him to say something unlawful. If he did, they would be able to hand him over to the Roman governor.

Pretending to be honest men, the spies questioned Jesus. "Teacher," one of them said, "we know that you preach about the ways of God and that you always speak the truth. So please tell us, is it right for us to pay taxes to Caesar or not?"

Jesus saw through these men and knew that they were trying to trap him. "Whose head and name appear on a denarius coin?" he asked them.

"Why, Caesar's," they replied.

"Then give to Caesar whatever is Caesar's, and to God whatever is God's," said Jesus. At that the spies fell silent, because they knew that these words told the truth and were not against the law.

Coins for Taxes
A Roman coin with the head of Emperor Hadrian and a Jewish coin of 134 CE, showing a temple.

LUKE 20.21–25

The Dishonest Steward

There was once a rich man who discovered that the steward who managed his business had been wasting his money. So the rich man called the steward in. "You cannot work for me any longer," the man said. "You will have to go. But before you leave, I want you to give me a full account of my business."

The steward had no idea what to do, now that he had lost his job. He was not strong enough for hard work and was ashamed to beg. So he thought up a plan that would make him popular with other tradespeople. He called in all those who were in debt to his master and asked them how much they owed.

"Eight hundred gallons of olive oil," said the first debtor. "Take your bill," said the steward," and change it to four hundred gallons."

The second debtor said he owed a thousand bushels of wheat.

"Take your pen quickly and change it to eight hundred bushels of wheat," said the steward.

When the master went through the accounts, he praised the dishonest steward for being so clever and for using his intelligence.

Jesus told this story to make people think about money and wealth. "Those who can be trusted with little can also be trusted with a lot," Jesus said. "And those who cheat in little ways also cheat in big ways. If you cannot be trusted with worldly wealth, who will trust you with true riches? No one can serve two masters at the same time, so you cannot be a slave to both God and money."

The Pharisees, who were listening to these words, sneered, because they loved money. "God can see into your hearts," Jesus told them, "and he hates the things that people like you value most highly."

AND THE LORD COMMENDED THE UNJUST STEWARD, BECAUSE HE HAD DONE WISELY: FOR THE CHILDREN OF THIS WORLD ARE IN THEIR GENERATION WISER THAN THE CHILDREN OF LIGHT.

(Luke 16.8)

THE LITTLE CHILDREN

AND THEY
BROUGHT YOUNG
CHILDREN TO HIM,
THAT HE SHOULD
TOUCH THEM: AND
HIS DISCIPLES
REBUKED THOSE
THAT BROUGHT
THEM. BUT WHEN
JESUS SAW IT, HE
WAS MUCH
DISPLEASED, AND
SAID UNTO THEM,
SUFFER THE LITTLE
CHILDREN TO COME
UNTO ME, AND
FORBID THEM NOT:
FOR OF SUCH IS THE
KINGDOM OF GOD.

(Mark 10.13–14
See also Matthew 18,
Luke 9.47)

M any of the people who believed in Jesus brought their babies and small children to him. They wanted him to place his hands on them and pray for them. When his disciples saw this, they grumbled at the parents because they thought they were taking up their master's valuable time.

But Jesus thought differently. "Let the little children come to me and do not turn them away," he said, "for the kingdom of God belongs to people like these children. Anyone who will not receive God's kingdom like a young child will never enter it."

Then he took the children in his arms, blessed them and said: "Whoever welcomes one of these children in my name also welcomes me. And whoever welcomes me also welcomes the one who sent me."

Martha, Mary and Lazarus

When Jesus and his disciples passed through the village of Bethany, near Jerusalem, a friend of Jesus named Martha welcomed them into her home. She wanted to make a special meal for her visitors and made herself busy getting the food ready.

While Martha worked hard, her sister Mary sat at the feet of Jesus and listened to every word he had to say. Before long, Martha became annoyed that her sister was not helping her. "Lord, my sister has left me with all the work," she said. "Please will you tell her to help me?"

But Jesus replied: "Martha, Martha, you are worried about many things, including your household chores. But Mary has chosen something more important. She is listening to what I have to say and no one can take that away from her."

> BUT MARTHA WAS CUMBERED ABOUT MUCH SERVING, AND CAME TO HIM, AND SAID, LORD, DOST THOU NOT CARE THAT MY SISTER HATH LEFT ME TO SERVE ALONE? BID HER THEREFORE THAT SHE HELP ME. AND JESUS ANSWERED AND SAID UNTO HER, MARTHA, MARTHA, THOU ART CAREFUL AND TROUBLED ABOUT MANY THINGS.
> (Luke 10.40–41)

Jewish burial
When a person died, the eyes were closed and the body washed and wrapped in cloth. It was carried on a stretcher to a burial place, often a cave. A large stone was rolled across to cover the opening of the cave. The bones of a dead person were moved to an "ossuary", a stone or wooden chest (above), about a year after the person had died.

Some time later, after Jesus had left Bethany, Martha and Mary were very troubled. Their brother Lazarus had fallen gravely ill. So the sisters sent a message to Jesus, asking for his help. When Jesus heard the news that Lazarus was so ill, he said to his disciples: "This sickness will not end in death, but is for the glory of God and God's son."

Rather surprisingly, Jesus did not rush back to Bethany, but two days later he told the disciples: "Our friend Lazarus has fallen asleep. I must go now to wake him up."

The disciples replied that surely there was no need to hurry, since sleep was usually the best cure. Then Jesus told them that it was no ordinary sleep. "Lazarus is dead," he explained. "But it was good that I was not there, because this will help you believe in me. Let us hurry to him now."

By the time Jesus arrived in Bethany, Lazarus had been in his tomb for four days. Many friends and neighbours had come to comfort Martha and Mary and to mourn their dead brother with them. Before Jesus had even entered the village, Martha rushed out to meet him, while Mary stayed at home with the mourners. "If only you had been here," Martha said, "my brother would not have died."

"Your brother will rise again," said Jesus. "For those who believe in me will never die. Do you believe this?"

"Yes, Lord," Martha replied. "I believe that you are the Christ, the Son of God." Then she ran home and told her sister Mary that Jesus had come and wanted to speak to her.

When the other mourners saw Mary leaving the house in a great hurry, they followed her, thinking that she was going to her brother's tomb. But she rushed to Jesus, knelt at his feet, and wept. "Lord, if you had been here, my brother would not have died," she said. Jesus was deeply moved by her tears and he too wept.

The raising of Lazarus
Lazarus had been dead for four days when Jesus asked Mary to show him the rock tomb in which he had been laid. Jesus then raised Lazarus to life and said: "Unbind him and let him go." Right, this fresco of Lazarus by Giotto (1266–1337) is from the church of St Francis in Assisi, Italy.

Then Jesus and all the mourners went to the tomb where Lazarus was buried. It was a cave with a large stone blocking the entrance. "Take the stone away," Jesus said.

"But Lord," Martha said, "my brother has been dead for four days. His body will be decaying."

"Did I not tell you that if you believed, you would see the glory of God?" Jesus reminded her. So they rolled away the stone. Then Jesus looked up to heaven and said: "Father, I know that you always hear me. I am doing this to prove to these people that sent me."

Then Jesus called in a loud voice: "Lazarus, come out!" The dead man came walking out of the tomb. He was wrapped in a shroud, and a cloth covered his face. "Take off those grave clothes," Jesus said, "and let him go home."

Many of the people who had seen Jesus perform miracles now believed in him. Some of them went and told the Pharisees how Lazarus had risen from the dead. But the Pharisees and chief priests did not want the people to put their faith in Jesus, because they feared they would lose their own authority and the Romans would close their temple.

From that time on, many people in Jerusalem were plotting to have Jesus arrested and killed.

Jesus Rides into Jerusalem

Palm Sunday
Excited crowds waved palm branches and spread them across the road in front of Jesus as he rode into Jerusalem on a donkey. Above, palm leaves were symbols of triumph and rejoicing.

Jesus and his disciples were travelling to Jerusalem. Before reaching the city, they stopped near a village on the Mount of Olives. Jesus sent two of his disciples on ahead. "When you get to the village," he told them, "you will find a donkey and her foal. Untie them and bring them back to me. If anyone asks what you are doing, say that the Lord needs them." The disciples went and fetched the donkey and her foal and spread cloaks over the donkey's back for Jesus to sit on.

Many people had heard that Jesus was on his way to Jerusalem, and crowds gathered all along the road. Some onlookers spread their cloaks on the road. Others cut palm leaves from the trees and threw them along the way. As the procession passed, people shouted:

"Hosanna to the Son of David! Blessed is the one who comes in the name of the Lord! Blessed is the King of Israel! Hosanna in the highest!"

When Jesus finally entered Jerusalem, the townsfolk asked each other, "Who is this?" And the crowds who were with him answered: "This is Jesus, the prophet from Nazareth!"

AND A VERY GREAT MULTITUDE SPREAD THEIR GARMENTS IN THE WAY; OTHERS CUT DOWN BRANCHES FROM THE TREES, AND STRAWED THEM IN THE WAY.

(Matthew 21.8
See also Mark 11.9, Luke 19.29–38, John 12.13)

THE TRADERS IN THE TEMPLE

When Jesus reached the temple in Jerusalem, he was horrified by what he saw. The courts around the temple, which should have been a calm place for religious discussion, were full of noisy people doing business. Many traders and moneylenders had set up their stalls. Some were buying and selling cattle, sheep or doves, while others sat at tables shouting and arguing as they bargained or exchanged money.

Jesus was furious that his Father's house had been turned into such a rowdy place. So he made a whip out of rope and drove all the traders out of the temple area, along with their animals. He cleared the benches of the dealers selling doves. Then he overturned the moneylenders' tables, scattering their coins everywhere.

"Get all your goods and animals out of here!" Jesus shouted. "How dare you turn my Father's house into this market? It is supposed to be a peaceful house of prayer for all nations, but you have turned it into a den of thieves!"

When the traders had been

Moneychangers
Someone in this profession converted foreign money into Jewish coinage, the only kind in which temple taxes could be paid. Above, carving of a moneychanger with a bag of coins.

255

The temple courtyard
Left, a reconstruction of Herod's temple. All four gospels relate a dramatic scene in which Jesus drove the traders and moneychangers out of the temple courtyard (the court of the Gentiles, left.) There, merchants were allowed to sell animals needed for sacrifice and moneychangers did business. Jesus may have been angry because the noisy merchants had set up their stalls "out of bounds" in the colonnades.

chased away, the people who had come with Jesus stayed in the temple to hear him speak. Blind and lame people came to the temple and he healed them. They saw the miraculous things that Jesus was doing, and they believed in him. But the chief priests and teachers of the law who heard and saw all this were very worried by his popularity. The more the crowds loved Jesus, the more they feared him. "We must find a way to arrest this man and silence him for ever," they whispered.

AND JESUS WENT INTO THE TEMPLE OF GOD,
AND CAST OUT ALL THEM THAT SOLD AND
BOUGHT IN THE TEMPLE, AND OVERTHREW
THE TABLES OF THE MONEYCHANGERS, AND
THE SEATS OF THEM THAT SOLD DOVES, AND
SAID UNTO THEM, IT IS WRITTEN, MY HOUSE
SHALL BE CALLED THE HOUSE OF PRAYER; BUT
YE HAVE MADE IT A DEN OF THIEVES.

(Matthew 21.12–13
See also Mark11.15, Luke 19.45–46,
John 2.14–16)

THE SINFUL WOMAN IS FORGIVEN

258

A Pharisee named Simon invited Jesus to have dinner at his house. While Jesus was there, a woman who had led a sinful life came and knelt beside the dinner table. The woman began to weep, and soon her tears flowed down on Jesus's bare feet. She had brought with her a jar of perfume, and as she gently wiped his feet dry with her hair, the woman kissed his feet and put perfume on them.

When he saw this, the Pharisee wondered if this man Jesus really could be a prophet. "How can he allow such a sinful woman to touch him?" he asked himself.

"Simon, answer me this," Jesus said. "Imagine that one man owes a moneylender five hundred silver coins and another man owes fifty. The moneylender, seeing that they cannot pay, cancels both debts. Which man, do you think, will love the moneylender more?"

"The one who owed him more, I suppose," the Pharisee replied.

"You have judged correctly," said Jesus. Then he turned towards the woman and said to Simon: "When I came into your house, you gave me no water for my feet, but this woman washed my feet with her tears and dried them with her hair. You did not greet me with a kiss, but this woman has not stopped kissing my feet. You did not put oil on my head, but she has put perfume on my feet. Her many sins have been forgiven, because she has shown so much love."

Then Jesus said to the woman: "Your faith has saved you. Go in peace."

Judas Plots Against Jesus

Precious perfumes
*In the hot, dry
climate of the Bible
lands, oil with added
perfume was rubbed
into the body to
soothe the skin.
Perfume was a luxury
and was kept in
expensive bottles and
containers.
Left, wall painting of
a young Roman
woman holding a
perfume bottle.*

259

Jesus went on teaching the people and every day the crowds listening to him grew larger. Many had heard how Jesus had raised Lazarus from the dead. News of this miracle was spread further by the people who had seen Jesus perform other miracles. Now more and more people wanted to hear him speak and watch him heal.

The chief priests and teachers of the law became ever more concerned at this growing popularity. "It is doing us great harm," they said. "Soon the whole world will follow this Jesus. We must silence him." They tried to think up ways to have Jesus arrested, but none of the traps they set worked. Even the spies who tried to get Jesus to say something that would upset the Roman rulers could not catch him out.

Two days before the feast of Passover, the High Priest Caiaphas called a meeting of the Jewish ruling council. When they were all assembled, the council members vowed to arrest Jesus and kill him. "But we must wait until after Passover," they decided, "or we will risk a riot among the people."

The priests did not know it then, but they were about to get help from a close follower of Jesus. Judas Iscariot was one of the twelve disciples. He was also a greedy man. Only a few days earlier, he had had a disagreement with Jesus. Martha, Mary and Lazarus had given a dinner in Jesus's honour at their house in Bethany. That evening, Mary had anointed him with valuable perfume, which Judas claimed was a foolish waste of money. "Why was that perfume not sold and the money given to the poor?" Judas asked. He had not said this out of love for the poor, but because he was the keeper of the disciples' money, to which he had often helped himself.

"This woman has done a beautiful thing," Jesus told Judas. "And it is good that she has done it now, because I will not always be with you." For Jesus knew that he was going to be betrayed.

Judas was sure that he could make money out of a deal with the priests. So he went to Caiaphas and offered his services. "How much are you willing to pay if I hand Jesus over to you?" he asked. Caiaphas and the other chief priests were delighted to find one of the twelve disciples ready to betray his master. They offered him thirty pieces of silver money.

"You can have the money now," they said, as they counted it out and handed it over to Judas. "All you have to do is to let us know where to find your master, at a time when he won't be surrounded by crowds of followers, so he can be arrested quietly."

From that moment on, Judas watched out for an opportunity to keep his side of the bargain and betray Jesus to the authorities.

THE LAST SUPPER

On the first day of the Feast of Unleavened Bread, Jesus asked his disciples Peter and John to make preparations for a special Passover supper.

"Where is the meal to take place?" the disciples asked.

"Go into the city," Jesus told them. "There you will meet a man carrying a jug of water. Follow him to see which house he goes into. Ask the owner of the house to show you his guest room. Tell him that your master wants to hold a Passover supper there, with his disciples. The man will take you upstairs to a large room

ready for the occasion. There you will find all that you need to prepare the Passover meal."

Peter and John did as Jesus said. They found the room and prepared the Passover supper. In the evening Jesus arrived and sat down with his twelve disciples. Just before the meal was served, Jesus stood up, poured water into a basin, took the towel that had been laid ready for a servant and began to wash the feet of his disciples. He knew that he would soon be leaving this world, and by this humble act he wanted to show his friends how much he loved them.

HE RISETH FROM SUPPER, AND LAID ASIDE HIS GARMENTS; AND TOOK A TOWEL AND GIRDED HIMSELF. AFTER THAT HE POURETH WATER INTO A BASIN, AND BEGAN TO WASH THE DISCIPLES' FEET, AND TO WIPE THEM WITH THE TOWEL WHEREWITH HE WAS GIRDED.

(John 13.4–5)

When it came to Simon Peter's turn to have his feet washed, he told Jesus that he could not allow him to wash his feet like a servant. Jesus replied that the day would come when Peter would understand what he was doing. "Unless I wash your feet," Jesus said, "you cannot share what is going to happen to me."

Wishing to share everything with his Lord, Peter wanted him to wash his hands and face as well! "I need only wash your feet, for you are clean," Jesus said, "though this is not true of every one of you." Jesus said this because he knew that one of the disciples would betray him, and he knew who it would be.

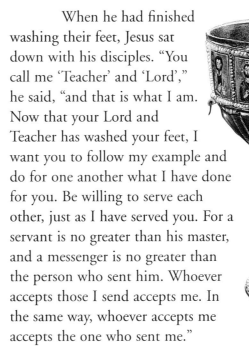

When he had finished washing their feet, Jesus sat down with his disciples. "You call me 'Teacher' and 'Lord'," he said, "and that is what I am. Now that your Lord and Teacher has washed your feet, I want you to follow my example and do for one another what I have done for you. Be willing to serve each other, just as I have served you. For a servant is no greater than his master, and a messenger is no greater than the person who sent him. Whoever accepts those I send accepts me. In the same way, whoever accepts me accepts the one who sent me."

Later, while they were eating their meal, Jesus spoke again to his disciples. "One of you will betray me to my enemies," he said. The disciples were horrified and stared at each other in disbelief and dismay. Surely there couldn't be a spy among them? Who could he mean? Each of the twelve said in turn: "Lord, surely it cannot be me! Who is it?"

"It is the one who dips bread into the bowl with me," Jesus replied. "The Son of Man will go, just as it was written. But for the one who betrays him, it would be better if he had never been born." Then Jesus dipped a piece of bread into the bowl

Holy Communion
Jesus and his disciples met to eat the Passover meal — a meal that became the most memorable of all meals, the Last Supper. The Last Supper is remembered by Christians as the occasion when Jesus took bread and wine and told his disciples that by these gifts, he would be both a memory and a living reality to his followers for ever more. The death of Jesus is remembered as a sacrifice that sealed a new covenant, or agreement, between God and his people. By sharing bread and wine during the Communion service, Christians remember Jesus's death and resurrection. Above, a chalice, or Communion cup, from Constantinople, used to hold wine for the service.

AND AS THEY DID EAT, JESUS TOOK BREAD, AND BLESSED, AND BRAKE IT, AND GAVE IT TO THEM, AND SAID, TAKE, EAT: THIS IS MY BODY. AND HE TOOK THE CUP, AND WHEN HE HAD GIVEN THANKS, HE GAVE IT TO THEM: AND THEY ALL DRANK OF IT. AND HE SAID UNTO THEM, THIS IS MY BLOOD OF THE NEW TESTAMENT, WHICH IS SHED FOR MANY.

(Mark 14.22–24 *See also* Matthew 26.26–28, Luke 22.19–20, I Corinthians 11.24–25)

264

The Last Supper
A fresco by the Florentine painter Domenico Ghirlandaio (1449–94). The scene is set in Renaissance Italy.

and gave it to Judas Iscariot. As Judas took the bread, Jesus looked at him with great sadness and said: "What you have planned to do, do quickly." Judas knew that Jesus had seen Satan in his heart. He quickly left the table and slipped off into the night.

The other disciples did not understand what Jesus had meant when he spoke to Judas Iscariot. They thought that perhaps he had been telling Judas to go out and give money to the poor, since Judas was in charge of their money. When he had gone, Jesus took the flat (unleavened) bread, gave thanks to God and broke it. Then he gave some to each of his disciples and said: "This bread is my body, which is given for you." Then Jesus took a cup of wine, gave thanks to God and passed it to his disciples. "Drink from this cup," Jesus said. "This wine is my blood, which is poured out for you. I will not drink the fruit of the vine again until the

day that I share it with you in my Father's kingdom."

When the supper was over, the disciples sang a hymn before going out to the Mount of Olives. On their way, Jesus tried to prepare them for what he knew was soon about to happen. "I will not be with you for much longer," he said.

But where are you going, Lord?" Simon Peter asked.

"Where I am going, you cannot follow now," Jesus replied. "But you will follow later."

"Why can't I come with you now?" Peter asked. "I am ready to go to prison, or even die for you." The others all said the same thing.

Then Jesus looked at Simon Peter and said: "Tonight, before the cock crows, you will say three times that you do not know me."

"Never!" Peter protested. "I will never do such a thing. I would rather die than disown you."

IN THE GARDEN
OF GETHSEMANE

J esus and his disciples reached Gethsemane, a peaceful garden near the Mount of Olives. There Jesus told the disciples to rest, while he went to pray.

Jesus took Peter, James and John with him. "Stay close and keep watch," he told them. "My heart is almost breaking and my soul is filled with sorrow." Then he went a little farther, knelt down and prayed: "Father, take this torment from me. But if this cup may not pass away, I will drink from it."

265

AND HE WAS
WITHDRAWN FROM
THEM ABOUT A
STONE'S CAST, AND
KNEELED DOWN, AND
PRAYED, SAYING,
FATHER, IF THOU BE
WILLING, REMOVE
THIS CUP FROM ME:
NEVERTHELESS NOT
MY WILL, BUT THINE
BE DONE.

(Luke 22.41–42
See also Matthew 26.39
Mark 14.36)

As he spoke, Judas Iscariot came rushing toward them, leading a group of men armed with swords and clubs. They were the guards of the chief priests, who had been sent to arrest Jesus. Judas had led them to where he knew Jesus would be, for he often went there to pray. To make sure the guards arrested the right man, he had arranged a special signal – a kiss.

Judas went straight up to Jesus. "Greetings, master," he said, and kissed him.

"Judas, are you betraying me with a kiss?" Jesus asked. But before he could say any more, the guards rushed up and seized him. While the others stood stunned, Peter grabbed a sword and in his fury swung it at one of the guards, cutting off his ear. Jesus told him to put the sword down. "Those who draw the sword will die by the sword," he said. He touched the guard's wound and it was healed. "I could easily ask my Father to send an army of angels to fight for me," Jesus told his disciples. "But all this has been planned and is happening according to the scriptures."

The disciples knew that there was nothing they could do. They watched as the guards led Jesus away.

When Jesus returned to the three disciples, he found them asleep. He woke them up and told them that they must keep watch: "The spirit is willing, but the body is weak." He went away for a second time and prayed to God, and again when he returned, he found the three disciples asleep. This time he just left them and went to pray for a third time. When he had finished praying, he came back and woke Peter, James and John. "Why are you still sleeping?" Jesus asked. "Wake up! The hour has arrived. Here comes my betrayer."

"I Don't Know Him!"

The guards bound Jesus and led him to the house of Caiaphas, the High Priest. Peter followed at a distance and cautiously managed to make his way into the High Priest's courtyard. He was hoping to be able to find out what was going to happen to Jesus. Nobody seemed to take any notice of him, so, as it was a cold night, he sat down near the guards and warmed his hands by their fire.

A servant girl saw Peter there, and watched him closely by the firelight. Eventually she came up and pointed at Peter. "This man was a follower of Jesus!" she said. Peter denied it. "I don't know him!" he replied.

Shortly afterward, a man came up to Peter and asked: "Aren't you one of the disciples of that Jesus?"

"I am not," Peter replied. "I tell you, I don't know the man!"

About an hour later, while Jesus was being questioned inside the house, another man came up and accused Peter. "I saw you with him in the olive garden," the man said. "You are definitely one of his lot!"

"I don't know what you're talking about," Peter cried. "I don't even know the man!" Just as Peter finished saying these words, he heard a cock crow. At once he remembered what Jesus had told him: "Before the cock crows, you will say three times that you do not know me."

Filled with shame, Peter rushed out of the courtyard, weeping.

One the servants of the High Priest, being his kinsman whose ear Peter cut off, saith, Did not I see thee in the garden with him? Peter then denied again: and immediately the cock crew.

(John 18.26–27
See also
Matthew 26.69–75
Mark 14.66–72
Luke 22.59–60)

267

JESUS ON TRIAL BEFORE THE JEWISH RULING COUNCIL

The night that Jesus was arrested, the men guarding him treated him very badly. They insulted him and beat him. One of the men tied a blindfold on Jesus and several others took it in turns to hit him. "Come on," they jeered. "You are supposed to know everything, so tell us who hit you!"

Members of the Sanhedrin, the Jewish ruling council, had come together at the house of the Chief Priest, Caiaphas. At daybreak, just around the time when Peter disowned him in the courtyard outside, Jesus was brought before the council. The Jewish leaders and chief priests had been trying their utmost to find evidence against Jesus, so that they could sentence him to death. But none of the charges they made up could be proved, and although they presented many false witnesses, their statements were all different.

Finally, one man came forward and said: "We heard him say that he would destroy the temple of God and build another in three days without the help of human hands." Others made similar claims, and Caiaphas demanded to know if the prisoner denied this charge. Jesus remained silent.

This infuriated the high priest. "Then simply answer us this," he yelled at Jesus. "Are you Christ, the Son of God?"

"I am," Jesus replied. "And soon you will see me sitting at the right hand of my Father."

"Well, we don't need any more witnesses," Caiaphas told the council. "The man's just given us all the proof we need. He has insulted

Jesus is mocked
"Then some began to spit at him; they blindfolded him, struck him with their fists, and said, 'Prophesy!'"
Right, this fresco by Fra Angelico (1400–55) is in the convent of San Marco, Florence, Italy.

God with his blasphemy and deserves death. Is everyone agreed?" All the members of the council agreed with the High Priest. "Death!" they shouted with one voice. Jesus was dragged away to appear before Pontius Pilate, the Roman governor, because only he could pass the death sentence.

When Judas Iscariot heard that Jesus had been condemned to death, he realised what a terrible thing he had done. He had betrayed an innocent man through greed and he was overcome with feelings of guilt. His first thought was to return the money that the chief priests had given him. "Take your money back! I have sinned. I have betrayed an innocent man!" he cried out.

"What has that got to do with us?" one of the priests replied. "That's your responsibility."

Judas was so desperate that he threw the coins on the temple floor and ran off. As it was against the law to put blood money into the temple treasury, the chief priests decided to use the silver coins to buy a field to use as a cemetery for foreigners. They didn't give another thought to Judas, who went off to a lonely place and hanged himself.

THE TRIAL BEFORE THE ROMAN GOVERNOR

The leaders of the Jewish council had their guards drag Jesus to the palace of Pontius Pilate. The Roman governor looked at the prisoner before him. "What crime is this man accused of?" he asked.

"He is a troublemaker who encourages our people not to pay taxes to Caesar," a council member replied. "He also claims to be Christ, our king."

Pilate was not convinced by the charges, and certainly had no wish to get involved in Jewish council affairs. So he told the priests to judge Jesus by their own laws. "But we are not allowed to put anyone to death," they objected. "We would not have handed him over to you if he wasn't a criminal."

The Roman governor felt he had no choice but to question Jesus himself. "Are you the king of the Jews?" Pilate asked.

Jesus answered: "It is as you say. But my kingdom is not of this world. If it were, my armies would defend me and I would never have been arrested."

Pilate announced to the Jews that he could find no reason for charging the prisoner. But the chief priests were determined to have their way, so they stirred up the crowd they had mustered against the man from Galilee, who was causing trouble in Jerusalem. Soon there were shouts of "Crucify him!" When Pilate heard that Jesus was from Galilee, he had an idea.

All Galileans came under the jurisdiction of King Herod Antipas, who at that moment was in Jerusalem. So why not send Jesus to him? Then Herod could decide if the man were guilty or not.

Herod was pleased when Jesus was brought before him. He had heard all about his miracles and hoped that he would perform one for him. Herod asked many questions, but Jesus gave no answers. He would not reply to the accusations brought against him, not even when Herod's soldiers mocked and made fun of him. So Herod had no choice but to send Jesus back to Pilate.

Once more the Roman governor spoke to the Jews. "I have questioned this man and so has King Herod," Pilate said. "But we have found no proof of his guilt. As it is the custom to release one prisoner of your choice at your time of Passover, I am proposing to set Jesus free."

The crowds outside the governor's palace thought differently. The chief priests persuaded them to shout for another prisoner to be set free, and the roar soon went up: "Barabbas! We want Barabbas!" Although Barabbas had been found guilty of murder, the leaders were happy for him to go unpunished as long as Jesus was executed. Then the crowds started to chant: "Crucify Jesus! Crucify Jesus! Crucify him!"

Pontius Pilate did not know what to do. He felt that Jesus was innocent, but the man would not help his case by defending himself. Even Pilate's wife had warned him. She had sent a message saying that she had been told in a dream that the governor must not execute an innocent man. Pilate turned again to Jesus. "It is in my power to free you or to crucify you," he said.

"You have power over me only because God has given it to you," Jesus replied. "Those who handed me over to you are more guilty than you."

Pilate turned to the crowd. "This man has not been found guilty of any crime," he said. "I intend to punish him, then set him free."

"No, crucify him! Crucify him!" the crowd shouted.

"Do you want me to crucify your king?" Pilate asked.

"Our king is Caesar," one of the chief priests shouted. Pilate saw that he had no choice but to set Barabbas free and condemn Jesus. So he had a basin of water brought to him and he washed his hands in front of the crowd. "I am innocent of this man's blood," Pilate said. "The death of Jesus will be your responsibility."

Pilate had Jesus flogged. Some of his soldiers decided that they would have some fun and make Jesus look more like a proper king. They dressed him in a purple robe and put a crown of thorns on his head. "Hail to the King of the Jews!" they jeered.

Good Friday
Good Friday is a solemn day on which Christians recall the arrest, trial and crucifixion of Jesus by the Roman rulers of Jerusalem.
Above, in this detail from a French painting of the 1500s, Jesus is being forced to carry his cross. It is believed that he carried the cross along the Via Dolorosa, "the way of sorrows." The route is today marked by fourteen "Stations of the Cross" recalling the events of the first Good Friday.

271

MATTHEW 27,
MARK 15,
LUKE 23,
JOHN 18

The Crucifixion

The soldiers tore off the purple robe that they had put on Jesus, before hitting him to the ground with their sticks. Then they dragged him to his feet, threw his own clothes back on him and showed him the heavy wooden cross on which he was to die. Jesus was made to carry the cross himself to Golgotha, which means "place of the skull". This was the place outside the city walls of Jerusalem where criminals were executed.

A crowd of people followed Jesus, and many women mourned and cried for him. Jesus turned to them and said: "Daughters of Jerusalem, do not weep for me." Weakened by the floggings, he stumbled under the weight of the cross. The soldiers wanted to get on with their job, so they forced a passer-by to carry the cross for Jesus. When at last they reached Golgotha, the soldiers offered Jesus some wine mixed with myrrh, but he refused to drink. Then they stripped Jesus of his clothes and nailed his hands and feet to the cross. When they raised the cross up, Jesus said: "Father, forgive them, for they do not know what they are doing."

Two other men, both thieves, were crucified along with Jesus. One was put up to his left and the other to his right. Pontius Pilate had a sign put on the cross on which Jesus was nailed, which read: "Jesus of Nazareth, King of the Jews." The Jewish chief priests objected to this, but Pilate told his soldiers that the sign must stay. When they saw the inscription, some of spectators began to sneer at Jesus. "I thought you said you were going to destroy the temple and build it in three days," one mocked. "So why don't you just come down from the cross?"

"They say you have saved many people," another person shouted out, "so show us one of your miracles and save yourself!"

One of the two thieves also spoke to Jesus. "If you really are the Christ," the man said, "why don't you

Sacrificial Lamb
The lamb was an animal used by the Hebrews for sacrifices. The early Christians adopted it as a symbol of Christ's sacrifice; for this reason it is often shown with a cross (above). The Hebrews believed that all things depended on God, and it became the custom to offer as a sacrifice the first fruits of crops and the firstborn of flocks. This was a way to acknowledge that everything belongs to God. Christians believe the death of Jesus on the cross to be the ultimate sacrifice that rescues humans from sins and makes all other forms of sacrifice unnecessary.

The Crucified Christ

Crucifixion was regarded as the most degrading form of death and was agonizingly painful. Jesus's crucifixion has inspired many artists through the ages. Right, a crucifixion by Simone Martini (1285–1344), from Siena, Italy.

274

save yourself and us too?"

The other thief said: "That's no way to talk. Don't you fear God? We have been rightly punished and deserve to die. This man has done nothing wrong." Then he begged Jesus to remember him when he was in his kingdom. Jesus promised: "Today you will be with me in paradise."

Meanwhile, the soldiers who had nailed Jesus to the cross shared his clothes out among themselves. They even threw dice to try and win his robe. Nearby stood Jesus's mother, Mary Magdalene, and the disciple John. When Jesus saw his mother crying bitter tears, he said to his favorite disciple: "John, look after my mother." Then he spoke to both of them. "Mother, there is your son," he said to Mary, and to John he said: "This is your mother."

At midday the Sun stopped shining, and for three hours it was as dark as night. Then Jesus cried out in a loud voice: "My God, my God, why have you forsaken me?" Seeing this terrible suffering, a man standing

nearby soaked a sponge in cheap wine, placed it on a stick and held it up to Jesus. When he had drunk from the sponge, Jesus bowed his head and called out: "It is over. Father, I place my spirit in your hands." Then Jesus breathed his last.

At that moment the ground shook and the curtain in the temple of Jerusalem was torn in two. A Roman centurion standing near the cross looked up at Jesus and said: "Surely this man was the Son of God!"

When the soldiers came to take down the crosses, they broke the legs of the robbers to make sure they were dead. Seeing that Jesus looked dead already, one of the soldiers pierced his side with a spear instead.

AND IT WAS ABOUT THE SIXTH HOUR, AND THERE WAS DARKNESS OVER ALL THE EARTH UNTIL THE NINTH HOUR. AND THE SUN WAS DARKENED, AND THE VEIL OF THE TEMPLE WAS RENT IN THE MIDST. AND WHEN JESUS HAD CRIED WITH A LOUD VOICE, HE SAID, FATHER INTO THY HANDS I COMMEND MY SPIRIT: AND HAVING SAID THUS, HE GAVE UP THE GHOST.

(Luke 23.44–46 *See also* Matthew 27.45–50, Mark 15.33–37, John 19.28–30)

Jesus is Buried and Rises Again

Joseph of Arimathea was a wealthy and important man. Although he was a member of the Jewish ruling council, he admired Jesus and had secretly become his follower. Wanting to give Jesus a decent burial, he asked Pontius Pilate for permission to take the body away. Pilate was only too happy to agree. Nicodemus, a Pharisee who had also become a believer, came to help Joseph.

The two men lifted the body from the cross, washed it with a mixture of herbs and incense and wrapped it in strips of perfumed linen. They took the body to a nearby garden and placed it in a new tomb cut into the rock. Finally, they rolled a big stone in front of the entrance to the tomb.

Mary Magdalene and the other women had followed Joseph and Nicodemus and they wept as they watched from a distance. Many hours after the two men had left, the exhausted women returned home.

The Holy Sepulchre
Above, the entrance to the Church of the Holy Sepulchre in Jerusalem, believed to stand on the site of Calvary, or Golgotha, where Jesus was crucified and buried.

275

Sabbath

Sabbath lasts from dusk on Friday until dusk on Saturday. On this day pious Jews meet in a synagogue to pray and hear the Bible read and taught. There are many stories in the New Testament of Jesus teaching in the synagogue.
Above, an illustration from a 14th-century Spanish manuscript showing the interior of a synagogue.

Jesus's Friends

Right, a painting of Mary Magdalene, Mary, the mother of James, and Salome entering the tomb. "They saw a young man sitting on the right side, clothed in a long white garment; and they were affrighted. And he saith unto them, Be not affrighted: Ye seek Jesus of Nazareth, which was crucified: he is risen; he is not here." The painting is by the Sienese artist Duccio di Buoninsegna (c.1255–1319).

The next day was the Sabbath, a day of rest. When at last this was over, the women prepared a special mixture of spices and myrrh to anoint the body of Jesus. At dawn, just as the sun was rising, they hurried back to his tomb.

On their way, the women wondered how they would be able to move the heavy stone that blocked the entrance to the tomb. But when they reached it, they saw that the stone had been rolled away. Their first thought was that someone had stolen the body and Mary Magdalene rushed back to find the disciples.

Hearing that the tomb had been disturbed, Peter and John rushed there as fast as they could. When the two disciples reached the tomb, they went inside and found that it was empty. The strips of linen in which Jesus had been wrapped were lying there, and his burial cloth was neatly folded up. But his body was gone. The two disciples, confused and wondering what they should do, went back to their homes.

Mary Magdalene stayed outside the tomb and wept. When Peter and John had left, she went back to the entrance and looked inside the tomb. There she saw two shining angels where the body of Jesus had lain, one sitting at the head and the other at the foot. "Woman, why are you crying?" one of the angels asked.

"They have taken away my Lord," Mary replied, "and I don't know where they have put him."

"He is not here," the angel said, "because he has risen."

Just then Mary felt the presence of someone behind her. She turned round and saw a man standing there, and thought he must be a gardener. "Who are you looking for?" the stranger asked.

"Sir," Mary pleaded, "if you have taken him away, please tell me where to find him."

"Mary," the man said, and as soon as she heard him speak her name, Mary knew that it was Jesus.

"Master!" she cried out, and this time she wept tears of joy.

"Go and tell my disciples that I have risen," Jesus said. "I am returning to my Father and your Father, to my God and your God."

For the second time that morning, Mary ran to find the disciples. Now she had wonderful news: "I have seen the Lord!"

JESUS SAITH UNTO HER, WOMAN WHY WEEPEST THOU? WHOM SEEKEST THOU? SHE SUPPOSING HIM TO BE THE GARDENER, SAITH UNTO HIM, SIR, IF YOU HAVE BORNE HIM HENCE, TELL ME WHERE THOU HAST LAID HIM, AND I WILL TAKE HIM AWAY. JESUS SAITH UNTO HER, MARY. SHE TURNED HERSELF, AND SAITH UNTO HIM, RABBONI; WHICH IS TO SAY, MASTER.

(John 20.15–16. *See also* Matthew 28, Mark 16)

TWO FRIENDS MEET A STRANGER

O n the same day that Mary Magdalene saw the risen Jesus, Cleopas and a friend were walking home to their village of Emmaus. They were both followers of Jesus and had been in Jerusalem when their master was crucified. On the long walk home, the two men talked about the amazing and terrible things that had happened over the past few days. They were so caught up in their discussion that they scarcely noticed a stranger who had suddenly appeared beside them.

Seeing that they looked very sad, the stranger asked what they were talking about. The two men assumed that this man had just

arrived in the region, because otherwise he would surely know about Jesus, his trial and execution. "He was a great prophet," Cleopas told the stranger, "and we hoped that he was going to save Israel." They went on to tell the stranger about the empty tomb and the two angels that Mary had seen there.

As the three men walked on along the dusty road, the stranger said: "Did not Moses and the other prophets say that the Christ, the chosen one, had to suffer such tortures before entering his glory?"

It was almost evening when they reached Emmaus and the two friends, by now feeling happier, invited their new companion to stay and have supper with them. The stranger accepted their invitation and, when they sat down, he took the bread, gave thanks to God, broke it and shared it between them. It was only then that Cleopas and his friend

recognized the stranger at their table. It was Jesus! When the two men looked across the table again, Jesus had vanished. Now they knew why they had felt so happy on the road to Emmaus. They were so excited that they returned at once to Jerusalem. Bursting in on the eleven disciples, they told them with great joy that they had seen their Lord and broken bread with him.

Celebrating Easter
Decorated eggs represent new life and the joy of Christ's resurrection. Hot cross buns are traditionally eaten on Good Friday. Pretzels (brittle, twisted, salted biscuits) were first made in eastern Europe as a reward for children who had learned their prayers. They were shaped to represent the crossed arms of children praying. Many countries have special Easter breads or cakes.

Doubting Thomas

While the disciples were talking about their master and wondering if he really was alive, Jesus suddenly appeared among them and said: "Peace be with you!" At first the frightened disciples thought they had seen a ghost, but Jesus comforted them. "Look at my hands and feet," he said. "Touch my wounds and forget your doubts, for ghosts are not made of flesh and bones."

The disciples were overjoyed, yet they still found it hard to believe that Jesus had really come back from the dead. When he said he was hungry, they gave him a piece of grilled fish and watched him eat it. This made them forget their doubts.

Jesus tried to make the disciples understand that everything that had been written about him in the scriptures had to be fulfilled. The scriptures said that the Christ would suffer and rise from the dead on the third day. "You are witnesses of these events," Jesus told the disciples. "Just as my Father sent me, I am sending you." Then he breathed on the disciples and said: "Receive the Holy Spirit. If you forgive someone their sins, they will be forgiven."

After Jesus had gone, the disciples told one of their number, whose name was Thomas, about what had happened. Thomas had not been with them when Jesus appeared, and he found their story very hard to believe. "Unless I touch his wounds myself, I will not believe it," Thomas said.

A week later the disciples were all together again. Although they had locked the door because they lived in fear of the Jewish authorities, Jesus suddenly appeared among them and said, "Peace be with you!" Then he turned to Thomas and asked him to touch the wounds on his hands and feel the spear wound in his side. "Stop doubting," Jesus said, "and believe!"

Thomas no longer had any doubts. "My Lord and my God," he said, falling to his knees in worship.

"You believe in me because you have seen me," Jesus told Thomas. "Blessed are those who have not seen me and yet believe in me."

The Ascension

The disciples left Jerusalem and went back home to Galilee. One evening Peter decided to go fishing, as he had always done before Jesus chose him to become a disciple. James, John and Thomas went with Peter in his boat across the starlit Sea of Galilee.

The four disciples fished all night, but by dawn they had not made a single catch. They were just starting to row back when they saw a stranger standing on the shore. "Friends," the stranger called out to them, "haven't you caught any fish?"

"No, nothing tonight!" Peter shouted back across the waves.

"Throw your nets over the right side of the boat," the man called. "You will make a good catch."

The disciples followed his advice. Soon their nets were so full of fish that they could hardly haul them into the boat. John looked again at the stranger on the shore and suddenly realized who it was. "It is the Lord!" he cried. Hearing this, Peter snatched up his coat, jumped into the water and swam ashore. The others followed in the boat, towing their huge catch behind them.

On the shore, Jesus welcomed his friends with a warming breakfast. Fish were already grilling

Jesus and Peter
Jesus called Peter the "rock" because of his firm faith. When Jesus said he would give Peter the keys of the kingdom, he meant that Peter was to take a leading role in the Christian Church. According to tradition, Peter is said to have died in Rome by being crucified upside down, during the reign of Emperor Nero.

281

on a fire, and there was bread to go with them. "Put on some of the fish you have just caught, too," Jesus said. He took the bread and shared it out among them, then he shared out the fish. There was no need now for any of the disciples to ask who he was. This was the third time that Jesus had come to them since he had risen from the dead.

When they had finished eating, Jesus walked along the shore with Peter and asked him three times: "Simon Peter, do you love me?"

Each time Peter said: "Yes, Lord, you know that I love you."

"Then take care of my sheep for me," Jesus said. "Look after my people when I am gone."

Once again Jesus left his disciples. So it happened for forty days after he had risen. Jesus would suddenly appear among his friends and speak to them about the kingdom of God. One day he told them not to leave Jerusalem, but to wait for the gift his Father had promised. "Soon you will be baptized

with the Holy Spirit," Jesus said. "This will give you great power and you will be my witnesses in Jerusalem, in all Judea and Samaria, and throughout the whole world."

When he had spoken these words, Jesus was taken up into heaven before the disciples' very eyes. As they looked up and watched their Lord rise into the sky, a cloud hid him from their sight. Then suddenly they realized that two men dressed in white had appeared next to them. "Why are you standing there looking up to heaven?" one of the men asked. "Jesus, who has been taken away from you up into heaven, will one day come back in the same way that you have seen him depart."

AND HE LED THEM OUT AS FAR AS TO BETHANY, AND HE LIFTED UP HIS HANDS, AND BLESSED THEM. AND IT CAME TO PASS, WHILE HE BLESSED THEM, HE WAS PARTED FROM THEM, AND CARRIED UP INTO HEAVEN. AND THEY WORSHIPPED HIM, AND RETURNED TO JERUSALEM WITH GREAT JOY.

(Luke 24.50–52)

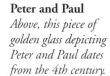

THE EARLY YEARS OF THE CHURCH

A secret sign
The word Paternoster *(Latin for "Our Father") is carved into this stone in a hidden form similar to a wordsearch that only a Christian would find.*

Peter and Paul
Above, this piece of golden glass depicting Peter and Paul dates from the 4th century.

The Acts of the Apostles – the fifth book of the New Testament – takes us on from the Ascension of Jesus and tells the story of the early years of the Christian Church. The Church began on the Jewish festival of Pentecost (what we now sometimes call Whitsun), fifty days after the death of Jesus. Jesus's close companions, the apostles (a word meaning "someone who is sent") were gathered together in one room in Jerusalem. Suddenly a mighty wind was heard rushing through the house and flickering tongues of fire hung over their heads – a sign that the Holy Spirit had come upon them. Amazingly, the apostles discovered that they could communicate their news in languages that foreigners recognized as their own.

After the day of Pentecost, the apostles became men with a mission: to preach the gospel, the message of Jesus, to everyone. People listened to them with admiration and many were admitted to the membership of the growing number of Jesus's followers.

It was not long before the apostles came into conflict with the Jewish authorities. When Peter and John healed a lame man and when Peter preached to a crowd about the power of the risen Christ, the Jewish leaders became very angry. Peter was taken before the High Priest for questioning. But it was a young man named Stephen who became the first of many believers to die for the new faith. Stephen was accused of blasphemy (dishonouring the name of God) and was stoned to death.

A person who watched with approval as Stephen was being stoned was a strict Jew named Saul, who was very much opposed to the followers of the teachings of Jesus. Saul was a Roman citizen, born in the important

THE APOSTLES

☞ The word "disciple" refers to all the close followers of Jesus. Only the chosen twelve were called "apostles" (although the term was sometimes used for Paul and Barnabas as "apostles of the Gentiles"). "Apostle" means "someone who is sent". The twelve apostles were all chosen by Jesus. They were his close companions and were given authority to teach and heal in his name. Except for **Matthew**, who was a despised tax-collector for the Romans, the apostles were all working men: **Peter**, a fisherman whom Jesus called "the rock" because of his strong faith; **Andrew**, Peter's brother and also a fisherman; **James**, another fisherman, and his brother **John**, "the disciple Jesus loved"; **Philip**, from Bethsaida; **Bartholomew**, perhaps the Nathanael mentioned in John's Gospel; **Thomas**, known as "doubting Thomas"; **James,** son of Alphaeus; **Simon**, "the zealot" or freedom-fighter; **Thaddaeus,** perhaps the same person as Judas, son of James; and **Judas Iscariot**, who looked after the money, betrayed Jesus, and killed himself.

city of Tarsus in Asia Minor. When Saul left Jerusalem on a mission to Damascus to arrest any followers of Jesus there, he was blinded on the journey by a dazzling light. Falling to the ground, he heard the voice of Jesus saying: "Saul, Saul why do you persecute me?" After this experience on the road to Damascus, Saul became a changed man. From being an enemy of the new faith, he became its most eloquent preacher and used a new name, Paul. He travelled widely, both along the network of Roman roads and by ship, to spread the Christian message. He made three main "missionary" journeys: the first to Cyprus and the southern coast of Asia Minor; next to northwest Asia Minor; and then to Macedonia, taking Christianity to Europe.

On his return to Jerusalem, Paul was arrested for causing a disturbance. His last journey was to Rome, where he asked to be sent – as a Roman citizen – to state his case to the emperor. On the voyage there, he was shipwrecked. When he eventually reached Rome, he was put under house arrest. While under arrest, Paul continued to write letters (epistles) of encouragement to friends or to groups of people and churches he had helped to establish. The epistles to the Ephesians, Philippians and Colossians talk about what it is like to be a Christian. The two letters to the Thessalonians are more concerned with the second coming of Jesus. What may be Paul's last letter was written to his old friend, Timothy: "I give you this charge: Preach the word; be prepared in season and out of season; correct, rebuke, encourage – with patience and careful instruction. For the time will come when men will not be able to endure sound doctrine."

The Acts of the Apostles
Above, this early 13th-century copy of the Acts of the Apostles was written in Syriac, a dialect of Aramaic, probably the main language spoken by Jesus and his apostles.

285

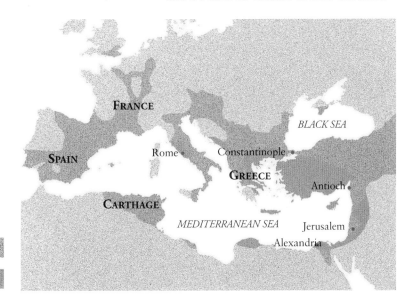

The spread of Christianity

100 CE

300 CE

FRANCE

BLACK SEA

SPAIN

Rome

Constantinople

GREECE

Antioch

CARTHAGE

MEDITERRANEAN SEA

Jerusalem

Alexandria

TONGUES OF FIRE

Jewish Pentecost
Pentecost is a Jewish festival that takes place fifty days after Passover. It is also known as the Feast of Weeks (Shavuot), when first fruits were offered to God in the temple, to celebrate the renewal of the covenant that he made with his people in the time of Moses.

286

In Jerusalem, the eleven original disciples met many of the other followers of Jesus. In the days shortly after Jesus ascended into heaven, they numbered about one hundred and twenty. Peter stood up and spoke to the believers. "Brothers and sisters," he said, "Jesus chose twelve disciples to be his apostles. We are his messengers, sent out to teach the people in his name. But we must now replace Judas Iscariot, who betrayed our Lord, so that the scriptures can be fulfilled. We must choose someone who has been a constant follower of Jesus and who was with us when we saw our Lord risen from the dead."

Two names were put forward: Matthias and Joseph Barsabbas. First the disciples prayed to be shown which of the two men to choose. Then they drew lots and Matthias was chosen to join the apostles.

At that time, Jews from many different countries were staying in Jerusalem for the celebration of Pentecost. News soon spread about the Galileans who could speak every language under the sun and large crowds gathered outside their house. There were people from Mesopotamia, Egypt, Libya, Rome, Crete, Arabia and many other regions, and every one of them was astonished to hear the apostles praising God in their own language. Other bystanders were less impressed. To them it seemed that the loud, excited Galileans had simply had too much wine to drink.

Then Peter stood up to address the crowd. "People of Jerusalem and friends from faraway lands," he began. "My fellow speakers are not drunk, as some of you suppose. It is only nine in the morning! What you see and hear was foretold by the prophet Joel long ago. Jesus promised us God's gift of the Holy

Christian Pentecost
At the first Pentecost after the death of Jesus, one of the most momentous happenings in the whole of the New Testament is recorded in the second chapter of Acts. The apostles received strange new powers, which they were sure came from God. They believed that they were filled with the power of God, the Holy Spirit. After the day of Pentecost, the apostles became men with a mission. Christians celebrate Pentecost (or Whitsun) as the birthday of the Church.

287

On the day of Pentecost, the apostles met to celebrate the festival. Suddenly great gusts of wind came down from heaven and swept through the house where they were gathered. Flaming tongues of fire flickered above each of the twelve men and they were filled with the Holy Spirit. When they began to talk about this, they were amazed to find that they could now communicate in different languages from other lands.

288

Spirit, and he has poured it on us so that you can hear God's word in your own languages. Jesus performed miracles in the name of God, who sent him to you. Yet you and your leaders nailed him to a cross and put him to death. But God raised Jesus from the dead, and we are his witnesses. Now Jesus sits at the right hand of God, who made him both Lord and Christ." Those listening felt deep shame and asked Peter what they should do. "Show sorrow for what you have done and be baptized in the name of Jesus Christ," Peter said. "Then your sins will be forgiven and you will receive the gift of the Holy Spirit." That day, about three thousand people were baptized and became followers of Jesus.

AND THEY CONTINUED STEADFASTLY IN THE APOSTLES'
DOCTRINE AND FELLOWSHIP AND IN BREAKING OF
BREAD AND IN PRAYERS. AND FEAR CAME UPON EVERY
SOUL: AND MANY WONDERS AND SIGNS WERE DONE BY
THE APOSTLES. AND ALL THAT BELIEVED WERE
TOGETHER, AND HAD ALL THINGS COMMON.

(Acts of the Apostles 2.42–44)

PETER PREACHES
AND HEALS

One afternoon, when Peter and John were about to go into the temple to pray, they heard a small, weak voice begging for money. This particular beggar had been lame from birth, and every day someone carried him to the temple gate. The two apostles looked down at the beggar, who was bent over facing the ground. "Look at us," Peter said. The beggar at once turned to look up.

"I have no silver or gold coins," Peter said, "but I will give you what I can." Then he took the man's right hand and said: "In the name of Jesus Christ, stand up and walk." As Peter helped him up, the beggar felt his legs growing in strength. He got to his feet and walked for the first time. Then, jumping and praising God at the top of his voice, he went with Peter and John into the temple courtyard.

The people in the temple could scarcely believe that this was the same beggar they had seen day after day at the gate. They were amazed at such a miracle. Many of them rushed up to Peter and John. "Why are you staring at us like that?" Peter asked the gathering crowd. "It was not our own power that made this man walk. It was faith in the name of Jesus that made him strong. Yet you handed Jesus over to be killed, before God raised him again from the dead. We are his witnesses, for we saw Jesus alive after he died on the cross. I know that you and your leaders did not know what you were doing when you killed Jesus. Everything that happened was God's way of making the prophets' words come true. Jesus will suffer, they foretold, and you made him suffer. But if you are sorry for what you have done and turn to God, who sent Jesus to you, your sins will be forgiven."

Peter carried on preaching about God and called on the people to turn to Jesus Christ, their saviour. Many did, and the number of believers

Peter heals
This 15th-century fresco by Massacio and Masolino da Panicale shows Peter raising the beggar to his feet (left) and bringing Tabitha back from the dead (right).

grew to about five thousand. But some of the High Priests and religious leaders were concerned at what they heard, especially the claim that Jesus had risen from the dead. They sent the temple guards to arrest Peter and John, and throw them into jail.

Next day the two apostles were brought before the ruling council and questioned by the High Priests Annas and Caiaphas. "By whose authority were you acting in the temple court?" they asked.

"We are being questioned about a simple act of kindness to a lame man," Peter replied. "But you should know this. The man was healed in the name of Jesus Christ of Nazareth, who was crucified by you and whom God raised from the dead."

THEN PETER SAID, SILVER AND GOLD HAVE I NONE; BUT SUCH AS I HAVE GIVE I THEE: IN THE NAME OF JESUS CHRIST OF NAZARETH RISE UP AND WALK. AND HE TOOK HIM BY THE RIGHT HAND, AND LIFTED HIM UP: AND IMMEDIATELY HIS FEET AND ANKLE BONES RECEIVED STRENGTH. AND HE LEAPING UP STOOD, AND WALKED, AND ENTERED WITH THEM INTO THE TEMPLE, WALKING, AND LEAPING, AND PRAISING GOD.

(Acts of the Apostles 3: 6–9)

The High Priests could not help but admire the courage of these two ordinary, uneducated men. They knew that they had been close friends of Jesus, but they could not charge them with any crime. The beggar had undoubtedly been healed, and this amazing miracle was admired by all who had seen and heard of it. As they could find no reason to hold Peter and John, they reluctantly decided to let them go. But they warned them first: "You must no longer preach in the name of Jesus."

"And you must judge for yourselves whether it is right for us to obey you or God," Peter replied. "For we cannot help speaking about what we have seen and heard."

In the weeks that followed, more people became believers. The followers of Jesus all helped each other, sharing everything they had. Rich people sold their land and took the money to the apostles, who gave it to the poor. There was great trust among the followers and everyone felt blessed by the love of Christ.

Some people found the new ways difficult, however. A man named Ananias had become a follower, along with his wife Sapphira, but when it came to selling their property, Ananias had second thoughts. It seemed a shame to give away all the money, so he suggested to his wife that they keep back some for themselves. Sapphira agreed. But when Ananias handed over the money to the apostles, saying it was the full amount, Peter knew at once what was going on. "Why are you lying to the Holy Spirit?" he asked Ananias. "The land was yours and after you sold it the money was yours and

Early followers
Left, a Roman image of a couple being blessed by Christ. The teachings of Jesus stress the worth of marriage and family, condemn adultery and are against divorce.

you had the power to give it all away. What made you think of keeping back some of it for yourself? You have not lied to us men, but to God."

When Ananias heard these words, he fell down dead. A short while later, his wife came to see the apostles. She did not know what had happened to Ananias and Peter asked her about the amount that she and her husband had received for their land. Sapphira looked at the money that Peter showed her. "Yes, that is all we were paid for the land," she said.

"How could you agree together to lie to God in such a way?" Peter asked. "Look outside and you will see the men who have just buried your husband. They will soon be coming to carry you out, too."

When Sapphira heard these words, she too fell down dead at Peter's feet. The men came and carried her body out to be buried next to her husband, just as Peter had said.

The story of Ananias and Sapphira quickly spread among the followers of Christ. It reminded all those who heard it that they must be truthful and obedient to God; if they tried to cheat him, then sooner or later they would come to experience his anger and his judgment.

Stephen Dies for his Beliefs

The twelve apostles went on spreading the good news about Jesus Christ and more and more people became believers. All followers were cared for and money was shared out fairly among those most in need. Looking after the funds took up a great deal of the apostles' time. It became clear that they needed help with this. So they decided to choose seven good men from among the true followers and put them in charge of this important work.

One of those chosen was a man named Stephen. He had great faith and did many miraculous deeds among the people. His calling was so strong that he even argued with members of the synagogue to prove that Jesus was the Messiah. They could not stand up to Stephen's wisdom and faith. This made him many enemies. Stephen's opponents secretly persuaded others to spread lies about him. They stirred up the people and invented false charges against him, reporting them to the High Priests and teachers of the law: "We have heard this man speaking badly of Moses and God," they said.

Stephen was brought before the Jewish ruling council. More false witnesses confirmed the accusations. "We heard Stephen say that Jesus of Nazareth will destroy this place and change the laws that Moses handed down to us," one witness claimed. What would Stephen have to say in his defence? "Are these charges true?" the High Priest asked him.

"Brothers and sisters, listen to me," Stephen replied. "All through the ages our nation has disobeyed God's commands. From the days of Abraham, jealousy and greed have turned the people away from God. Our ancestors treated the prophets badly and fought against the Holy Spirit. They refused to listen to God's message and even killed those who told them about the coming of his son, Jesus Christ. And now you have betrayed and murdered him."

The council members were furious at being rebuked in this way. But before they could say or do anything, Stephen looked up and said: "I can see heaven opening, with Jesus standing at the right hand of God."

This was too much for many of those listening. Some of them even covered their ears so that they would not have to hear Stephen's words. A group of angry people rushed at Stephen, yelling at the tops of their voices. They dragged him outside and began hurling rocks and stones at him. As they did so, Stephen cried out: "Lord, do not hold this sin against them." The maddened crowd did not even hear these words as they stoned Stephen to death.

Many of those who killed Stephen had left their cloaks with a young man named Saul. From that day, Saul and others went throughout Jerusalem from house to house, dragging off believers in Jesus and throwing them into prison.

Christian martyrs
Stephen was the first Christian martyr (the word originally meant witness). When Rome was badly damaged by fire in 64 CE, Nero blamed it on the Christians and had them hunted down. Many were killed. Christians were widely persecuted in the 3rd and 4th centuries: torture, executions, and mass destruction of church buildings were common. Above, the illustration shows the martyrdom of Saints Giulitta and Quircino, from a Spanish altarpiece.

293

AND THEY STONED STEPHEN, CALLING UPON GOD, AND SAYING, LORD JESUS, RECEIVE MY SPIRIT. AND HE KNEELED DOWN, AND CRIED WITH A LOUD VOICE, LORD, LAY NOT THIS SIN TO THEIR CHARGE. AND WHEN HE HAD SAID THIS, HE FELL ASLEEP.

(Acts of the Apostles 7.59–60)

On the Road to Damascus

Saint Paul
Saul, later called by his Roman name Paul, was a Jew and a Roman citizen. After his conversion, he travelled widely in the Mediterranean region, sharing and spreading the Christian message.

294

S aul came from a Jewish family and was born in Tarsus, the capital of the Roman province of Cilicia. He was a Roman citizen and the Roman form of his name was Paul, but as a Pharisee and strict defender of the Jewish laws he proudly called himself Saul. He had been trained as a rabbi in Jerusalem and bitterly opposed all believers in Jesus Christ. Saul saw it as his mission to put a stop to the teachings of the disciples of Jesus. The High Priests permitted him to arrest anyone who supposedly broke the laws of Moses, and he ruthlessly hunted people down.

When Saul found out that some Jews in Damascus were following the teachings of Jesus, he asked the ruling council for a letter of authority to the leaders of the synagogue there. He was determined to bring these people back to Jerusalem to be tried and punished. Accompanied by armed guards, Saul set off for Damascus. As he approached the city, a dazzling bright light suddenly came down from heaven and flashed all around him. Blinded by its brilliance, Saul fell to the ground and heard a voice saying: "Saul, Saul, why do you keep on persecuting me?"

"Who are you, Lord?" Saul cried, his body shaking in terror.

"I am Jesus, whom you want to destroy," the voice replied. "Now get up and go into the city. There you will be told what you must do."

The guards who were travelling with Saul saw the bright light and heard strange sounds, but they could not make out what was said. They watched as Saul picked himself up from the ground. But when he opened his eyes, Saul could not see them – or anything else. The guards realised that he really had been blinded by the light. So they took him by the hand and led him into the city of Damascus.

Saul was taken to the house of a man named Judas, who lived in Straight Street. He stayed there for three days, and during that time he did not eat or drink – he only prayed. Then a faithful disciple of Jesus, whose name was Ananias, heard the Lord's voice calling to him. "Ananias," the voice said, "go to Straight Street and ask for Saul of Tarsus. He is praying there and has had a vision that a man named Ananias will bring back his sight."

"But Lord, I can't do that," the disciple replied. "That man has caused great harm to your followers in Jerusalem. He is here with authority from the chief priests to arrest anyone who believes in you."

As he journeyed, he came near Damascus: and suddenly there shined round about him a light from heaven: and he fell to the earth, and heard a voice saying unto him, Saul, Saul, why persecutest thou me?

(Acts of the Apostles 9.3–4)

moment it was as if scales fell from Saul's eyes. Light returned and he could see again. Filled with joy, Saul got up and was baptised by Ananias.

Now that he was a believer, Saul stayed with the other disciples in Damascus. He went to the synagogue and preached to everyone there that Jesus was the Son of God. All those who heard him were amazed at the change that had come over Saul. "Didn't he come here to arrest these people of the Way?" someone asked.

Many of the Jews of Damascus came to regard Saul as their enemy, and decided that he must be stopped. Waiting for an opportunity to kill him, they kept watch on the city gates day and night to make sure he did not leave Damascus. Saul's followers learned of this, however, and worked out a plan of escape. One night they took Saul secretly to the city wall and lowered him over in a basket.

Saul went straight back to Jerusalem. When he arrived in the city, he tried to join the disciples, but they were all afraid of him. They found it difficult to believe him after all the terrible things he had done to their brothers and sisters in the past. But a disciple named Barnabas trusted him. He took Saul to the apostles, telling them what had happened on the road to Damascus and how Saul had fearlessly preached in the synagogue. From that day on, Saul was accepted by all the followers of Jesus, and went everywhere with them, praying and preaching.

"Go!" Jesus said to Ananias. "Do as I ask. I have chosen Saul to tell all the people about me. I will guide him and be with him when he comes to suffer in my name."

Ananias went at once and found Saul at the house of Judas. He placed his hands on Saul and said: "Jesus, who appeared to you on the road to Damascus, has sent me so that you may see again and be filled with the Holy Spirit." At that very

PETER AND CORNELIUS

Cornelius was a Roman centurion stationed with his troops in Caesarea. He and his family respected Jewish customs, prayed to their God and gave generously to the poor. One day Cornelius had a vision. He saw an angel of God calling out his name. The centurion was frightened by this and asked what he should do. The angel told him that God was pleased with his prayers and kind gifts to the poor. "Send men to Joppa," the angel said. "Tell them to bring back a man named Peter, who is staying there in the house of Simon, a leather-worker. He will tell you what to do." Cornelius immediately instructed two of his most trusted servants and a Roman soldier to do as the angel said.

Jewish Food Laws

Old Testament law (found in Leviticus and Deuteronomy) detailed what the Israelites could and could not eat. Only animals that chew the cud and have divided hooves could be eaten. This ruled out pigs. Only fish with fins and scales were allowed. Many of these laws may have been based on hygiene.

Peter was staying in Joppa because some time earlier a kind seamstress named Tabitha had died there and her friends had sent for Peter. They took him to the room where her body lay. He knelt and prayed, before turning to Tabitha and telling her to get up. At once she opened her eyes and Peter helped her to her feet. News of this miracle spread throughout Joppa, where many more people began believing in Jesus.

While Peter was wondering what this was supposed to mean, he heard a voice say: "Peter, three men are looking for you. Go with them, for I sent them to you." Peter rushed downstairs and saw that three strangers had just arrived. They explained how an angel had told their master Cornelius to send them. The men spent the night at Simon's house as guests and, next morning, the four of them left together for Caesarea.

Peter arrived to find that Cornelius had arranged a great reception for him and had invited his family and friends to meet him. When Peter entered his house, the centurion fell to his knees, but Peter said: "Stand up, please, for I am only a human being, just like you."

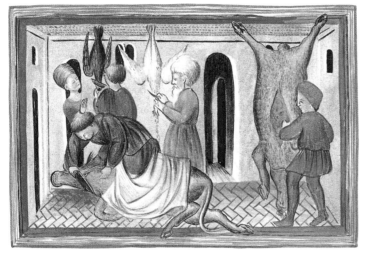

AND THERE CAME A VOICE TO HIM, RISE, PETER; KILL, AND EAT, BUT PETER SAID, NOT SO LORD; FOR I HAVE NEVER EATEN ANYTHING THAT IS COMMON OR UNCLEAN. AND THE VOICE SPAKE UNTO HIM AGAIN THE SECOND TIME, WHAT GOD HATH CLEANSED, THAT CALL NOT THOU COMMON.

(Acts of the Apostles 10.13–15)

On the day that Cornelius's men were travelling to Joppa, Peter went up onto the roof of Simon the leather-worker's house to pray. There, as if in a dream, Peter saw heaven open and a large white sheet come down to earth. On the sheet were all kinds of animals, including some that Jews were not allowed to eat because they were considered unclean. As Peter watched, he heard a voice say: "Get up, Peter. Kill and eat." Peter refused, saying that he had never eaten anything unclean. The voice spoke to Peter again: "Do not call unclean anything that God has made clean." This happened three times, and then the sheet went back up to heaven.

Inside the house, Peter saw that all the people waiting to meet him were non-Jews. Now he understood the message that God had sent him in Joppa. Peter spoke to them all. "We all know that it is against our law for a Jew to visit Gentiles," he said. "But God has shown me that we should not call anyone unclean. For God has no favourites and accepts people from every nation who obey him and do what is right." Later that day, many of those who listened to Peter were baptised in the name of Jesus Christ.

When the disciples in Jerusalem heard about this, they were unhappy and asked Peter why he had baptised Gentiles. After telling them of his vision, Peter said: "How could I disobey God? Just as he gave the gift of the Holy Spirit to us, so he gives it to all, wherever they come from, who believe in Jesus Christ."

PETER IN PRISON

King Herod Agrippa was now the ruler of Judea under the Romans. Since he was eager to be on good terms with the Jewish ruling council, Herod hunted down those who believed in Jesus and treated them cruelly. He had the apostle James, brother of John, put to death. When he realised how much this execution pleased some of the High Priests, Herod arrested another apostle – Peter – and threw him into prison. He planned to stage a public trial for Peter, but as it was the time of Passover, he decided to wait until the festival had ended.

Peter was heavily guarded by four separate squads of four soldiers each. The night before his trial, he was chained between two guards as he slept and sentries were posted at the cell gate. Suddenly a light shone in the cell and an angel woke Peter. "Get up quickly!" the angel said. As he spoke, the chains fell from Peter's wrists. The angel told Peter to put on his cloak and sandals and to follow him out of the prison.

AND, BEHOLD, THE ANGEL OF THE LORD CAME UPON HIM, AND A LIGHT SHINED IN THE PRISON; AND HE SMOTE PETER ON THE SIDE, AND RAISED HIM UP, SAYING, ARISE UP QUICKLY. AND HIS CHAINS FELL OFF FROM HIS HANDS.

(Acts of the Apostles 12.7)

299

Peter walked with the angel past two sets of guards. When they came to the heavy iron gate that led to the city, it just opened by itself. When they had walked the length of one street, the angel suddenly disappeared. Peter looked around and, seeing that he really was free, realised that God had sent an angel to rescue him. He quickly made his way to the house of Mary, the mother of Mark, where he knew his friends would be praying for him. How pleased they would be to see him alive and free from Herod's clutches.

A servant girl named Rhoda came to the door when Peter knocked and recognised his voice at once. In her excitement, Rhoda shut the door on him and rushed inside to tell the others Peter was there. No one believed her. But when she insisted that it was true, one disciple said: "Then it must be his angel." Peter kept knocking and when his friends finally opened the door, they were amazed to see that it really was him. He quickly told them how an angel had helped him escape. "Tell James and the other believers," he said, before leaving for a safer place.

Next morning the chief prison guard had no choice but to report Peter's escape to Herod. After ordering a thorough search of the prison and questioning all of the guards without success, Herod in his fury had every one of them executed.

Angels
Angels appear on several occasions in the Acts of the Apostles. They rescue people from prison and give people guidance through dreams and visions. Right, this 12th-century gold icon from Byzantium is of the Archangel Michael.

PAUL'S JOURNEYS

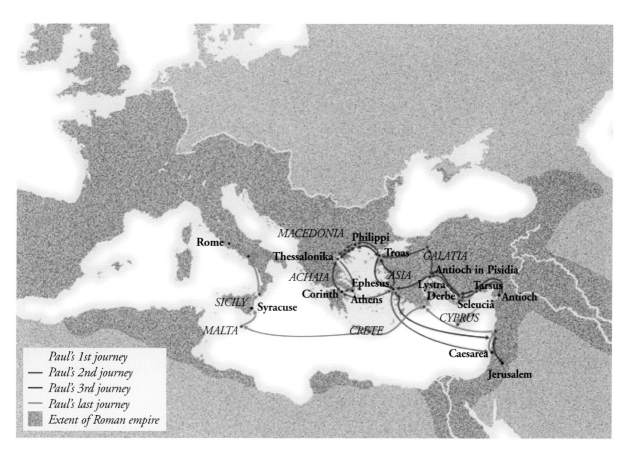

Rome
MACEDONIA Philippi
Thessalonika Troas
ACHAIA ASIA GALATIA
Corinth Ephesus Antioch in Pisidia
Athens Lystra Tarsus
SICILY Syracuse Derbe Seleucia Antioch
MALTA CRETE CYPRUS
Caesarea
Jerusalem

Paul's 1st journey
Paul's 2nd journey
Paul's 3rd journey
Paul's last journey
Extent of Roman empire

With Barnabas in Antioch

After meeting the apostles in Jerusalem, Saul returned to his birthplace, the city of Tarsus, in the Roman province of Cilicia. There he lived simply and spent his time helping the poor and sick. Meanwhile Barnabas, the disciple who had helped Saul in Jerusalem, had been sent to the Syrian city of Antioch. Barnabas and other disciples brought the good news about Jesus to the people there, and many became believers. Hearing that Saul was in nearby Tarsus, Barnabas went there to find him. Pleased to see each other again, Saul went with Barnabas to help him with his work in Antioch.

Many persecuted believers had also made their way to Antioch, and it was there that the followers of Jesus Christ began to call themselves Christians. They also called Saul by his Roman name – Paul – and this is how he was known from that time on.

One day, as the Christians were fasting and praying, they were told by the Holy Spirit that they must say farewell to Paul and Barnabas. God had chosen these two men to be his missionaries; they were to take the good news about Jesus to other lands.

Paul's First Journey

Paul and Barnabas left Antioch at once, taking with them Barnabas's cousin Mark. First they travelled south to the town of Seleucia, on the Mediterranean coast. From there they took a ship to the island of Cyprus, which was where Barnabas originally came from. Arriving at the town of Salamis, they soon began preaching the word of God in the synagogues belonging to the Jews.

Next the missionaries crossed the island to Paphos, where they were sent for by the Roman proconsul, Sergius Paulus, who wanted to learn about Jesus. His attendant, a sorcerer named Elymas, had other plans. Elymas tried to turn the proconsul away from the faith. Paul saw through him straight away. "You are a child of the devil," Paul told him. "But the hand of the Lord is against you, and you will not see the light of day for some time." Elymas was struck blind, and people had to lead him away. Seeing the Lord's power, the Roman proconsul became a Christian believer.

Paul and Barnabas sailed from Cyprus to the coast of Asia Minor, where Mark left them to return to Jerusalem. They visited several towns in the Roman province of Galatia and preached in the synagogues. Some of the Jewish people there were unhappy that the Christians accepted Gentiles so readily into their faith, and plotted against the missionaries. But Paul and Barnabas simply moved on to the next town, happy to spread the word to anyone who listened.

In the town of Lystra, Paul healed a man who had never before been able to walk. Some of the locals were convinced that Paul must be Hermes, the messenger of the ancient Greek gods, and offered sacrifices to him. Paul told them that he was not a god, just an ordinary man who had come to give them good news about the one true God. Other people were so unhappy at what Paul had to say that they threw stones at him and tried to kill him. But Paul and Barnabas were happy to face any hardship in order to spread the word. They went on their way to Derbe, before retracing their steps to Attalia and then sailing back to Antioch.

Travelling in the Roman Empire
A magnificent road system linked all parts of the Roman Empire. Messengers bearing Paul's letters to the faithful would have journeyed along the straight, wide roads. Above, the oldest Roman road, the Appian Way, ran from Rome to the seaport of Brindisi in the southeast of Italy. Paul would have travelled along it to reach Rome on his final journey.

302

The Greek gods
The chief Greek god was Zeus, known to the Romans as Jupiter. The people of Lystra hailed Barnabas as Zeus, and Paul as Hermes (Mercury to the Romans), the messenger of the gods. Right, a Greek vase depicting a man holding an olive branch as he performs a libation to honour the gods.

AND THERE SAT A CERTAIN MAN AT LYSTRA, IMPOTENT IN HIS FEET, BEING A CRIPPLE FROM HIS MOTHER'S WOMB, WHO NEVER HAD WALKED. THE SAME HEARD PAUL SPEAK: WHO STEADFASTLY BEHOLDING HIM, AND PERCEIVING THAT HE HAD FAITH TO BE HEALED, SAID WITH A LOUD VOICE, STAND UPRIGHT ON THY FEET. AND HE LEAPED AND WALKED.

(Acts of the Apostles 14,8–10)

Paul's Second Journey

Paul and Barnabas went to Jerusalem to report on their missionary work. There, many church leaders made it clear that they thought that all Gentile Christians should strictly follow the laws of Moses. The apostle Peter reminded them that God accepted people from every nation, and Paul told of the wonders God had performed through him in many of the Gentile cities.

Paul told Barnabas that he wanted to go back to the towns they had visited, to see how the newly converted Christians were getting on. Barnabas agreed and suggested they take his cousin Mark with them. Paul was not happy about this, because on their first journey, Mark had soon wanted to return home. After this disagreement, Paul chose another disciple – Silas – to go with him, while Barnabas and Mark sailed for Cyprus.

Paul and Silas travelled north to Asia Minor, before sailing across the sea to Macedonia. This was the first time that Christians had set foot in Europe. They met with some opposition in Macedonia and were beaten and even thrown into prison in Philippi. Later, a disciple named Timothy joined them. He had a Greek father and a Jewish mother. With him, they travelled south into Greece, to the ancient city of Athens. There, many of the people were discussing philosophy. They asked Paul about his beliefs and took him to a meeting of the Athenian council, where Paul explained his faith in God and Jesus in a way that they could understand. The Athenians listened politely, but though some were convinced, many were not.

Paul next moved on to Corinth, where he met a Jewish couple, Aquila and Priscilla. They were tentmakers, just as Paul had once been, and had recently arrived from Rome. They had come because the Emperor Claudius had ordered all Jews to leave the imperial capital. His new friends went with Paul to Ephesus, where they stayed. Paul, Silas, and Timothy then took a ship back to Jerusalem, and Paul made his way from there to Antioch.

Athena
Above, a statue of the Greek goddess of war and wisdom, from the Parthenon, Athens.

303

AND BECAUSE HE WAS OF THE SAME CRAFT, HE ABODE WITH THEM, AND WROUGHT: FOR BY THEIR OCCUPATION THEY WERE TENTMAKERS. AND HE REASONED IN THE SYNAGOGUE EVERY SABBATH, AND PERSUADED THE JEWS AND THE GREEKS.

(Acts of the Apostles 18.3–4)

Paul's Third Journey

On his third missionary journey, Paul travelled alone. He first returned to Ephesus, on the Aegean coast of Asia Minor, which was the greatest port in the region. Pleased to see his friends Aquila and Priscilla again, Paul stayed in Ephesus for two years, teaching and converting people to Christianity. This led to trouble with the locals, who believed he was insulting their guardian goddess, Artemis. Eventually Paul moved on to Macedonia.

After travelling through Macedonia and Greece and revisiting many cities there, Paul returned to Troas, a port on the coast of Asia Minor. He stayed there for seven days,

before leaving on foot for Assos. Then he took a ship to Miletus, where he called the elders of the church at Ephesus to meet him. Paul told the elders that there was still much work to be done. "My life is worth nothing to me," Paul said, "if only I may complete the task the Lord Jesus gave me. But be on your guard, for after I leave, savage wolves will come and try to destroy your flock." Then he told the Ephesians that they would never see him again. They wept as Paul set sail for Jerusalem.

After stopping at the islands of Kos and Rhodes on the way, Paul finally landed at the seaport of Tyre. Then he went by land to Jerusalem.

I HAVE SHOWED YOU ALL THINGS, HOW THAT SO LABOURING YE OUGHT TO SUPPORT THE WEAK, AND TO REMEMBER THE WORDS OF THE LORD JESUS, HOW HE SAID, IT IS MORE BLESSED TO GIVE THAN TO RECEIVE. AND WHEN HE HAD THUS SPOKEN, HE KNEELED DOWN, AND PRAYED WITH THEM ALL. AND THEY ALL WEPT SORE, AND FELL ON PAUL'S NECK, AND KISSED HIM, SORROWING MOST OF ALL FOR THE WORDS WHICH HE SPAKE, THAT THEY SHOULD SEE HIS FACE NO MORE. AND THEY ACCOMPANIED HIM UNTO THE SHIP.

(Acts of the Apostles 20.35–38)

In Prison in Philippi

In the Roman colony of Philippi, Paul and Silas went outside the city gates to a quiet place near the river, where they prayed. There they were approached by a slave girl, who told them that a spirit helped her predict the future and earn money for her Roman owners by fortune-telling. The girl followed Paul and Silas everywhere, shouting: "These men are servants of the most high God, and will tell you how to be saved!" After being followed by the screaming girl for many days, Paul turned to her and spoke to the spirit. "In the name of Jesus Christ," he said, "I order you to come out of her." The girl was freed from the spirit at once.

The slave girl's owners were furious when they found she could no longer tell fortunes. They had Paul and Silas arrested and taken before the magistrates. "These men are Jews," the slave owners said, "and they want us to do things that are against Roman law." The crowds shouted for punishment. Soldiers seized Paul and Silas, beat them and threw them into prison.

The jailer was ordered to guard the prisoners carefully, so he chained them to the wall of the deepest, darkest cell. That night, Paul

AND THE KEEPER OF THE PRISON AWAKING OUT OF HIS SLEEP, AND SEEING THE PRISON DOORS OPEN, HE DREW OUT HIS SWORD, AND WOULD HAVE KILLED HIMSELF, SUPPOSING THAT THE PRISONERS HAD BEEN FLED. BUT PAUL CRIED OUT WITH A LOUD VOICE, SAYING, DO THYSELF NO HARM; FOR WE ARE ALL HERE.

(Acts of the Apostles 16.27–28)

306

and Silas sang hymns to God, while the other prisoners listened. Suddenly, around midnight, a violent earthquake shook the very foundations of the prison. All the doors flew open and the chains fell from the prisoners' arms and legs. When the jailer woke in terror and saw the prison gates wide open, he was sure that all the prisoners must have escaped. Knowing that he would have to pay for this with his life, the jailer drew his sword to kill himself. But Paul shouted: "Do not harm yourself, we are all here!"

Trembling, the jailer rushed into the cell and knelt down in front of Paul and Silas. "Tell me," he begged, "what must I do to be saved?"

"Believe in the Lord Jesus," Paul replied, "and you and your family will be saved." The jailer thanked Paul and Silas and then washed their wounds. Later, he was baptised.

Next morning, the jailer received the order to release Paul and Silas. First, Paul demanded to speak to the officers. He said to them: "We were stripped, beaten and thrown into jail, even though we are Roman citizens. Tell the magistrates that they can't get rid of us so quietly. Let them come and escort us out themselves."

The magistrates were very worried when they learned that Paul and Silas were Roman citizens. They had no choice but to do as Paul had said. After leading Paul and Silas out of the prison, they asked them politely to leave the city. The missionaries were only too happy to agree, and went on their way.

BUT PAUL SAID UNTO THEM, THEY HAVE BEATEN US OPENLY UNCONDEMNED, BEING ROMANS, AND HAVE CAST US INTO PRISON; AND NOW DO THEY THRUST US OUT PRIVILY? NAY, VERILY; BUT LET THEM COME THEMSELVES AND FETCH US OUT.

(Acts of the Apostles 16.37)

TROUBLE IN EPHESUS

Ephesus was famous for its temple dedicated to the Greek goddess Artemis, who was named Diana by the Romans. When they came to the temple, which was one of the Seven Wonders of the Ancient World, visitors generally bought small figurines of the goddess. These souvenirs had become a good source of income for local craftsmen, so they were not happy when people became Christians and no longer wanted to buy their souvenirs.

A silversmith named Demetrius called a meeting of his workers and told them that something had to be done about Paul. "He and his companions have convinced many people in the province that hand-made gods are no gods at all," Demetrius said. "Soon we will lose our good name, and the temple, and even the goddess herself, will be despised."

Some of the workers started shouting: "Great is Artemis of Ephesus!" Then the whole city joined the protest and the meeting looked like turning into a riot. When Paul heard what was happening, he rushed to speak to the people. But the provincial officials would not let him speak, fearing that his presence would make matters worse. The whole city was in uproar, though most of the people didn't really know why they were there or what it was all about.

After listening to the crowd chanting for Artemis for two hours, the city clerk finally managed to calm things down. He told the people that the city of Ephesus would always be the guardian of the goddess and her temple and that Paul had neither robbed the temple nor insulted Artemis. "If Demetrius wishes to make an official complaint," the city clerk said, "then he must take his case to the authorities and press charges. As it is, you are in danger of being charged with rioting."

Most of the people accepted this explanation, calmed down and began to make their way home.

Artemis
Paul caused a riot when he preached in the temple of Artemis in Ephesus, a seaport and the capital of the Roman province of Asia. Above, this statue of the goddess Artemis (Diana to the Romans) was found in Ephesus.

ACTS OF THE
APOSTLES 19

307

AND THERE SAT IN A WINDOW A CERTAIN YOUNG MAN NAMED EUTYCHUS, BEING FALLEN INTO A DEEP SLEEP: AND AS PAUL WAS LONG PREACHING, HE SUNK DOWN WITH SLEEP, AND FELL FROM THE THIRD LOFT, AND WAS TAKEN UP DEAD. AND PAUL WENT DOWN, AND FELL ON HIM, AND EMBRACING HIM SAID, TROUBLE NOT YOURSELVES; FOR HIS LIFE IS IN HIM.

(Acts of the Apostles 20.9–10)

308

EUTYCHUS IS RAISED FROM THE DEAD

Early worship
Early Christians shared what they owned. They met frequently to share a meal and to worship Jesus. Their main "service" then — as now — was the Eucharist (the "Thanksgiving") when the "Last Supper" is remembered and reenacted and when Jesus becomes a living reality to his followers. Right, this carving of a shared meal is from a Christian stone coffin of the 3rd century CE.

Paul stayed at Troas, on the west coast of what is now Turkey, for seven days. On his last evening he met with some friends in an upstairs room to share a meal. Knowing that he was leaving the next day, Paul talked to the other disciples until midnight. Among them was a young man named Eutychus, who sat on the window-sill listening to Paul.

As Paul talked at great length, Eutychus eventually nodded off to sleep, toppled over and fell out of the window. The room was on the third storey, so the disciples rushed downstairs as fast as they could. But when they reached Eutychus, he was lying on the ground, dead. Paul quickly knelt down and put his arms around the young man. "Don't be alarmed," Paul told the others. "He is alive." Then he went back upstairs, continued his meal and went on talking until daybreak. Some of the others took Eutychus home, overjoyed to find that he was alive, just as Paul had said.

PAUL IS ARRESTED

When Paul arrived in Jerusalem, he was warned by Christian believers that many Jewish people had turned against him. They had heard rumours that on his travels, Paul had been encouraging Jews to live like Gentiles and break the laws of Moses. Paul had already been warned by others that he would not be safe in Jerusalem, but he was determined to go there.

One day when Paul was in the temple court, some Jews from Asia Minor stirred up a crowd against him. "People of Israel, help us!" they cried as they seized Paul. "This is the man who breaks our laws and brings Gentiles into our temple!"

People came running from all directions. Paul was soon surrounded by an angry mob. They dragged him out of the temple and began to beat him severely. Just in time, news of the riot reached the Roman commander, who sent in his soldiers to control the mob. The commander arrested Paul, put him in chains and asked the people who he was and what he had done. By then the crowd was in such a frenzy that it was impossible to understand what they were accusing him of. Some

Jews and Gentiles
Gentile is a term denoting a non-Jew. Paul believed that Gentiles wishing to become Christians should not be required to first convert to Judaism. Above, this limestone slab is inscribed with a warning in Greek that prohibits the entry of non-Jews into the temple. It dates from the time of the Second Temple.

309

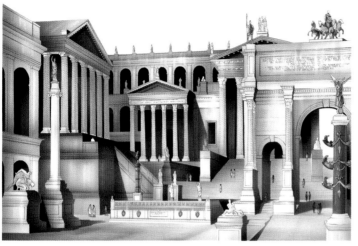

The Roman forum
A reconstruction of Rome's city centre during imperial times, when temples and government buildings surrounded an open market. The forum was also a central meeting place where Romans went to discuss important questions of the day.

shouted one thing and some another. In the end, the Roman soldiers had to carry Paul into their barracks to stop the crowd tearing him to pieces.

Later Paul asked to be allowed to speak to the crowd. He explained how at first he had been opposed to the followers of Jesus, but later had come to see that Jesus's teaching was for the whole world. The crowd remained against him. "He's not fit to live!" someone shouted out.

The commander then ordered his soldiers to flog Paul. Just as they were about to carry out the order, Paul said: "Is it right to flog a man who was born a Roman citizen and who has not even been found guilty of any crime?" When the commander heard this, he decided it would be best to refer the case to the Jewish ruling council. But this achieved nothing, as rival groups within the council argued with each other. Some of the Jews hatched a plot to kill Paul. When the Roman commander was told of this, he sent Paul to Caesarea to appear before the Roman governor, Felix.

Paul was kept in prison for two years, while Felix listened to his accusers but did nothing. Eventually Felix was succeeded by Festus. The Jews of Jerusalem asked the new governor to turn Paul over to them. "No one has the right to hand me over to these people," Paul said. "I should stand before Caesar's court. I am a Roman citizen. I claim that privilege. I appeal to the emperor!"

At last the Roman governor agreed. Paul was to be sent to Rome.

SHIPWRECKED!

For the long voyage to Rome, Paul and the other prisoners were under the charge of a Roman centurion named Julius. The first part of the voyage, past Cyprus and Crete, went well. But as they headed on towards southern Greece, the weather changed.

Julius regretted not having listened to Paul, who had warned them of the dangers ahead. Instead, he had taken the captain's advice to sail on from Crete. Now severe storms made it impossible to turn back. Huge waves battered the decks, timbers cracked and the masts broke. The desperate sailors slung ropes around the hull to stop the ship from being ripped apart. Cargo and equipment had to be thrown overboard to help keep it afloat. Days turned into everlasting nights, when neither sun nor stars came out to give them any hope.

Paul stood up and shouted above the noise of the wind and waves: "Keep up your courage, for you will all be saved. Last night an angel of God told me that I will reach Rome to stand trial before Caesar."

The crew were encouraged by Paul's words, and some time later saw that the ship was drifting in shallower water. During the days of terror, nobody had eaten much and they had very little strength left. Paul now urged everyone to eat some bread, so that they would be ready for the tough challenges ahead. At dawn, they could see land not far off, but as they made for it, the ship was driven on to a sandbank and began to break up.

Dangerous seas
In Roman times, many ships crossing the Mediterranean Sea never reached their destinations. Storms, pirates and rocks took their toll, sending sailors and ships to the sea bed. Above, a Roman relief of a ship in a storm.

311

AND WHEN NEITHER SUN NOR STARS IN MANY DAYS APPEARED, AND NO SMALL TEMPEST LAY ON US, ALL HOPE THAT WE SHOULD BE SAVED WAS THEN TAKEN AWAY.
(Acts of the Apostles 27.20)

bit his hand. The islanders looked at each other in horror, and whispered among themselves: "This man must be a murderer because, although he escaped from the sea, he will surely now die from the snake bite." But Paul just shook the snake off, and the islanders were amazed to see that he was not affected by its bite. "The man must be a god!" one said.

The travellers spent the winter on Malta and the Roman governor invited Paul and his friends to be his guests. When Paul heard that the governor's father was ill, he went to his bedside and healed him. From then on, many islanders came to Paul to be cured. When spring arrived, Paul and the others took another ship and sailed to Sicily. On his arrival in Puteoli, on the Italian mainland, Paul was welcomed by Christians who had heard that he would be landing there. Some of them travelled with him on the overland journey to Rome.

In Rome, Paul was not thrown into prison, but was allowed to stay in a rented house, where a Roman soldier guarded him. He was told he could receive visitors, so he invited the Jewish leaders in Rome to come to the house. He explained to them that many people in Jerusalem had taken against him and he had been forced to appeal to Caesar for judgment. Then he told them about Jesus Christ. His words and faith convinced some to become Christians, but others did not want to give up their old beliefs.

Paul stayed in the house in Rome for two years. During that time, he welcomed all who came to see him and told them about the kingdom of God and the Lord Jesus Christ.

AND WHEN PAUL HAD GATHERED A BUNDLE OF STICKS, AND LAID THEM ON THE FIRE, THERE CAME A VIPER OUT OF THE HEAT, AND FASTENED ON HIS HAND. AND WHEN THE BARBARIANS SAW THE VENOMOUS BEAST HANG ON HIS HAND, THEY SAID AMONG THEMSELVES, NO DOUBT THIS MAN IS A MURDERER.

(Acts of the Apostles 28.3–4)

As the ship broke apart, the Roman soldiers expected the centurion to order them to kill the prisoners. But instead he just yelled that it was up to everyone to save themselves. Those who could swim headed for the shore, while others grabbed pieces of wood to keep themselves afloat. Amazingly, every single soldier, sailor and prisoner reached land safely.

The people from the ship discovered that they were on an island named Malta. The local islanders were friendly and helped the survivors build a fire. Paul picked up a log and was about to throw it onto the flames, when a snake slid out and

LETTERS TO THE FAITHFUL

Paul was a great traveller and Christian missionary. Wherever he went, he wrote letters to friends and people in many countries, encouraging all those who had turned to Jesus Christ. Paul also wrote many letters while he was under house arrest in Rome. These are some extracts from Paul's letters to the faithful.

TO THE ROMANS
(From *Romans* 8.31–39)

"If God is for us, who can be against us? God even gave up his own Son for us, to show that he will give us all things. Jesus Christ, who died and was raised back to life, is at the right hand of God.

"Nothing can separate us from the love of Christ, not even trouble, hardship or persecution. Neither death nor life, neither angels nor demons, neither the present nor the future can separate us from the love of God that is in Jesus Christ our Lord."

TO THE CORINTHIANS
(From *1 Corinthians* 13.1–13)

"Love is patient and kind. Love does not envy or boast. Love is not easily angered. Love always protects, trusts and hopes. Love never fails.

"When I was a child, I talked like a child, I thought like a child, I understood like a child. But when I became a man, I put childish things behind me.

"Now these three remain: faith, hope and love. And the greatest of these is love."

TO THE GALATIANS
(From *Galatians* 5.14–23)

"The whole of law can be summed up in one command: Love your neighbour as you love yourself. If you keep on fighting each other, watch out or you will end up being destroyed by each other.

"The fruit of the Holy Spirit is love, joy, peace, patience, gentleness, goodness and faithfulness. Let us all live by the Spirit and keep in step with the Spirit."

TO THE EPHESIANS
(From *Ephesians* 6.10-17)

"Be strong in the Lord's mighty power. Put on the full armour of God, so that you can stand up to the schemes of the devil. We must struggle against the powers and rulers of the darkness of this world and we must fight evil. So put on the full armour of God, so that you can stand up to the day of evil and remain standing. Put on the belt of truth and the breastplate of right. Carry the shield of faith, which will protect you from all the flaming arrows of evil. Then put on the helmet of salvation and take up the sword of the Spirit, which is the word of God."

TO THE PHILIPPIANS
(From *Philippians* 2.2–4)

"Make my joy complete by having the same love, being in agreement and of one mind. Do not act out of ambition or vanity, but be

The martyrdom of St Paul
It is believed that Paul was kept under house arrest for two years. He was then released and continued his missionary work, but was rearrested in about 67 CE. The end of his life is uncertain. The 4th-century Church historian Eusebius records that Paul was executed in Rome during the persecutions of Christians by the Emperor Nero (54–68 CE), and one tradition claims that he was beheaded. Above, a painting from the workshop of Pacino di Buonaguida, Italy.

313

humble and hold others in higher esteem than yourselves. Do not simply look after your own interests, but always look out for the interests of others."

To Timothy (a friend):
"Be strong and endure hardship as a good soldier of Jesus Christ. Soldiers who go into battle try to carry out the orders of their commander. A competitor only wins if he obeys the rules. A farmer who works hard is the first to receive the fruit of his crops. Think about what I am saying, and the Lord will help you to understand everything."

To Philemon (a church leader at Colossae in Asia Minor):
"I appeal to you concerning Onesimus, who was once your slave and became my friend when I was in prison. I am sending him back to you. I would have liked to keep him with me, but perhaps he only left you for a while so that one day you could have him back for good. But do not receive him as a slave, but as a brother. If you count me as a partner, welcome him as you would welcome me. If he has done you any wrong, put it down to me.

"I, Paul, write this with my own hand, knowing that you will do even more than I ask."

314

A Vision of Heaven

I John, saw a new heaven and a new earth. And I saw the holy city, a new Jerusalem, coming down out of heaven from God. Then I heard a loud voice from heaven, saying: "God will now live with men and women, and they will be his people."

The one who sat on the throne in heaven said: "I am making everything new. Write these words down, for they are the truth. I am Alpha and Omega, the first and the last, the beginning and the end. I will give to those who are thirsty drink from the spring of the water of life."

One of the seven angels carried me away to a high mountain and showed me the shining city of Jerusalem as it came down from heaven. Its streets were made of pure gold and it had a high wall made of beautiful stone, with twelve pearly gates and an angel at each one. On the gates were written the names of the twelve tribes of Israel. These gates will never be shut, because there will be no night there. The wall had twelve foundations decorated with jewels and on them were written the names of the twelve apostles of Jesus. The city does not need the sun to shine on it, because the glory of God gives it light and Jesus is its lamp.

Then the angel showed me the river of the water of life, which flowed crystal clear from the throne of God and Jesus. On each side of the river stood the tree of life, bearing twelve different fruits that appear twelve times each year. And the leaves of the tree were there to heal all nations.

I, John, saw and heard all these things. Then I fell to my knees and worshiped at the feet of the angel who had shown them to me. But he said to me: "Do not worship me, for I am a fellow servant of you, of the prophets, and all those who keep the words of this book. Worship God."

AND HE THAT SAT UPON THE THRONE SAID, BEHOLD, I MAKE ALL THINGS NEW. AND HE SAID UNTO ME, WRITE: FOR THESE WORDS ARE TRUE AND FAITHFUL. AND HE SAID UNTO ME, IT IS DONE. I AM ALPHA AND OMEGA, THE BEGINNING AND THE END. I WILL GIVE UNTO HIM THAT IS ATHIRST OF THE FOUNTAIN OF THE WATER OF LIFE FREELY.

(Revelation 21.5–6)

The Revelation of St John
The Book of Revelation *was written by the disciple John while he was imprisoned on the Greek island of Patmos. John sees a vision of the heavenly Jerusalem and the glory of the risen Christ. The vision is full of symbols. Heaven is unlike anywhere we know on earth. Above, this illustration is from a medieval Spanish commentary on the* Book of Revelation.

Who's Who in the Bible

AARON: Moses's brother who acted as his spokesman when they asked Pharoah to let the Israelites leave Egypt.

ABEDNEGO: One of Daniel's friends who was also in the service of King Nebuchadnezzar.

ABEL: The second son of Adam and Eve, and brother of Cain.

ABIGAIL: The wife of King David.

ABRAHAM (Abram): The first Patriarch of Israel. A man devoted to God, and a great leader.

ABSALOM: One of King David's sons.

ADAM: The first man that God created, and the father of Cain and Abel.

AHAB: The Israelite king who reigned at the time of the prophet Elijah. Married to Jezebel.

AMOS: A prophet from Judah who was sent by God to speak to the Israelites.

ANANIAS: The Christian whose prayers helped restore Saul's sight.

ANDREW: A fisherman and brother of Peter and one of Jesus's twelve disciples.

ARTAXERXES: The king of Persia who allowed Nehemiah to return to Jerusalem.

AUGUSTUS: Roman Emperor during the time of Jesus.

BALAAM: A prophet who refused Balak's request to put a curse on the Israelites.

BALAK: The Moabite king who asked Balaam to put a curse on the people of Israel.

BARABBAS: The criminal who was freed instead of Jesus.

BARTHOLEMEW: One of Jesus's twelve disciples.

BATHSHEBA: The wife of King David, and Solomon's mother.

BELSHAZZAR: The king of Babylon who was given a warning by God, which appeared as writing on a wall.

BENJAMIN: Jacob's youngest son and Joseph's brother.

BOAZ: A farmer from Bethlehem who became Ruth's second husband.

CAIAPHAS: The high priest in Jerusalem when Jesus was arrested and crucified.

Cain: The eldest son of Adam and Eve. He murdered Cain, his brother.

CALEB: One of the Joshua's spies who was sent into Jericho to find out about the Promised Land.

CLEOPAS: One of the two men who saw Jesus on the road to Emmaus.

CYRUS: King of Persia who gave Judaens the freedom to return to Judah.

DANIEL: A Jewish prophet in exile in Babylon who was given an important post by King Nebuchadnezzar after God gave him the ability to interpret dreams.

DARIUS: A king of the Medes who took possession of the kingdom of Babylon after the death of Belshazzar.

DAVID: A shepherd from Bethlehem who went on to become king of Israel.

DELILAH: A Philistine woman who betrayed Samson by revealing the secret of his strength.

DEMETRIUS: A silversmith who lived in Ephesus.

ELI: A high priest who brought up Samuel.

ELIJAH: A prophet of Israel who competed against the priests of Baal to prove that there was only one true God.

ELISHA: The man who succeeded Elijah as God's prophet.

ELIZABETH: Mary's cousin and the mother of John the Baptist. Married to Zechariah.

ESAU: One of Isaac and Rebekah's twin sons, who was tricked out of his inheritance by his brother, Jacob.

ESTHER: A young Jewish woman and Queen of Persia upon her marriage to King Xerxes, who prevented the massacre of her own people.

EUTYCHUS: A young man who fell asleep and fell out of a window while Paul was preaching.

EVE: The first woman that God created. The wife of Adam, and mother of Cain and Abel.

EZEKIEL: A prophet in exile in Babylon who had a vision of hope for the Israelites.

GABRIEL: The angel who was sent by God to tell Mary that she would give birth to Jesus.

GIDEON: A judge who saved the Israelites by defeating the Midianites with only a very small army.

GOLIATH: A giant Philistine soldier who was killed by David.

HAGAR: Sarah's servant and Ishmael's mother.

HAM: One of the three sons of Noah.

HAMAN: King Xerxes' prime minister whose plot to massacre the Jewish exiles was stopped by Queen Esther.

HANNAH: The mother of Samuel.

HEROD ANTIPAS: Herod the Great's son who ordered the execution of John the Baptist.

HERODIAS: Herod Antipas' wife who told her daughter Salome to ask for John the Baptist's head to be brought to her on a dish.

HEROD THE GREAT: The king of Judea when Jesus was born who ordered the slaughter of all baby boys in Bethlehem under the age of two.

HEZEKIAH: King of Judah during the time of Isaiah.

HOSEA: A prophet of Israel who warned the people to change their sinful ways.

ISAAC: Abraham and Sarah's son. The father of Jacob and Esau, and husband of Rebekah.

ISAIAH: A prophet of Israel who warned the people to obey God's laws and told them of the coming of the Messiah.

ISHMAEL: Abraham and Hagar's son, and the servant of Sarah.

JACOB: One of Isaac and Rebekah's twin sons. Stole the inheritance of his brother, Esau. Married Leah and then Rachel. Father of the twelve tribes of Israel.

JAIRUS: The head of the synagogue whose daughter was healed by Jesus.

JAIRUS' DAUGHTER: A young girl who was healed by Jesus.

JAMES: The name of two of Jesus's twelve disciples.

JAPHETH: One of the three sons of Noah.

JEPHTHAH: An Israelite general who had to sacrifice his daughter because of a promise he had made to God in order to defeat the Ammonites.

JEREMIAH: A prophet from Judah who foretold that Jerusalem would be destroyed.

JESSE: The father of David.

JESUS CHRIST: The Son of God and the Messiah foretold by the Old Testament prophets. The central figure of Christianity and the New Testament.

JETHRO: The father of Moses' wife, Zipporah.

JEZEBEL: The evil wife of King Ahab who planned the death of Naboth.

JOAB: The commander of King David's army.

JOHN: The brother of James and one of Jesus' disciples who wrote the fourth Gospel.

JOHN THE BAPTIST: A prophet and the cousin of Jesus who prepared people for Jesus' coming.

JONAH: The prophet who was swallowed by a whale after he disobeyed God.

JONATHAN: King Saul's son and one of David's closest friends.

JOSEPH: Married to Mary, the mother of Jesus.

JOSEPH: The favourite of Jacob's twelve sons, and his first with Rachel. His jealous brothers sold him into slavery in Egypt, but he rose to power and became the saviour of Egypt and the Israelites.

JOSEPH (Barsabbas): One of the men who was considered as a replacement for Judas.

JOSEPH OF ARIMATHEA: A rich Jewish man who provided a tomb in which to bury Jesus.

JOSHUA: After Moses' death, he led the Israelites into Canaan, the Promised Land. With God's help he conquered Jericho.

JOSIAH: Became king of Judah when he was just eight years old.

JUDAH: One of Jacob's twelve sons.

JUDAS ISCARIOT: The disciple who betrayed Jesus.

JULIUS: A Roman centurion who escorted Paul on the journey to Rome.

LABAN: The brother of Rebekah, and Rachel and Leah's father. Laban tricked Jacob into marrying his eldest daughter Leah, although he was in love with Rachel.

LAZARUS: Mary and Martha's brother who was raised from the dead by Jesus.

LEAH: One of Laban's two daughters, and Jacob's first wife.

LOT: The nephew of Abraham. Lived in Sodom.

LUKE: A doctor and one of Jesus' twelve disciples who wrote the third Gospel.

MARK: The writer of the second Gospel, and one of Jesus' twelve disciples.

MARTHA: Lazarus and Mary's sister and one of Jesus' close friends.

MARY: The wife of Joseph and mother of Jesus.

MARY: Lazarus and Martha's sister and one of Jesus' close friends.

MARY MAGDALENE: The first person to witness Jesus' resurrection.

MATTHEW: A collector of taxes who became one of Jesus' twelve disciples. The writer of the first Gospel.

MATTHIAS (Barsabbas): He replaced Judas Iscariot as one of Jesus's twelve disciples.

MESHACH: One of Daniel's friends who was also in the service of King Nebuchadnezzar.

MICHAL: The daughter of Saul who married David.

MIRIAM: Moses and Aaron's sister.

MORDECAI: Queen Esther's cousin and protector.

MOSES: The man who led the Israelites out of slavery in Egypt, in search of the Promised Land. He was given the ten commandments by God on Mount Sinai.

NAAMAN: The commander of the Syrian army who was cured of his leprosy by Elisha.

NABAL: The husband of Abigail.

NABOTH: An Israelite farmer who was killed by King Ahab after Queen Jezebel plotted to get his vineyard.

NAOMI: Ruth's mother-in-law.

NATHAN: A prophet who was sent to deliver God's word to King David, and who helped Solomon become king.

NEBUCHADNEZZAR: The king of Babylon who captured Jerusalem and took the people of Judah into exile.

NEHEMIAH: Cupbearer to Artaxerxes, the king of Persia. He returned to Jerusalem to help rebuild the city.

NICODEMUS: A Jewish leader who helped with the preparations for the burial of Jesus'.

NOAH: The man who saved his family from the great flood by building an ark according to God's instructions.

ORPAH: The daughter-in-law of Naomi.

PETER (Simon Peter): A fisherman who was a disciple and a close friend of Jesus.

PHILIP: One of Jesus's twelve disciples.

PONTIUS PILATE: The Roman governor of Judea who ordered that Jesus be crucified.

POTIPHAR: An Egyptian courtier whose wife was responsible for putting Joseph, who worked for him, in prison.

QUEEN OF SHEBA: The queen who travelled from her own land to test King Solomon's wisdom.

RACHEL: Jacob's second and favourite wife, who was mother to his sons Joseph and Benjamin. She was the daughter of Laban, and sister of Leah, Jacob's first wife.

RAHAB: A woman living in Jericho, who hid two of Joshua's spies in her house.

REBEKAH: The wife of Isaac, and Jacob and Esau's mother.

REHOBOAM: King of Israel after his father Solomon died. Divided the kingdom of Israel.

REUBEN: The first son of Jacob and Leah.

RUTH: Naomi's devoted daughter-in-law who travelled with her to Bethlehem where she married for a second time, to Boaz.

SALOME: Herodias' daughter who danced for King Herod and who asked for the head of John the Baptist.

SAMSON: An Israelite man with great strength who fought against the Philistines.

SAMUEL: A prophet and judge who anointed the first two kings of Israel, Saul and David.

SARAH (Sarai): Abraham's wife, and the mother of Isaac.

SAUL: The first Israelite king, and father of Jonathan.

SAUL (Paul): A Jew who persecuted Christians, he converted to Christianity after he had a vision of Jesus, and became a great Christian leader.

SENNACHERIB: An Assyrian king who sent his army to attack Jerusalem and order Hezekiah to surrender.

SHADRACH: One of Daniel's friends who was also in the service of King Nebuchadnezzar.

SHEM: One of the three sons of Noah.

SILAS: A Christian who accompanied Paul on some of his missionary journeys.

SIMEON: An old man who saw Mary and Joseph presenting the baby Jesus to the Lord in the Temple.

SIMON: One of Jesus's twelve disciples.

SOLOMON: Became King of Israel on the death of his father, David. He was given great wisdom by God, and built the Temple in Jerusalem.

STEPHEN: One of the first Christian leaders and the first to be a martyr.

TERAH: The father of Abraham.

THADDAEUS: One of Jesus' twelve disciples.

THOMAS: One of Jesus's twelve disciples who doubted that Jesus had risen from the dead.

TIMOTHY: A friend of Paul who accompanied him on his missionary journeys.

URIAH: Bathsheba's first husband, who King David sent to his death.

XERXES (Ahasuerus): The king of Persia who was married to Esther.

ZACCHAEUS: The tax collector who climbed a tree in order to see Jesus.

ZECHARIAH: Married to Elizabeth, and father of John the Baptist.

ZEDEKIAH: The last king of Judah.

ZIPPORAH: The wife of Moses.